SPECIAL FUNCTIONS

The Mathematical Physics Monograph Series

A. S. Wightman, Editor
Princeton University

Ralph Abraham *Princeton University*	FOUNDATIONS OF MECHANICS
Vladimir I. Arnold *University of Moscow* André Avez *University of Paris*	ERGODIC PROBLEMS OF CLASSICAL MECHANICS
Freeman J. Dyson *The Institute for Advanced Study*	SYMMETRY GROUPS IN NUCLEAR AND PARTICLE PHYSICS
Robert Hermann *Argonne National Laboratory*	LIE GROUPS FOR PHYSICISTS
Rudolph C. Hwa *State University of New York at Stony Brook* Vigdor L. Teplitz *Massachusetts Institute of Technology*	HOMOLOGY AND FEYNMAN INTEGRALS
John R. Klauder E. C. G. Sudarshan *Syracuse University*	FUNDAMENTALS OF QUANTUM OPTICS
André Lichnerowicz *College de France*	RELATIVISTIC HYDRODYNAMICS AND MAGNETOHYDRODYNAMICS
George W. Mackey *Harvard University*	THE MATHEMATICAL FOUNDATIONS OF QUANTUM MECHANICS
Roger G. Newton *Indiana University*	THE COMPLEX *j*-PLANE
David Ruelle *Institut des Hautes Etudes Scientifiques*	STATISTICAL MECHANICS
R. F. Streater *Imperial College of Science and Technology* A. S. Wightman *Princeton University*	PCT, SPIN AND STATISTICS, AND ALL THAT
James D. Talman *The University of Western Ontario*	SPECIAL FUNCTIONS
René Thom *Institut des Hautes Etudes Scientifiques*	STABILITE STRUCTURELLE ET MORPHOGENESE

SPECIAL FUNCTIONS

A Group Theoretic Approach

Based on Lectures by Eugene P. Wigner

JAMES D. TALMAN

The University of Western Ontario

With an Introduction by Eugene P. Wigner

W. A. Benjamin, Inc.

New York 1968 Amsterdam

SPECIAL FUNCTIONS
A Group Theoretic Approach

Library of Congress Catalog Card Number 68-54038
Manufactured in the United States of America
12345R321098

*The manuscript was put into production on March 14, 1968;
this volume was published on November 30, 1968.*

W. A. Benjamin, Inc.
New York, New York 10016

Preface

In theoretical physics, routine use is made of many properties, such as recurrence relations and addition theorems, of the special functions of mathematical physics. These properties are for the most part classical, and their derivations are usually based on the methods of classical analysis. The purpose of this book is to show how these functions are also related to the theory of group representations and to derive their important properties from this theory. This approach elucidates the geometric background for the existence of the relations among the special functions. Moreover, the derivations may be more rationally motivated than are the usual complicated manipulations of power series, integral representations, and so on. I hope that the reader may find in this book reasonably simple derivations of many of the relations commonly used in theoretical physics for which the proofs may otherwise be somewhat unfamiliar.

In order that the book be fairly self-contained, approximately the first third delves into a preliminary discussion of such topics as Lie groups, group representations, and so on. The remaining chapters are devoted to various groups, and the special functions are discussed in conjunction with the group with which it is associated. Because of the inclusion of the introductory material, the only prerequisite is a reasonable knowledge of linear algebra.

The original impetus for the writing of this book was provided by a lecture course given by Professor Eugene P. Wigner a number of years ago. I am greatly indebted to Professor Wigner for his suggestion that I pursue the subject of the lectures further and for his continued friendly interest and advice in the work. I wish to thank Dr. Trevor Luke for carefully checking the manuscript. I also wish to thank my wife, whose encouragement contributed greatly to the writing of the book.

James D. Talman

London, Canada
July 1968

CONTENTS

General Introduction

All of us have admired, at one time or another, the theory of the higher transcendental functions, also called special functions of mathematical physics. The variety of the properties of these functions, which can be expressed in terms of differential equations which they satisfy, in terms of addition theorems or definite integrals over the products of these functions, is truly surprising. It is surpassed only by the variety of the properties of the elementary transcendentals, that is the exponential function, and functions derived therefrom, such as the trigonometric functions. At the same time, special functions, as their full name already indicates, appear again and again as solutions of problems in theoretical physics.

These higher transcendentals are analytic functions of their arguments and their properties are usually derived on the basis of their analytic character, using the methods of the theory of analytic functions. Neither the present volume, nor the earlier lectures which gave the incentive to this volume, intend to question the beauty of the analytic theory of the special functions, nor the generality of the results which this theory furnishes. In fact, the lectures started with the observation that the results of the analytic theory are more general than those furnished by the method to be employed in the lectures, thus pointing to a drawback of the considerations to be presented. Though this has been substantially eliminated by subsequent developments, presented also in the present volume and at least partially in other publications, this in no way diminishes the beauty and elegance of the analytic theory, or the inventiveness that was necessary to its development.

Rather, the claim of the present volume is to point to a role of the "special functions" which is common to all, and which leads to a point of view which permits the classification of their properties in a uniform fashion. The role which is common to all the special functions is to be matrix elements of representations of the simplest Lie groups, such as the group of rotations in three-space, or the Euclidean group of the plane. The arguments of the functions are suitably chosen group parameters. The addition theorems of the functions then just express the multiplication laws of the group elements. The differential equations which they obey can be obtained either as limiting cases of the addition theorems or as expressions of the fact that multiplication of a group element with an element in the close neighborhood of the unit element furnishes a group element whose parameters are in close proximity of the parameters of the element multiplied. The integral relationships derive from Frobenius' orthogonality relations for matrix elements of irreducible representations as generalized for Lie groups by means of Hurwitz's invariant integral. The completeness relations have a similar origin. Further relations derive from the possibility of giving different equivalent forms to the same representation by postulating that the representatives of one or another subgroup be in the reduced form. Finally, some of the Lie groups can be considered as limiting cases of others; this furnishes further relations between them. Thus, the Euclidean group of the plane can be obtained as a limit of the group of rotations in three-space. Hence, the elements of the representations of the former group (Bessel functions) are limits of the representations of the latter group (Jacobi functions).

Because of the important role which representations of simple groups play in problems of physics, the significance of the "special functions" in physical theory also becomes more understandable. In fact, it appears that the elementary transcendentals are also "special functions," the corresponding group being the simplest Lie group of all: the one parametric and hence Abelian Lie group. On the other hand, the field opens up in the opposite direction and one will wonder, when reading this book, what the role and what the properties are of representation coefficients of somewhat more complex Lie groups.

Naturally, the common point of view from which the special functions are here considered, and also the natural classification of their properties, destroys some of the mystique which has surrounded, and still surrounds, these functions. Whether this is a loss or a gain remains for the reader to decide.

Eugene P. Wigner

Chapter 1

INTRODUCTION

In addition to the elementary transcendental functions such as e^x and sin x, an important role is played in mathematical physics by the <u>special functions.</u> Examples of these functions are the Bessel functions, Legendre functions, and hypergeometric functions. For the most part the properties of these functions are studied on the basis of their analytic properties as solutions of ordinary differential equations. For example, the Bessel functions J_n are the solutions of the differential equation

$$J_n''(x) + \frac{1}{x} J_n'(x) + \left[1 - \frac{n^2}{x^2}\right] J_n(x) = 0 \tag{1.1}$$

that behave as $x^n/2^n n!$ for $x \to 0$. The Bessel functions are analytic functions of their argument and their order n, although in the original form of (1) the variable x was taken to be real, and the order is frequently restricted to be an integer.

The special functions are treated from this point of view in many excellent books. The best known among physicists are those of Courant and Hilbert [1] and Morse and Feshbach [2] but there are many other treatises, such as those of Rainville [3] and Lebedev [4] devoted to the subject.

The purpose of the present monograph is to demonstrate some of the properties of special functions from the point of view of group theory, or more specifically, from the theory of group representations. It will be seen that many of the special functions are matrix elements, or are simply related to matrix elements, of the representations of elementary groups such as rotation groups and Euclidean groups. Many properties of the special functions can then be derived from a unified point of view from the group representation property. For example, the Legendre functions are matrix elements of repretations of the rotation group in three dimensions. The addition theorems for these functions then follow from the group multiplication law. The differential equations for Legendre functions are a consequence of the differential equations that relate the derivatives of group representations to the corresponding representations of the Lie algebra of the group. The orthogonality and completeness relations are the orthogonality and completeness relations of the group representations. Further relations can be obtained by transforming a given representation to an equivalent form and by reducing the direct product of two representations into a sum of irreducible representations.

The group theoretic treatment shows that the special functions are special only in that they are related to specific groups. The usefulness of group representation theory for the solution of a variety of physical problems makes it natural that representation matrix elements are important special functions for many problems in mathematical physics. It may further be true that the properties that can be derived group theoretically are their most important ones, since they originate from the "geometric" properties of the functions.

Although it provides a unified basis for the treatment of special functions, the group theoretic approach has a number of limitations. Not all special functions arise as elements of group representation matrices; for example, no group theoretic basis is known for the gamma and elliptic functions. The special functions that occur in group representations have restricted indices; for example, only the Legendre functions of the first kind of integer order arise in a natural way. Certain other properties, such as the many integral representations, are not obvious consequences of the representation property.

The special functions that will be considered in detail in this work are the complex exponential function, Jacobi functions and Legendre functions (which are related to hypergeometric functions), Bessel and spherical Bessel functions, Gegenbauer polynomials, associated Laguerre polynomials, and Hermite polynomials. These arise in connection with the groups of pure rotations in two, three, and four dimensions, the Euclidean groups (rigid transformations) in two and three dimensions, and a less familiar group that corresponds to the Lie algebra generated by the position and momentum operators of quantum mechanics.

The approach that we will follow has a certain resemblance to one that has received considerable attention recently and that is related to the <u>factorization method</u> of Infeld and Hull [5]. In the factorization method, a single second-order differential equation is replaced, if possible, by a pair of first-order differential equations for a whole set of special functions, that is, a pair of equations of the form

$$L_n^+ f_n = f_{n+1}, \qquad L_n^- f_n = f_{n-1} \tag{1.2}$$

where L_n^+ and L_n^- are first-order differential operators. The second-order equation can then be written in the two alternate forms

$$L_{n+1}^- L_n^+ f_n = f_n, \qquad L_{n-1}^+ L_n^- f_n = f_n.$$

It is possible to identify the operators L_n^+ and L_n^- (together with additional operators) with a Lie algebra, and the possible factorizations can be classified by the study of these Lie algebras. The special functions constitute basis functions in representation spaces (as will be defined), for Lie algebras and many of their properties can be obtained in this way. This approach has been thoroughly investigated by W. Miller [6] and B. Kaufman [7].

The approach that will be followed here differs from this in that the primary emphasis will be on groups rather than on the corresponding Lie algebras, and most of the special functions will be related to matrix elements of group representations rather than basis functions in representation spaces, although some interesting results will also be obtained in this way.

A large amount of work has been done in the past few years on the relationship of special functions to group representations, particularly by Miller [8], and a book by N. I. Vilenkin [9] on the subject has been published in Russian. Our attention in this book will be limited for the most part to those properties that seem to be of most interest for mathematical physics. A considerable part of the material in this book arises from the lecture notes of Wigner on the subject [10].

Chapter 2

ABSTRACT GROUPS

It seems natural to commence the study of the application of group theory to the special functions with a review of group theory itself. This chapter is included to meet this possible need and to define some of the terms that are met in the remainder of the book. The contents of this chapter will be familiar, at least in outline, to many readers, and they are invited either to omit it or to take pleasure in the review of familiar concepts. This chapter is for this reason brief and rather tedious, without the examples and observations which give rise to the interest in the subject.

It is instructive, in the study of group theory, to view it as an investigation of the 1-1 mappings of a set S onto itself. The group elements are functions f defined for all $x \in S$ such that $f(x) \in S$, that is, the domain and range of f are both S. The function f must be 1-1; that is, for each $y \in S$, there must be a unique x such that $y = f(x)$ A group composed of such mappings is called a transformation group. As an example, the set S might consist of the first n integers, in which case the group is the permutation group on n objects.

The requirement that the mapping be 1-1 implies that it has a well-defined inverse f^{-1}; f^{-1} is the mapping that undoes the operation of f.

If f and g are 1-1 mappings, the composition mapping gf defined by $[gf](x) = g(f(x))$ is easily seen to be 1-1. This mapping is called the product of g and f. It is this type of multiplication that is the basic operation in group theory, adjoining an element, the product gf, to each ordered pair of elements g and f.

Some groups are sets of mappings of a set onto itself that are restricted in some further way than the 1-1 condition that has been imposed. For example, the group of transformations of a plane into itself that keep the distance between points fixed and also keep one point fixed is the rotation group in the plane. It is with groups of this nature that we will be principally concerned.

2-1 ABSTRACT GROUPS

A group G is a set in which an operation is defined which associates with every ordered pair of elements in G a third element of G. This operation is called multiplication; each of the given pair is called a factor, and the third element is called the product. If (a, b) is the given pair, the product is usually denoted simply by ab. The set G and the multiplication law must further satisfy the following properties known as group axioms.

A. The multiplication is associative; that is,

$$(ab)c = a(bc). \tag{2.1}$$

B. There is one element, the identity e, with the property that for all $a \in G$

$$ae = ea = a. \tag{2.2}$$

C. For each $a \in G$, there is an element a^{-1}, the inverse of a, such that

$$a^{-1}a = aa^{-1} = e. \tag{2.3}$$

An important consequence of A is that the product of three (or more) factors in a particular order is independent of the order in which the multiplications are performed. Thus, a product of the form abcd can be interpreted to be any one of (ab)(cd), a((bc)d), ((ab)c)d, and so on.

It is important to observe that either of the equations $ax = b$ and $xa = b$ has a unique solution for x. In the former case $x = a^{-1}b$, in the latter $x = ba^{-1}$, as can be seen by left (right) multiplication with a^{-1}. It follows from this that if $ab = b$, or if $ba = b$, then $a = e$, since $a = e$ is a solution of either equation. Therefore, e is the only element multiplication with which leaves any element unchanged, and this applies to both left and right multiplication. Similarly, if $ab = e$, or $ba = e$, then $b = a^{-1}$. The inverse element is therefore unique; that is, a^{-1} is the only element with the property C.

If $a^2 = a$, multiplication with a^{-1} shows that $a = e$: the identity is the only element equal to its square (although it is possible that $a^n = a$, $n \neq 2$). Since $e^2 = e$, the identity element is its own inverse.

Another rule which is frequently used is that the inverse of the product ab is $b^{-1}a^{-1}$.

A result of considerable significance is that the mapping f_a of G into G defined by $f_a(x) = ax$ is a 1-1 correspondence between the group and itself. For any $y \in G$, $f_a(a^{-1}y) = aa^{-1}y = y$, so that y is the image of an element in G, that is, f_a maps G onto G. Furthermore, if $f_a(x_1) = f_a(x_2)$, $x_1 = x_2$, since multiplying each side of $ax_1 = ax_2$ with a^{-1} gives $x_1 = x_2$. Therefore, each $y \in G$ is the image of exactly one $x \in G$ and the mapping f_a has a well-defined inverse. The mapping f_a in effect rearranges or permutes the elements of G.

Each group element can therefore be identified with a unique mapping of the group onto itself with the property that the product $x_2^{-1}x_1$ is invariant. It is obvious that each group element generates such a mapping. Conversely, if F is such a mapping, the group element is such that $F = f_a$ can be identified as $a = F(x)x^{-1}$; the invariance of $x_2^{-1}x_1$ guarantees that this choice is independent of x.

We consider now some examples of groups. One simple example is the set C of all nonzero complex numbers under complex multiplication. Another example is the set of all nonsingular $n \times n$ matrices with complex elements; the multiplication in this group, and in all matrix groups to be considered in this work, is the usual matrix multiplication.

A third example has been alluded to in the introduction. It is the <u>permutation group</u> which can be defined as follows For any set S the set of all mappings f of S onto itself which have a well-defined inverse constitutes a group with the multiplication defined as in the introduction. The identity of the group is the mapping defined by $f(x) = x$. It is necessary to verify that the associative law is valid, that is, that $(fg)h = f(gh)$; this can be seen to be true since each of these is the mapping $x \rightarrow f(g(h(x)))$.

It may happen that two groups, which are defined in quite different ways, are identical as far as their mathematical structure is concerned. If this is the case, the groups are said to be isomorphic. The precise definition of isomorphism is as follows: two groups G and G' are <u>isomorphic</u> if there is a 1-1 correspondence between them such that if $a \longleftrightarrow a'$ and $b \longleftrightarrow b'$, then $ab \longleftrightarrow a'b'$ for all a and b in G. This correspondence is called an <u>isomorphism</u>. One can see immediately that $e \in G$ must correspond to e', the identity in G', by the following argument. Suppose $e \longleftrightarrow c'$. Then for any a and corresponding a', $ae \longleftrightarrow a'c'$ and, hence, $a \longleftrightarrow a'c'$. This implies that $a'c' = a'$ and, hence, as we have seen, that $c' = e'$. It can also be proved easily that if $a \longleftrightarrow a'$, $a^{-1} \longleftrightarrow (a')^{-1}$. As a simple example of isomorphism, we remark that the group of complex numbers mentioned above is isomorphic to the group of matrices of the form

$$\begin{pmatrix} a & b \\ -b & a \end{pmatrix}$$

where a and b are real and not both zero and the above matrix corresponds to the complex number a + bi under the isomorphism.

If two elements have the property that ab = ba, they are said to commute. A group that has the property that all pairs of elements commute is said to be Abelian, or commutative. One can devise many examples of Abelian groups; the simplest is, perhaps, the set of real numbers with addition as the group operation. We mention also that if a group has a finite number n of elements, it is said to be a finite group of order n.

2-2 SUBGROUPS AND FACTOR GROUPS

A subset of a group G which is itself a group with the same law of multiplication as that in G is called a subgroup. To be more explicit, a subgroup H is a nonempty subset of G such that if a and b are in H, then a^{-1} and ab are in H. It is unnecessary to specify the associative property since this is guaranteed by the multiplication law in G. Furthermore, $e \in H$ since if $a \in H$, $a^{-1} \in H$, and $aa^{-1} = e \in H$. Two trivial examples of subgroups of G are the group G itself and the subgroup consisting of only e. If a subgroup is neither of these, it is said to be a proper subgroup. An example of a subgroup is the set of all n × n matrices with unit determinant as a subgroup of the set of all n × n matrices. Another example is provided by the group of permutations on a set S. If S' is a subset of S, the set of permutations that have the property f(x) = x for all $x \in S'$ is a subgroup of the full permutation group; this subgroup is in fact the permutation group on the set S − S'. Another subgroup, which is larger, is the set of all permutations that map S onto itself and S − S' onto itself.

If a is any element of a group G and B is any subset of the group, it is convenient to denote by aB the set of all elements of the form ab where $b \in B$; similarly Ba denotes the set of all elements of the form ba. If A and B are subsets, we will denote by AB and BA respectively the sets of all elements of the form ab and ba where $a \in A$ and $b \in B$. These sets satisfy certain associativity properties such as (AB)C = A(BC), which are easily verified and will henceforth be taken for granted. As examples of this notation, we observe that eA = A for any A, and that if H is a subgroup, $HH = H^2 = H$. We will also denote by A^{-1} the set of all inverses of elements of A. We can observe that $(AB)^{-1} = B^{-1}A^{-1}$ and that if H is a subgroup, $H^{-1} = H$. It is also true that if $H^2 = H^{-1} = H$, H is a subgroup.

A subgroup H of a group G can be used to subdivide G into disjoint pieces known as the left cosets of H. These are the subsets of G of the form aH where a is any element of G. Each element x of G is in exactly one left coset. It is certainly in the left coset xH since

$x = xe \in xH$. Suppose, however, that x is in two cosets, aH and bH. Then x can be written either as ah_1 or as bh_2, where h_1 and h_2 are elements of H. Then $ah_1 = bh_2$ (= x) or $a = bh_2h_1^{-1}$ and $aH = bh_2h_1^{-1}H = bh_2H = bH$ so that aH and bH are identical. We remark further that a and b are in the same left coset if and only if a can be expressed in the form bh, $h \in H$; this is equivalent to the condition $b^{-1}a \in H$, which is a useful criterion for determining whether two elements are in the same left coset

If the subgroup H contains a finite number m of elements, and there are p, a finite number, left cosets, the group G contains $p \times m$ elements since each left coset contains exactly m elements. This implies that in a finite group the order of a subgroup must divide the order of the group, a result known as Lagrange's theorem.

It is clear that <u>right cosets</u> can be defined analogously to left cosets and that the foregoing remarks will be equally applicable. We observe that two elements a and b are in the same right coset if, and only if, $ba^{-1} \in H$. In general the right cosets will differ from the left cosets; if, however, $aH = Ha$ for all $a \in G$, the two types of cosets coincide and the subgroup H is said to be <u>normal</u> or <u>invariant</u>. It can be seen that a condition equivalent to $aH = Ha$ for all $a \in G$ is that $aHa^{-1} \subset H$ for all $a \in G$, and the condition of normality will usually be expressed in this form. If a group has no proper normal subgroup, it is called <u>simple</u>.

If N is a normal subgroup of G, an important new group can be formed which is known as the <u>factor</u> or <u>quotient</u> group and is denoted by G/N. The elements of G/N are the cosets of N. Multiplication is defined in G/N by defining the product of two cosets aN and bN to be the coset $(aN)(bN) = aNbN = abNN = abN$; that is, the product of aN and bN is the coset containing ab. (It is not difficult to show that this definition is independent of the choice of a and b from their respective cosets.) The identity of G/N is N itself since $(aN)N = aNN = aN$. The associative law is readily seen to be valid since $(aNbN)cN = abcN = aN(bNcN)$. Finally, the inverse of aN is clearly $a^{-1}N$.

An example of a normal subgroup is the group of matrices of unit determinant as a subgroup of a complete matrix group; it will be left to the reader to show that this is a normal subgroup, and that the corresponding factor group is isomorphic to the group of nonzero complex numbers.

A few rather elementary properties of subgroups will now be formulated as a theorem, for which the proofs will not be given.

THEOREM 2-1. Let G be a group.

(a) If H and K are subgroups of G, then $H \cap K$, the set of elements contained in both H and K, is a subgroup of G.

(b) If H is a subgroup of G, and N is a normal subgroup of G, then

$N \cap H$ is a normal subgroup of H.

(c) If H is a subgroup of G, and N is a normal subgroup of G, then NH is a subgroup of G.

(d) If H and N are normal subgroups of G, then NH and $H \cap N$ are normal subgroups of G.

2-3 HOMOMORPHISMS

A more general relation between two groups than isomorphism is that of homomorphism. A mapping f from a group G onto a group G' is said to be a homomorphism if for every pair of elements a, b in G, $f(a)f(b) = f(ab)$. (Note that f(a), f(b), and f(ab) are elements of G'.) A homomorphism is more general than an isomorphism in that several elements of G may be mapped into a single element of G', so that f may not have a single-valued inverse. It is required, however, that every element of G' be the image of some element of G. (This is implied by the preposition "onto.")

In this section a few simple properties of homomorphisms will be described. The image of e, the identity in G, is e', the identity in G'; that is, $f(e) = e'$. This can be shown in the way that the same result was proved for isomorphisms. Similarly, the images of reciprocals are again reciprocals: $f(a)f(a^{-1}) = f(e) = e'$ or $f(a^{-1}) = [f(a)]^{-1}$.

It is interesting to observe that the set of elements of G that are mapped by f into the identity e' of g' is a normal subgroup of G. This set is called the kernel of f and is often denoted by K. An element k of G is in K if $f(k) = e'$. If k_1 and k_2 are both in K, $f(k_1k_2) = f(k_1)f(k_2) = e'^2 = e'$ showing that k_1k_2 is also in K. Moreover, if $f(k) = e'$, $f(k^{-1}) = e'^{-1} = e'$, showing that $k^{-1} \varepsilon K$ and hence that K is a subgroup. To show that K is a normal subgroup, we consider its cosets. It will be shown that all elements of a coset of K map onto a single element of G', and conversely, that all the elements of G that are mapped onto a single element of G' belong to the same coset of K. Let aK be a left coset of K and suppose $x \varepsilon aK$. Then $x = ak$, $k \varepsilon K$, and $f(x) = f(a)f(k) = f(a)$, showing that all elements of aK are mapped by f into f(a). Conversely, if $f(x) = f(a)$, $f(a^{-1}x) = f(a)^{-1}f(x) = e'$, implying that $a^{-1}x \varepsilon K$ and that $x \varepsilon aK$. It can be concluded that the coset aK is the set of all elements x such that $f(x) = f(a)$. These considerations apply just as well to Ka so that $aK = Ka$ and K is normal.

It is evident that there is a 1-1 correspondence between cosets of K and elements of G' defined by the relation

$$aK \longleftrightarrow f(a) . \tag{2.4}$$

Furthermore, this 1-1 correspondence is an isomorphism between G' and the factor group G/K composed of the cosets of K, as is shown by the calculation $(aK)(bK) = abK \quad f(ab) = f(a)f(b)$. These findings can be summarized as a theorem.

THEOREM 2-2. Let f be a homomorphic mapping of a group G onto a group G'. Then the set K of elements of G that map onto the identity of G' is a normal subgroup of G, the set of elements of G that map onto an element a' of G' is a coset of K, and G/K is isomorphic to G'.

If N is a normal subgroup of G, it is easy to see that the mapping of G onto G/N that maps each element of G onto the coset of which it is a member is a homomorphism. This is known as the natural homomorphism of G onto G/N; the kernel of the natural homomorphism is obviously N, since N is the identity of G/N.

2-4 SOME FURTHER ASPECTS OF GROUPS

Our review of some of the concepts from abstract group theory will be concluded in this section with discussions of miscellaneous topics: equivalence classes in groups, direct products of groups, and two important subgroups. The discussion will be limited to definitions and results more or less pertinent to the sequel.

An important classification of elements within a group G is provided by the conjugacy or equivalence classes in the group defined as follows. An element $b \in G$ is said to be equivalent, or conjugate, to $a \in G$ if there is some element t such that $tat^{-1} = b$. If this is the case, t is said to transform a into b. Since e transforms a into a, a is equivalent to itself, and since t^{-1} transforms b into a, a is equivalent to b. Furthermore, if c is equivalent to b, that is, $c = sbs^{-1}$, and b is equivalent to a, $b = tat^{-1}$, then c is equivalent to a since c $= (st)a(st)^{-1}$. The group G can be divided into disjoint subsets with the property that any two elements common to one subset are equivalent and any two elements from different subsets are not equivalent; these subsets are called the equivalence or conjugacy classes of G. The class to which any element a belongs will be denoted by C_a. As an example, we note that C_e consists only of e since $tet^{-1} = e$ for all $t \in G$. If G is Abelian, it is clear that each class consists of only a single element.

It is worth while to observe that a subgroup N of G is normal if and only if it is composed of entire classes. This follows since, if $a \in N$, $tat^{-1} \in N$ if N is normal, so that $C_a \subset N$. On the other hand, if $C_a \subset N$ for each $a \in N$, $tNt^{-1} \subset N$ and N is normal. The subgroup N can itself be regarded as a group composed of classes $\bar{C}$ with respect to N. Two elements n_1 and n_2 are in the same class $\bar{C}$ if there is an element $t \varepsilon N$ such that $tn_1t^{-1} = n_2$; it follows that if two elements are in the same class $\bar{C}$ of N, they are in the same class C of G. On the other hand, two elements common to a class C in G may be in different classes in N, since the element which transforms one to the other may be outside of N. We can conclude from this discussion that each class C in G that is contained in N is composed of entire classes $\bar{C}$ of N.

If two groups G_1 and G_2 are known, it is possible to form a third group from them. The direct product $G_1 \otimes G_2$ of the two groups is defined to be the set of all pairs of the form (g_1, g_2) where $g_1 \varepsilon G_1$ and $g_2 \varepsilon G_2$. The product of two such pairs is defined in a rather obvious way by

$$(g_1 g_2)(h_1, h_2) = (g_1 h_1, g_2 h_2). \tag{2.5}$$

The identity in $G_1 \otimes G_2$ is (e_1, e_2) and the inverse of (g_1, g_2) is (g_1^{-1}, g_2^{-1}).

The direct product has no interesting algebraic structure other than that of each of its factors. A question of some interest is: given a group G, does it have subgroups G_1 and G_2 such that G is (isomorphic to) the direct product of G_1 and G_2? It will now be shown that if G has normal subgroups N_1 and N_2 such that $N_1 \cap N_2 = \{e\}$ and $N_1N_2 = G$, then G is isomorphic to $N_1 \otimes N_2$. It will first be shown that if $n_1 \varepsilon N_1$ and $n_2 \varepsilon N_2$, then $n_1n_2 = n_2n_1$. This is proved by considering the commutator $q = n_1n_2n_1^{-1}n_2^{-1}$ of n_1 and n_2. Since N_2 is a normal subgroup, $n_1n_2n_1^{-1} = n_2' \varepsilon N_2$ and $q = n_2'n_2^{-1} \varepsilon N_2$. Similarly, since N_1 is a normal subgroup, $n_2n_1^{-1}n_2^{-1} = n_1' \varepsilon N_1$ and $q = n_1n_1' \varepsilon N_1$. Therefore, $q \varepsilon N_1 \cap N_2$ and q is necessarily e. It follows immediately that $n_1n_2 = n_2n_1$. Since $N_1N_2 = G$, each element $g \varepsilon G$ can be expressed in the form n_1n_2. This representation is, moreover, unique, since if $g = n_1n_2 = m_1m_2$ where n_1 and m_1 are in N_1 and n_2 and m_2 are in N_2, then $m_1^{-1}n_1 = m_2n_2^{-1}$. The left-hand side is in N_1, the right-hand side is in N_2, so that each is necessarily e and $m_1 = n_1$, $m_2 = n_2$. The isomorphism between $N_1 \otimes N_2$ and G is now given by the relation

$$(n_1, n_2) \longleftrightarrow n_1n_2. \tag{2.6}$$

This correspondence is an isomorphism, since if $(n_1, n_2) \longleftrightarrow n_1n_2$ and $(m_1, m_2) \longleftrightarrow m_1m_2$, then $(n_1, n_2)(m_1, m_2) = (n_1m_1, n_2m_2) \longleftrightarrow n_1m_1n_2m_2 = (n_1n_2)(m_1m_2)$ from the fact that $n_2m_1 = m_1n_2$.

The set Z of all elements that commute with every element of a group G is called the center of G. It is easy to show that Z is a subgroup of G, since if z_1 and z_2 are in Z and g is any element of

G, $z_1z_2g = z_1gz_2 = gz_1z_2$ and $z_1z_2 \varepsilon Z$. It is also clear that $e \varepsilon Z$ and that if $z \varepsilon Z$, $z^{-1} \varepsilon Z$, so that Z is a subgroup. Since $gZ = Zg$ for all $g \varepsilon G$, Z is also a normal subgroup of G. Any subgroup of Z is also necessarily a normal subgroup of G; such a subgroup is called a central normal subgroup.

We have defined the commutator of two elements a and b to be $aba^{-1}b^{-1}$. The commutator subgroup of G is defined to be the set of all elements that can be expressed as a product of commutators. The commutator subgroup is commonly denoted by G'. It is clear that the product of two elements of G' is again in G' and that $e \varepsilon G'$. If q is the commutator of a and b, q^{-1} is the commutator of b and a. It follows from this that the inverse of any element in G' is again in G', and, hence, that G' is a subgroup. To show that G' is a normal subgroup, we observe first that if q is the commutator of a and b, tqt^{-1} is the commutator of tat^{-1} and tbt^{-1} so that t transforms any commutator into another commutator. If $x = q_1q_2 \cdots q_n$ is an element of G', then $txt^{-1} = (tq_1t^{-1})(tq_2t^{-1}) \cdots (tq_nt^{-1})$ is also an element of G', which is, therefore, a normal subgroup.

An interesting property of G' is that G/G' is an Abelian group. Let aG' and bG' be two cosets of G'. Their inverses in G/G' can be written $a^{-1}G'$ and $b^{-1}G'$ respectively. The commutator of aG' and bG' is $(aG')(bG')(a^{-1}G')(b^{-1}G') = aba^{-1}b^{-1}G' = G'$, since $aba^{-1}b^{-1} \varepsilon G'$. Since G' is the identity in G/G', G/G' is Abelian.

Chapter 3

LIE GROUPS

Although the study of group theory originated with finite groups, the theory of Lie groups has achieved greater importance than that of finite groups, and it is Lie groups that are of primary significance for our purposes. Whereas the elements of a finite group form a discrete set, those of a Lie group form a continuum; they depend differentiably on one or more parameters. Because of this, topological considerations, the concepts of neighborhood, open sets, closed sets, and so on, play an important role in the basic theory of Lie groups. Many remarkable results, for example that continuity of the group implies differentiability of the group under certain circumstances, have been established for Lie groups. However, in the present discussion we will avoid involved topological considerations as much as possible, often by making more restrictive assumptions than are necessary (differentiability instead of continuity, and so on).

Many of the properties of a Lie group are determined by the elements in an arbitrarily small neighborhood of the identity, since such a neighborhood can be multiplied by itself repeatedly to generate at least a large part of the group. For example, if the elements in any neighborhood of the identity commute, the group is Abelian. There is no corresponding situation in finite groups, in which a small subset cannot be expected to determine most of the group properties.

Whereas the theory of finite groups can stand alone, without relying on any other part of mathematics, the theory of Lie groups often makes extensive use of the theory of ordinary and partial differential equations. In addition, many Lie groups have connectedness properties which, if perhaps not complicated, are still different from the connectedness properties of ordinary Euclidean spaces. An example of this, that of the group of rotatiohs in two dimensions, will be found in the next section. There are Lie groups with even more complicated "topology in the large." As a result of these circumstances, particularly the reliance on the theory of differential equations, the theory of Lie groups is much less independent of other parts of mathematics than is the theory of finite groups.

3-1 LIE GROUPS

A Lie group of dimension n is a group with the following properties.

A. The group is composed of a finite number of subsets, which are not necessarily disjoint, such that the elements of each subset can be placed in 1-1 correspondence with the points of open regions in n-dimensional space. These regions will be called parameter domains and the n coordinates of a point in one of them will be called group parameters or coordinates and will be used as coordinates for the corresponding group element.

B. A given group element may have parameters in more than one parameter domain; if this is the case the coordinates in one region must be arbitrarily differentiable functions of the coordinates in the other region.

C. The group operations must be differentiable in the group parameters; the exact meaning of this condition will be explained shortly.

D. The group is closed (or has the closure property) and is connected. These properties will be defined precisely later.

It would be most convenient if one open region in the parameter space were sufficient to label all the group elements. Unfortunately, it is usually necessary for topological reasons, that is, reasons of connectedness, to introduce different coordinate systems into different parts of the group. For the most part, this complication will, however, be ignored and we may refer to the coordinates of a group element without mentioning explicitly that they are in a particular parameter domain.

The various parameter domains could be made to be nonoverlapping by discarding from some of them those elements that they have in common with others. The reason that this is not done is that the resulting domains, which would be differences of open sets, would not be open, and it is desirable that the parameter domains be open sets. In fact, one of the difference sets could conceivably be a single point, in which case the differentiability condition would become meaningless.

As an example of all this, consider the set of rotations of a plane, which can be labelled by the rotation angle θ.

This θ is, however, a cyclic variable and rotations by θ and by $\theta \pm 2\pi n$ (n an integer) are identical. It is, therefore, impossible to introduce a variable with a finite domain which would depend continuously on the group element: the group is, like the circle, multiply connected whereas any finite domain of a variable is singly connected. Hence, one introduces two domains to cover the group. The variable of the first domain is $\theta_1 = \theta$ and is restricted to the open region $-\pi < \theta_1 < \pi$. The second one is $\theta_2 = -\pi$ and can also be restricted to the domain $-\pi < \theta_2 < \pi$. The only point the first domain does not cover is the point $\theta = \pi$, the only point the second domain does not cover is $\theta = 0$, that is, the unit element. Of course, both domains could be chosen to be smaller as long as they cover all points $-\pi < \theta \leq \pi$.

The reason for the need of several open domains in parameter space (actually only two for the groups to be considered) is always the same in principle, but the situation may be somewhat more complicated than in the case just considered.

A particular group will naturally admit many different coordinate systems, each of which will be called a parametrization.

The set of coordinates of a group element will be denoted by a boldface letter. We will frequently not distinguish between a group element and the point in the parameter space that represents it; for example, we may refer to the product of elements $\mathbf{p}$ and $\mathbf{q}$.

It is convenient to assume that the identity element has coordinates zero in at least one parameter domain. This is no real restriction since it can be achieved by a coordinate translation.

An example of a Lie group is the group of n x n nonsingular matrices with real elements. This is an n^2-dimensional group, in which the matrix elements, with 1 subtracted from the diagonal elements, can be regarded as the group parameters.

If two group elements a and b, with coordinates $\mathbf{p}$ and $\mathbf{q}$ respectively, are given a third element c, their product ab is determined by the group multiplication property. The coordinates of c will be denoted by $\mathbf{r}$. The numbers $r^1, r^2, \ldots, r^n$ depend on the coordinates of a and b and they are therefore functions of the variables $\mathbf{p}$ and $\mathbf{q}$. There are n such functions, one for each coordinate of c, and each function depends on 2n variables, the coordinates of a and b. There seems to be no standard terminology for these functions; we will call them product functions and denote them by $\mathbf{f}$. The coordinates of c = ab are therefore given by $\mathbf{f}(\mathbf{p}, \mathbf{q})$. For a given pair $\mathbf{p}$, $\mathbf{q}$ there may be more than one function $\mathbf{f}$ since c = ab may have coordinates in more than one parameter domain. The various possible functions are, because of B, connected by a differentiable transformation.

The group multiplication laws (2.1) and (2.2) impose certain conditions on the functions $\mathbf{f}$. For example, the property ae = ea = a requires that

$$\mathbf{f}(\mathbf{p}, 0) = \mathbf{f}(0, \mathbf{p}) = \mathbf{p}. \tag{3.1}$$

The associative law (ab)c = a(bc) imposes a rather more complicated condition on the $\mathbf{f}$. We again denote the coordinates of a, b, and c by $\mathbf{p}$, $\mathbf{q}$, and $\mathbf{r}$ respectively. The group element ab has coordinates $\mathbf{f}(\mathbf{p}, \mathbf{q})$ and (ab)c therefore has coordinates $\mathbf{f}(\mathbf{f}(\mathbf{p}, \mathbf{q}), \mathbf{r})$. In a similar way it can be found that a(bc) has coordinates $\mathbf{f}(\mathbf{p}, \mathbf{f}(\mathbf{q}, \mathbf{r}))$. The equality of the two group elements requires that

$$f(f(p, q), r) = f(p, f(q, r)). \tag{3.2}$$

This relation will be called the associative law, since it is equivalent to (2.1).

The differentiability condition for the group operations is formulated in terms of the functions $f(p, q)$ and is that they must have uniformly bounded derivatives of all orders with respect to the variables p^{α} and q^{β}.

The meaning of the closure property imposed on a Lie group is that if any sequence $\{p_n\}$ of group coordinates in some parameter domain D converges to a point p, the group elements g_n corresponding to p_n converge to a group element g. This is actually the definition of the convergence of group elements. This condition is significant only if p is on the boundary, and hence outside of D. The meaning is then that there must be a second parameter domain D' in which, at least past a certain point in the sequence, the group elements g_n have coordinates q_n, and the q_n converge to q, an interior point of D'. This assumption is a condition on both the group and the admissible parametrizations.

The nature of this assumption can perhaps be clarified by the following example. The group R of real numbers, with addition playing the role of group multiplication, is closed in the usual parametrization. A new parameter $y = \tan^{-1} x$ could be introduced for which $-\pi/2 < y < \pi/2$. This parametrization is inadmissible, since there is no group element corresponding exactly to the limit elements at $y = \pm\pi/2$.

The group of rotations in the plane is closed although there is apparently no limit element at $\pm\pi$ for the parameter θ_1 mentioned above. The rotation by π corresponds, however, to an interior point in the θ_2 coordinate system, thereby satisfying the condition given above.

The property that the group is connected is that the coordinates (in at least one parameter domain) of every group element can be connected to the coordinates of the identity, in the parameter domain in which they are zero, by a continuous curve. This curve can pass from one parameter domain to another, but in doing so must pass continuously through the region of overlap of the two domains. If any two such curves, joining the identity to an arbitrary group element, can be deformed continuously into one another, the group is simply connected; otherwise it is multiply connected. These properties do not, however, play an important role in the work that we are considering here.

3-2 COMPACT GROUPS

The theory of representations has particularly simple results for a certain class of groups, the compact groups. The property of compactness also simplifies the derivation of some general theorems. In this section we will define a compact group.

A simple example of a compact (not group theoretical) set is a closed finite interval on the real line. Such an interval, [a, b], has two important properties. The first is that for any infinite set of points $\{x_i\}$, $a \le x_i \le b$, there is (at least) one limit point also in [a, b]. If every neighborhood of a point x contains an infinite number of the points x_i, x is said to be a limit element of the set $\{x_i\}$. The second property of a closed finite interval could be called the Heine-Borel property. This stipulates that from any set of open intervals $I_\alpha = (x_\alpha, y_\alpha)$ that covers [a, b], it is possible to select a finite subset of intervals $I_{\alpha_1}, I_{\alpha_2}, \ldots, I_{\alpha_n}$ that again cover [a, b]. The verb "cover" means in this case that each element of [a, b] is also in one of the covering open intervals. The classic Heine-Borel theorem is that the second property is a consequence of the first property.

A Lie group will be defined to be compact if there is a parametrization in which the group is covered by coordinates in a finite number of bounded parameter domains. It is essential, of course, that the parametrization be such that the differentiability and closure properties described above are satisfied. A bounded parameter domain is one that can be enclosed in a rectangle in the coordinate space. Specifically, there are numbers a^i, b^i, $i = 1, 2, \ldots, n$ such that $a^i < p^i < b^i$ for the coordinates p^i of points in the domain.

Let $\{g_n\}$ be an infinite set of elements of a compact Lie group. Then one of the parameter domains must also contain the coordinates of an infinite number of the g_n and these coordinates must have a limit element either in or on the boundary of the parameter domain. (The proof can be found in many books on advanced calculus.) The closure property of the group then assures that the limit element is a group element. The first property of closed finite intervals, that any infinite sequence of group elements has a limit element, is therefore satisfied by a compact Lie group.

It is also possible to adapt the usual proof of the Heine-Borel theorem to show that a compact Lie group G has the second property of closed finite intervals in the following sense. Suppose a family of open regions U_α covers G by including the coordinates of each element of G from at least one parameter domain. It is then possible to select a finite number of the U_α that cover G in the same way. (The definition is complicated here by the possibility that a given group element may have coordinates in several parameter domains.)

It is obvious that the group of rotations in the plane is compact since it is covered by two finite intervals. On the other hand, the group R of real numbers cannot be compact since the sequence of the integers 1, 2,... cannot have a limit element in any parametrization.

3-3 LOCALLY ISOMORPHIC GROUPS

It may happen that two groups which are essentially different appear to be identical if one is permitted to view only a part of them. We will give a rather simple example of this situation. We consider again the group R of all real numbers with addition being the operation of group multiplication. This group has a normal subgroup, the group Z of all integers. The factor group R/Z, whose elements are cosets of Z, consists of sets of numbers such that the difference of any two of the numbers in a set is an integer. Each element can, therefore, be characterized by a number p satisfying $-1/2 < p \leq 1/2$. The product of two elements of R/Z corresponding to p and q corresponds to p+q if $-1/2 < p + q \leq 1/2$; if p + q is outside this interval it can be reduced by ± 1 to bring it back into the interval. The groups R and R/Z are certainly different; for example, R/Z is compact (it is isomorphic to the group of rotations in the plane) whereas R is not. The two groups are identical, however, if one considers only elements corresponding to $|p| < 0.1$.

The groups R and R/Z are said to be locally isomorphic. This property can be defined as follows. Lie groups G and G' are locally isomorphic if there exist neighborhoods of the identity in each group and parametrizations such that the product functions are equal if their arguments are in these neighborhoods.

3-4 PROPERTIES OF THE PRODUCT FUNCTIONS

The following discussion will contain the calculation of derivatives of the product functions at various points in the group. The customary notation for partial derivatives can be rather misleading, so that we will introduce and adhere to the following convention. The symbol $\partial f^\alpha/\partial p^\beta$ will be used to represent the derivative of the product function f^α with respect to the βth coordinate of the first set of arguments of f^α, regardless of the point at which this function is actually evaluated. Similarly, $\partial f^\alpha/\partial q^\gamma$ denotes the derivative of f^α with respect to the γth coordinate of the second argument. The summation convention of summing over repeated indices will also be used.

We will now discuss a few properties of the derivatives of the product functions. The first of these are rather trivial and are obtained by differentiating (1) with respect to p^β:

$$\frac{\partial f^\alpha}{\partial p^\beta}(\mathbf{p}, 0) = \delta^\alpha{}_\beta, \qquad \frac{\partial f^\alpha}{\partial q_\beta}(0, \mathbf{q}) = \delta^\alpha{}_\beta. \tag{3.3}$$

These imply further that

$$\frac{\partial^2 f^\alpha}{\partial p^\beta \partial p^\gamma}(\mathbf{p}, 0) = \frac{\partial^2 f^\alpha}{\partial q^\beta \partial q^\gamma}(0, \mathbf{q}) = 0. \tag{3.4}$$

If $r^\alpha = f^\alpha(\mathbf{p}, \mathbf{q})$, it is possible to show that the Jacobian

$$\frac{\partial(r^1, r^2, \ldots, r^n)}{\partial(p^1, p^2, \ldots, p^n)} = \frac{\partial f^\alpha}{\partial p^\beta}(\mathbf{p}, \mathbf{q})$$

is nonzero. The parameters of the inverse of the element with the parameters $\mathbf{p}$ will be denoted by $i^1(\mathbf{p}), i^2(\mathbf{p}), \ldots, i^n(\mathbf{p})$ so that

$$\mathbf{f}(\mathbf{i}(\mathbf{p}), \mathbf{p}) = 0. \tag{3.5}$$

Consider then the derivative with respect to p^β of the identity $f^\alpha(\mathbf{f}(\mathbf{p}, \mathbf{q}), \mathbf{i}(\mathbf{q})) = p^\alpha$, which is a reflection of the identity $abb^{-1} = a$. The derivative is

$$\frac{\partial f^\alpha}{\partial p^\gamma}(\mathbf{f}(\mathbf{p}, \mathbf{q}), \mathbf{i}(\mathbf{q}))\, \frac{\partial f^\gamma}{\partial p^\beta}(\mathbf{p}, \mathbf{q}) = \delta^\alpha{}_\beta. \tag{3.6}$$

This shows that the matrix whose elements are $\partial f^\gamma/\partial p^\beta$ has an inverse and hence that the Jacobian is nonzero. It is possible to show in a similar way that

$$\frac{\partial f^\alpha}{\partial q^\gamma}(\mathbf{p}, \mathbf{q}) \neq 0.$$

These results are simply reflections of the fact that the transformations $\mathbf{r}(\mathbf{p}) = \mathbf{f}(\mathbf{p}, \mathbf{q})$ with $\mathbf{q}$ fixed, and $\mathbf{r}(\mathbf{q}) = \mathbf{f}(\mathbf{p}, \mathbf{q})$ with $\mathbf{p}$ fixed, are necessarily invertible.

It is now possible to calculate the derivatives of the functions $\mathbf{i}(\mathbf{p})$ that are determined by the inversion operation. Consider the derivative with respect to p^β of the identity (5):

$$\frac{\partial f^\alpha}{\partial p^\gamma}(\mathbf{i}(\mathbf{p}), \mathbf{p})\, \frac{\partial i^\gamma}{\partial q^\beta}(\mathbf{p}) + \frac{\partial f^\alpha}{\partial q^\beta}(\mathbf{i}(\mathbf{p}), \mathbf{p}) = 0.$$

This equation can be solved for $\partial i^\gamma/\partial p^\beta$ by using equation (6) which instructs us how to invert the matrix whose elements are $\partial f^\alpha/\partial p^\beta$. The desired result is

$$\frac{\partial i^\gamma}{\partial p^\beta}(\mathbf{p}) = -\frac{\partial f^\gamma}{\partial p^\alpha}(0, \mathbf{i}(\mathbf{p}))\frac{\partial f^\alpha}{\partial q^\beta}(\mathbf{i}(\mathbf{p}), \mathbf{p}). \tag{3.7}$$

It is apparent that higher derivatives of $\mathbf{i}$ could be calculated by differentiation of this result.

In the next section we will have occasion to use functions $v^\alpha{}_\beta$ defined by

$$v^\alpha{}_\beta(\mathbf{p}) = \frac{\partial f^\alpha}{\partial q^\beta}(\mathbf{p}, \mathbf{0}). \tag{3.8}$$

These functions satisfy an identity which can be derived by differentiating equation (2), the associative law, with respect to r^γ and then setting $\mathbf{r} = 0$. Using the chain rule and (1) gives

$$\frac{\partial f^\alpha}{\partial q^\gamma}(\mathbf{f}(\mathbf{p}, \mathbf{q}), 0) = \frac{\partial f^\alpha}{\partial q^\beta}(\mathbf{p}, \mathbf{q})\frac{\partial f^\beta}{\partial q^\gamma}(\mathbf{q}, 0)$$

or, from (8),

$$v^\alpha{}_\gamma(\mathbf{f}(\mathbf{p}, \mathbf{q})) = \frac{\partial f^\alpha}{\partial q^\beta}(\mathbf{p}, \mathbf{q})\, v^\beta{}_\gamma(\mathbf{q}). \tag{3.9}$$

This equation will play an important role in Chapter 5 when an invariant integral over the group will be defined.

3-5 ONE-PARAMETER SUBGROUPS

The investigation of the structure of a Lie group G is facilitated by the construction of the one-parameter subgroups of G. A one-parameter subgroup is a "curve" a(t) in the group with the property that

$$a(s)a(t) = a(s+t). \tag{3.10}$$

The variable t is a real number that serves to label the group elements in the subgroup; it is the "one-parameter." Corresponding to an element $a(t) \in G$, there is a point $\mathbf{p}(t)$ in a parameter domain. An additional requirement on the one-parameter subgroup is that the points $\mathbf{p}(t)$ constitute one or more continuous curves in each parameter domain through which it passes. A rather trivial one parameter subgroup is defined by $a(t) = e$. If a(t) is a one-parameter subgroup, $a(\alpha t)$ is also one consisting of the same group elements but differing in the scale of the parameter.

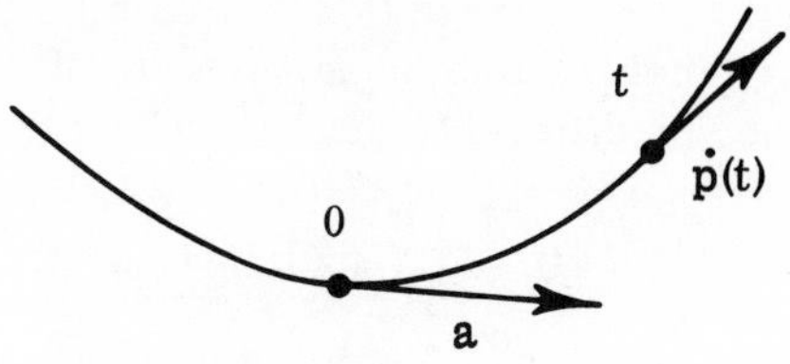

Fig. 3-1

A one-parameter subgroup showing **a**, the tangent at e, and $\dot{\mathbf{p}}(t)$, the vector into which $v^{\alpha}{}_{\beta}(\mathbf{p}(t))$ transforms **a**.

It is evident from (10) that $a(0) = e$ and that $[a(t)]^{-1} = a(-t)$. The one-parameter subgroup can be shown to be isomorphic to either R, the group of real numbers under addition, or to R/Z, the factor group discussed in Section 3 of this chapter, depending on whether or not there is a number t_1 such that $a(t_1) = e$.

It has been implied that the one-parameter subgroups may pass through several parameter domains. It may also cross the boundary of a parameter domain and reenter it at another point.

We shall first assume the existence of a one-parameter subgroup and obtain some of its properties. It will then be shown that there are one-parameter subgroups and that in a sufficiently small neighborhood of e, each element is contained in a one-parameter subgroup.

We restrict our attention now to the parameter domain containing the coordinates of e (which is the origin in the coordinate system of that domain). If it is assumed that the coordinates $\mathbf{p}(t)$ are differentiable functions, a first-order differential equation can be derived for the subgroup. The tangent vector to $\mathbf{p}(t)$ at $t = 0$ will be denoted by **a**; that is,

$$\mathbf{a} = \dot{\mathbf{p}}(0). \tag{3.11}$$

From equation (10) and the definition of the product functions **f** we can write

$$p^{\alpha}(s+t) = f^{\alpha}(\mathbf{p}(s), \mathbf{p}(t)), \tag{3.12}$$

at least for s and t close enough to 0 so that **p**(s), **p**(t), and **p**(s + t) remain in the original parameter domain. A differential equation for **p**(t) is obtained by differentiating (12) with respect to t,

$$\dot{p}^{\alpha}(s+t) = \frac{\partial f^{\alpha}}{\partial q^{\beta}}(\mathbf{p}(s), \mathbf{p}(t))\, \dot{p}^{\beta}(t),$$

and setting t = 0. Using (8) and (11), one obtains

$$\dot{p}^{\alpha}(s) = v^{\alpha}{}_{\beta}(\mathbf{p}(s))\, a^{\beta}. \tag{3.13}$$

Equation (13) shows that the matrix whose elements are $v^{\alpha}{}_{\beta}(\mathbf{p})$ transforms the tangent vector at e of a one-parameter subgroup into the tangent vector at **p**, as shown in Fig. 3-1. It should be noted that, according to (3) and (8),

$$v^{\alpha}{}_{\beta}(0) = \delta^{\alpha}{}_{\beta}. \tag{3.14}$$

This is necessary if (13) is to be consistent at e. It is also observed that matrix $v^{\alpha}{}_{\beta}(\mathbf{p})$ is nonsingular, since it is a special case of the matrix $\partial f^{\alpha}/\partial q^{\beta}$.

The initial condition $p^{\alpha}(0) = 0$ can be added to the system of equations (13). A standard result, the Picard-Lindelöf theorem [1], of the theory of ordinary differential equations guarantees that if the functions $v^{\alpha}{}_{\beta}(\mathbf{p})\, a^{\beta}$ have bounded derivatives with respect to their arguments (the p^{γ} in this case), then there is an interval $(-\varepsilon, \varepsilon)$ such that the equations (13) have a unique solution for s in this interval. The differentiability condition is satisfied in the present case since the product functions are at least twice differentiable in the parameter domain. We consider now a solution of (13), satisfying **p**(0) = 0, for some particular choice of the a^{β}. It is to be expected that these solutions will also satisfy (12) and therefore describe at least part of a one-parameter subgroup. The components of the tangent at e to the subgroup will then be the a^{β}. This is the content of the following theorem.

THEOREM 3-1. A set of functions **p**(s) that satisfy (13) for s in the interval $(-\varepsilon, \varepsilon)$ with initial condition p(0) = 0 also satisfy (12) for s, t, and s + t in the same interval. These functions can be used to generate a complete one-parameter subgroup.

Proof. The method of proof is to show that each side of (12), considered as a function of t, satisfies the same first-order differential equation with the same initial conditions; the uniqueness theorem for the solution then guarantees that the two sides are the same. The left-hand side of (12) will be denoted by $l^{\alpha}(t)$; differentiating with respect to t and using (13) gives

$$\dot{l}^{\alpha}(t) = \dot{p}^{\alpha}(s+t) = v^{\alpha}{}_{\beta}(\mathbf{p}(s+t))\, a^{\beta} = v^{\alpha}{}_{\beta}(\boldsymbol{l}(t))a^{\beta}. \tag{3.15}$$

This equation is in fact identical to (13) but with the initial condition $\boldsymbol{l}(0) = \mathbf{p}(s)$. The right-hand side of (12) will be denoted by $r^{\alpha}(t)$. Differentiating $\mathbf{r}$ with respect to t and using successively (13), (9), and the definition of $\mathbf{r}$ gives

$$\begin{aligned} \dot{r}^{\alpha}(t) &= \frac{\partial f^{\alpha}}{\partial q^{\gamma}}(\mathbf{p}(s), \mathbf{p}(t))\, \dot{p}^{\gamma} = \frac{\partial f^{\alpha}}{\partial q^{\gamma}}(\mathbf{p}(s), \mathbf{p}(t))\, v^{\gamma}{}_{\beta}(\mathbf{p}(t))\, a^{\beta} \\ &= v^{\alpha}{}_{\beta}(\mathbf{f}(\mathbf{p}(s), \mathbf{p}(t)))\, a^{\beta} = v^{\alpha}{}_{\beta}(\mathbf{r}(t))\, a^{\beta}. \end{aligned} \tag{3.16}$$

This equation is identical to (15) so that it can be concluded that $\mathbf{r}(t)$ and $\boldsymbol{l}(t)$ satisfy the same differential equation. Furthermore, $\mathbf{r}(0) = \mathbf{f}(\mathbf{p}(s), 0) = \mathbf{p}(s)$ so that $\mathbf{r}$ and $\boldsymbol{l}$ satisfy the same initial condition. The uniqueness theorem for the solution of the differential equations guarantees that $\mathbf{r}(t)$ and $\boldsymbol{l}(t)$ are the same in any interval in which the solutions exist, that is, provided s, t, and s + t are all in $(-\varepsilon, \varepsilon)$ since the solution of (15) or (16) is then obviously $\mathbf{p}(s + t)$.

If a solution of (13) is known in the interval $[-\varepsilon, \varepsilon]$, which can be assumed to be closed, it can be continued outside the interval by expressing an arbitrary parameter t in the form $n\varepsilon + \delta$ where n is an integer and $0 \leq \delta < \varepsilon$. The group element a(t) can then be defined to be $[a(\varepsilon)]^n a(\delta)$. It can be seen that the function a(t) defined in this way is a one-parameter subgroup since the various factors involved in the construction all commute. This subgroup is constructed in the group; a particular parameter domain may contain the coordinates of only a limited part of the subgroup. Henceforth, when we refer to the coordinates $\mathbf{p}(t)$ of a one-parameter subgroup, we mean the arc connected to the origin in the domain that contains the coordinates of the identity. It is also convenient to call $\mathbf{p}(t)$ one-parameter subgroup, even though it may really only be part of one.

3-6 CANONICAL COORDINATES

It has been seen that a solution to (13) exists for every tangent vector $\mathbf{a}$ so that a one-parameter subgroup passes through e in every direction. It will now be shown that there is a neighborhood V of e such that a one-parameter subgroup passes through each point in V. It is first noted that if $\mathbf{p}(t)$ is a one-parameter subgroup with tangent vector $\mathbf{a}$, $\mathbf{p}(ct)$ is a one-parameter subgroup with tangent vector $c\mathbf{a}$. We will now show the dependence of $\mathbf{p}(t)$ on $\mathbf{a}$ explicitly by writing

$\mathbf{p}(t) = \mathbf{z}(\mathbf{a}, t)$ where $\mathbf{a} = \dot{\mathbf{p}}(0)$. Then the above observation shows that $\mathbf{z}(\mathbf{a}, ct) = \mathbf{z}(c\mathbf{a}, t)$. Consider now the function $\mathbf{w}(\mathbf{a}) = \mathbf{z}(\mathbf{a}, 1)$. It can be seen from the above identity that $z^{\alpha}(\mathbf{a}, t) = w^{\alpha}(t\mathbf{a})$. If this identity is differentiated with respect to t we find

$$\frac{\partial w^{\alpha}}{\partial a^{\beta}}(t\mathbf{a})\, a^{\beta} = \dot{z}^{\alpha}(\mathbf{a}, t) = v^{\alpha}{}_{\beta}(\mathbf{z}(\mathbf{a}, t))\, a^{\beta}$$

from the differential equation (13). The theory of ordinary differential equations guarantees that the derivatives $\partial w^{\alpha}/\partial a^{\beta}$ exist. Putting $t = 0$ now shows that

$$\frac{\partial w^{\alpha}}{\partial a^{\beta}}(0)\; a^{\beta} = \delta^{\alpha}{}_{\beta}\; a^{\beta}$$

and, since the numbers a^{β} can be chosen arbitrarily, that

$$\frac{\partial w^{\alpha}}{\partial a^{\beta}}(0) = \delta^{\alpha}{}_{\beta}\,.$$

It can be concluded that the Jacobian of the transformation $\mathbf{w}(\mathbf{a})$ is 1 at $\mathbf{a} = 0$. The implicit function theorem can now be used to prove that there are open regions V in the parameter space and U in the space of tangent vectors such that the equation $\mathbf{p} = \mathbf{w}(\mathbf{a})$ can be solved to give $\mathbf{a}$ as a single-valued function of $\mathbf{p}$. In other words, for every $\mathbf{p} \in V$, there is a unique $\mathbf{a} \in U$ such that $\mathbf{p} = \mathbf{w}(\mathbf{a})$. It is therefore possible to use the components of the tangent vectors in U as a new set of group parameters characterizing the group element with old coordinates $\mathbf{p} = \mathbf{w}(\mathbf{a})$, provided $\mathbf{p} \in V$. The new coordinates of a group element are the components of the tangent at e to the one-parameter subgroup that passes through the point at $t = 1$. This new coordinate system is said to be canonical.

The one-parameter subgroups have the very simple parametric equations $\mathbf{a}(t) = \mathbf{a}t$ as long as $\mathbf{a}t$ is in U. This is proved as follows. Let $\mathbf{p}(t)$ be the old coordinates of a one-parameter subgroup with tangent vector $\mathbf{a} \in U$; then $\mathbf{p}(1)$ has new coordinates $\mathbf{a}$. Consider the curve $\mathbf{p}_s$ in the old parameters defined by $\mathbf{p}_s(t) = \mathbf{p}(st)$. The tangent at 0 to $\mathbf{p}_s$ is $s\mathbf{a}$ and $\mathbf{p}_s(1)$ has new coordinates $s\mathbf{a}$ (provided $s\mathbf{a} \in U$). On the other hand $\mathbf{p}_s(1) = \mathbf{p}(s)$, showing that the new coordinates of $\mathbf{p}(s)$ are simply $s\mathbf{a}$, provided $\mathbf{p}(s) \in V$ (or $s\mathbf{a} \in U$).

It is also possible to prove that any continuous one-parameter subgroup (the arc going through the unit element), not assumed differentiable, must have a parametric equation of the form $\mathbf{p}(t) = \mathbf{a}t$ for some $\mathbf{a}$[2]. Therefore, the coordinates must actually be differentiable functions of t in the open region U and must satisfy equation (13). The proof of this fact will be omitted.

This has the following consequence that will be useful in the next chapter. Suppose that f is a homomorphic mapping of a Lie group G onto another Lie group G'. If a(t) is a one-parameter subgroup in G, f(a(t)) is a one-parameter subgroup of G'. If further, the coordinates of G and G' are canonical, the coordinates of a(t) and f(a(t)) are expressible as **a**t and **a**'t respectively. It will be assumed that **a** and **a**' are in the neighborhoods U and U' in which canonical coordinates for G and G' are defined; this can always be achieved by a change of scale in the parameter t. If f is regarded as a mapping from the coordinates of G to the coordinates of G', we can write

$$f^{\alpha}(\mathbf{a}t) = a'^{\alpha}(\mathbf{a})t \tag{3.17}$$

where a'^{α} is independent of t but depends on **a**.

It can be proved that the f^{α} are linear functions of their arguments. It is first necessary to prove that they are differentiable at the origin. To show this we put $a^{\mu} = \delta_{\mu\nu}$ so that (17) becomes

$$f^{\alpha}(0,0,\ldots,t,\ldots,0) = a'^{\alpha}(0,0,\ldots,1,\ldots,0)t.$$

Differentiation with respect to t shows that $\partial f^{\alpha}/\partial a^{\nu}(0)$ exists and is $a'^{\alpha}(0,0,\ldots,1,\ldots,0)$, the 1 being the νth argument of a'^{α}.

The derivative of (17) with respect to t, evaluated at t = 0, is

$$\frac{\partial f^{\alpha}}{\partial a^{\mu}}(0)\, a^{\mu} = a'^{\alpha}(\mathbf{a}).$$

On the other hand, if we put t = 1 in (17), we find that

$$f^{\alpha}(\mathbf{a}) = a'^{\alpha}(\mathbf{a}) = \frac{\partial f^{\alpha}}{\partial a^{\mu}}(0)\, a^{\mu}. \tag{3.18}$$

Equation (18) shows that f^{α} is a linear function of **a**.

The transformation to canonical coordinates from an arbitrary parametrization is differentiable and invertible in the neighborhood of the origin. From this it can be shown, in view of the differentiability of (18), that a homomorphic mapping of one Lie group onto another must be a differentiable mapping of the coordinates in the neighborhood of the origin. In particular, two parametrizations in a Lie group must be connected by a differentiable transformation. In this case the transformation must also be invertible, since in each parametrization there are neighborhoods of the origin in which the points can be placed in one-to-one correspondence with the group elements, and therefore with each other.

3-7 ONE-PARAMETER SUBGROUPS OF MATRIX GROUPS

To provide an illustration of the concept of one-parameter subgroup, these subgroups of the group L(n) of $n \times n$ nonsingular matrices will be calculated. A parametrization of the group is obtained by expressing each matrix element in the form $\delta^{ij} + p^{ij}$ so that the coordinates of the identity are zero. Rather than attempt to use a single index, it is much more convenient to use a pair of indices, namely, (ij), $i = 1, 2, \ldots, n$, $j = 1, 2, \ldots, n$ to label the parameters. The product functions for the matrix group are then given by

$$f^{ij}(\mathbf{p}, \mathbf{q}) = p^{ij} + q^{ij} + p^{ik} q^{kj}. \tag{3.19}$$

From this we obtain

$$v^{ij}{}_{mn}(\mathbf{p}) = \frac{\partial f^{ij}}{\partial q^{mn}}(\mathbf{p}, 0) = \delta^{i}{}_{m} \delta^{j}{}_{n} + p^{im} \delta^{j}{}_{n}. \tag{3.20}$$

The differential equation (13) is therefore

$$\dot{p}^{ij} = [\delta^{i}{}_{m} \delta^{j}{}_{n} + p^{im} \delta^{j}{}_{n}] a^{mn} = a^{ij} + p^{im} a^{mj} \tag{3.21}$$

where the a^{mn} are the matrix elements of the "tangent" matrix A. This equation can be conveniently written in matrix form as

$$\dot{P} = A + PA. \tag{3.22}$$

It can be verified that this equation has the solution

$$P(t) = e^{At} - 1 \tag{3.23}$$

where

$$e^{At} - 1 = \sum_{r=1}^{\infty} \frac{A^r t^r}{r!} \tag{3.24}$$

is a convergent (for all t) power series solution of (22). (The largest matrix element of A^r is smaller in absolute value than $(nA_m)^r$ where A_m is the absolute value of the largest matrix element of A.) We can conclude that the one-parameter subgroups of L(n) can be written in the form e^{At} where A is an arbitrary $n \times n$ matrix.

Chapter 4

LIE ALGEBRAS

The properties of a Lie group that pertain to elements in the neighborhood of the identity can be investigated and characterized by considering another mathematical structure associated with the group, the Lie algebra of the group. The purpose of this chapter is to define Lie algebras, and to discuss, rather superficially, the relation between a Lie group and the corresponding Lie algebra.

The Lie algebra of an arbitrary Lie group will be defined in Section 1, and in the second section this definition will be related to the Lie algebra of a matrix group, which can be defined, somewhat differently, as a matrix algebra.

Further properties of Lie algebras are developed in Sections 4, 5, and 6. In Section 7 the Lie algebras of some of the important matrix groups are calculated, and in Section 8 all the Lie algebras of dimension 1, 2, and 3 are catalogued.

Some of the theorems which are more difficult to prove will be stated without complete proof in this chapter. These theorems concern the relation between Lie groups and Lie algebras; their proofs can be found in Pontrjagin's classic work [1].

The term Lie algebra was introduced by H. Weyl to replace the earlier somewhat misleading term, infinitesimal group, used by Lie.

4-1 ABSTRACT DEFINITION OF A LIE ALGEBRA

The elements of a Lie algebra are real, n-dimensional vectors $\mathbf{a}$, and a Lie algebra Λ is an n-dimensional vector space. A Lie algebra is constructed from a Lie group G by defining the vectors $\mathbf{a}$ to be the tangents at the identity to (at least twice) differentiable curves in the group These curves may, but need not, be one-parameter subgroups. In any event, for any $\mathbf{a} \in \Lambda$ there is, according to Theorem 3-1, a one-parameter subgroup $\mathbf{p}(s)$ such that

$$\dot{\mathbf{p}}(0) = \mathbf{a}. \qquad (4.1)$$

The linear properties of Λ are related to the group properties of G. If, for example, **a** and **b** are tangent to curves **p**(s) and **q**(t) respectively in the group, **a** + **b** is tangent to the curve **r**(s) = **p**(s) **q**(s). The parameters of **r**(s) are given by $r^\alpha(s) = f^\alpha(\mathbf{p}(s), \mathbf{q}(s))$; therefore

$$\dot{r}^\alpha(0) = \frac{\partial f^\alpha}{\partial p^\beta}(0,0)\dot{p}^\beta(0) + \frac{\partial f^\alpha}{\partial q^\beta}(0,0)\dot{q}^\beta(0) = a^\alpha + b^\alpha$$

because of (3.3) and (1). If **a** is tangent to the curve **p**(s), α**a** is tangent to **p**(αs). In particular, if **p**(s) is a one-parameter subgroup, and α is an integer, α**a** is tangent to $[\mathbf{p}(s)]^\alpha$. In a very loose sense, Λ can be regarded as the space of "logarithms" of group elements.

In an algebra, not only linear combinations, but also products of elements are defined. In the case of a Lie algebra, the product of two elements is called the commutator and is constructed from the group commutator. Suppose **a** and **b** are tangent to twice differentiable curves **p**(s) and **q**(t) respectively. It is convenient, but not necessary, to assume that **p**(s) and **q**(t) are one-parameter subgroups. We form the function

$$a(s,t) = \mathbf{p}(s)\mathbf{q}(t)\mathbf{p}(s)^{-1}\mathbf{q}(t)^{-1}, \tag{4.2}$$

where **p**(s), **q**(t) represent the group elements with these parameters. Equation (2) determines, in general, a surface in the group. The parameters **r** of a(s, t) are given by

$$r^\alpha(s,t) = f^\alpha(\mathbf{f}(\mathbf{p}(s),\mathbf{q}(t)),\mathbf{f}(\mathbf{p}(-s),\mathbf{q}(-t))) \tag{4.3a}$$

if **p**(s) and **q**(t) are one-parameter subgroups. We consider expanding $r^\alpha(s, t)$ to second-order in a Taylor series in s and t:

$$r^\alpha(s,t) = a_0{}^\alpha + a_1{}^\alpha s + a_2{}^\alpha t + a_{11}{}^\alpha s^2 + a_{12}{}^\alpha st + a_{22}{}^\alpha t^2 + \ldots. \tag{4.3b}$$

This is possible since **p**(s), **q**(t), and also the product functions are at least twice differentiable.

It can be seen from (2) that a(0, t) = e for all t since $\mathbf{p}(0) = \mathbf{p}(0)^{-1} = e$ and hence that $r^\alpha(0, t) = 0$. Putting s = 0 in (3b) shows that $a_0{}^\alpha = a_2{}^\alpha = a_{22}{}^\alpha = 0$. Similarly, it can be shown by putting t = 0 that $a_1{}^\alpha = a_{11}{}^\alpha = 0$, so that

$$r^\alpha(s,t) = a_{12}{}^\alpha st + \ldots. \tag{4.3c}$$

The coefficients $a_{12}{}^\alpha$ can be calculated from equations (3):

$$a_{12}{}^\alpha = \frac{\partial^2 r^\alpha}{\partial s \partial t}(0,0) = \left[\frac{\partial^2 f^\alpha}{\partial p^\beta \partial q^\gamma}(0,0) - \frac{\partial^2 f^\alpha}{\partial q^\beta \partial p^\gamma}(0,0)\right]\dot{p}^\beta(0)\dot{q}^\gamma(0)$$
$$= c^\alpha{}_{\beta\gamma} a^\beta b^\gamma \tag{4.4a}$$

where

$$c^{\alpha}{}_{\beta\gamma} = \frac{\partial^2 f^{\alpha}}{\partial p^{\beta}\partial q^{\gamma}}(0,0) - \frac{\partial^2 f^{\alpha}}{\partial p^{\gamma}\partial q^{\beta}}(0,0). \tag{4.4b}$$

The commutator $[\mathbf{a}, \mathbf{b}]$ of the elements $\mathbf{a}$ and $\mathbf{b}$ of Λ is the vector whose components are defined by

$$[\mathbf{a}, \mathbf{b}]^{\alpha} = a_{12}{}^{\alpha} = c^{\alpha}{}_{\beta\gamma}\, a^{\beta} b^{\gamma}. \tag{4.5a}$$

The coefficients $c^{\alpha}{}_{\beta\gamma}$ defined in (4b) are known as the structure constants of the Lie algebra.

The choice of $\mathbf{p}(s)$ and $\mathbf{q}(t)$ as one-parameter subgroups was made to simplify the discussion and is not essential. It can be shown, but we will not do this, that the definition of $[\mathbf{a}, \mathbf{b}]$ is independent of the choice of curves to which $\mathbf{a}$ and $\mathbf{b}$ are tangent.

The unit vectors in Λ, that is, the vectors $\mathbf{e}_{\alpha}$ with components defined by $(\mathbf{e}_{\alpha})^{\beta} = \delta_{\alpha\beta}$, can be seen to satisfy

$$[\mathbf{e}_{\beta}, \mathbf{e}_{\gamma}] = c^{\alpha}{}_{\beta\gamma}\mathbf{e}_{\alpha}. \tag{4.5b}$$

Another definition of the commutator is that it is the tangent vector to the curve $a(\sqrt{s}, \sqrt{s})$, as defined by (2). The advantage of this definition is that it is independent of the parametrization in the group.

Two simple consequences of equations (4b) and (5a) can be stated as a theorem.

THEOREM 4-1. The commutation operation satisfied the antisymmetry property

$$[\mathbf{a}, \mathbf{b}] = -[\mathbf{b}, \mathbf{a}] \text{ or } c^{\alpha}{}_{\beta\gamma} = -c^{\alpha}{}_{\gamma\beta}, \tag{4.6}$$

and the linearity properties

$$[\alpha_1\mathbf{a}_1 + \alpha_2\mathbf{a}_2, \mathbf{b}] = \alpha_1[\mathbf{a}_1, \mathbf{b}] + \alpha_2[\mathbf{a}_2, \mathbf{b}] \tag{4.7a}$$

$$[\mathbf{a}, \beta_1\mathbf{b}_1 + \beta_2\mathbf{b}_2] = \beta_1[\mathbf{a}, \mathbf{b}_1] + \beta_2[\mathbf{a}, \mathbf{b}_2]. \tag{4.7b}$$

Equations (6) imply that $[\mathbf{a}, \mathbf{a}] = 0$ and that $c^{\alpha}{}_{\beta\beta} = 0$.

The structure constants depend on the parametrization chosen for the group G. Under a change in parametrization of G, the vectors $\mathbf{e}_{\alpha}$ of equation (5b), which are unit vectors along the coordinate axes, must be expressed in terms of $\mathbf{f}_{\beta}$, the unit vectors along the new coordinate axes. Explicitly, $\mathbf{e}_\alpha = s_\alpha{}^\beta \mathbf{f}_\beta$, $\mathbf{f}_\beta = t_\beta{}^\alpha \mathbf{e}_\alpha$, where $s_\alpha{}^\beta = \partial p'^\beta/\partial p^\alpha(0)$ and $t_\beta{}^\alpha = \partial p^\alpha/\partial p'^\beta(0)$. If $\bar{c}^\rho{}_{\sigma\tau}$ are the structure constants in the new representation, we can write

$$[\mathbf{f}_\sigma, \mathbf{f}_\tau] = t_\sigma{}^\beta t_\tau{}^\gamma [\mathbf{e}_\beta, \mathbf{e}_\gamma] = t_\sigma{}^\beta t_\tau{}^\gamma c^\alpha{}_{\beta\gamma} \mathbf{e}_\alpha$$
$$= t_\sigma{}^\beta t_\tau{}^\gamma s_\alpha{}^\rho c^\alpha{}_{\beta\gamma} \mathbf{f}_\rho = \bar{c}^\rho{}_{\sigma\tau} \mathbf{f}_\rho.$$

This shows that in the new parametrization the structure constants are given by

$$\bar{c}^\rho{}_{\sigma\tau} = s_\alpha{}^\rho t_\sigma{}^\beta t_\tau{}^\gamma c^\alpha{}_{\beta\gamma}. \tag{4.8}$$

If two Lie algebras are of the same dimension and their structure constants are the same or can be connected by a transformation of the form (8), where the $t_\sigma{}^\beta$ are the matrix elements of the inverse of the matrix whose elements are $s_\alpha{}^\rho$, the Lie algebras are said to be <u>isomorphic.</u> All isomorphic Lie algebras are essentially the same; the properties of one of them imply all the algebraic properties of the others.

If the commutator of any pair of elements in a Lie algebra is zero, the algebra is said to be <u>Abelian.</u>

4-2 LIE ALGEBRA OF A MATRIX GROUP

If a Lie group is a matrix group, it is possible to define its Lie algebra not as tangents in the parameter space, but as a set of matrices. The result is a Lie algebra isomorphic to that of the definition of the previous section, that is, it is a vector space of the same dimension and has a commutation operation defined with the same structure constants. The commutation operation is in this case, moreover, the operation of forming matrix commutators, that is,

$$[A, B] = AB - BA. \tag{4.9}$$

We consider a Lie group G of matrices $A(\mathbf{p})$ with the group operation being that of matrix multiplication. It will be assumed that the elements of A are differentiable functions of the parameters $\mathbf{p}$. Suppose that $\mathbf{a} = \dot{\mathbf{p}}(0)$ is an element of the Lie algebra Λ of G; $\mathbf{a}$ is the tangent at 0 to a curve $\mathbf{p}(t)$ in the parameter space.

Corresponding to the curve $\mathbf{p}(t)$ there is a matrix function $A(\mathbf{p}(t))$. We can calculate

$$\dot{A}(\mathbf{p}(0)) = \frac{\partial A}{\partial p^\alpha}(0)\, \dot{p}^\alpha(0) = I_\alpha a^\alpha \tag{4.10}$$

where

$$I_\alpha = \frac{\partial A}{\partial p^\alpha}(0). \tag{4.11}$$

It will be assumed, although it can be proved on the basis of the previous axioms, that the I_α are linearly independent. This will be evident in all the examples that are considered. There is then a nonzero matrix $I_\alpha a^\alpha$ corresponding to each $\mathbf{a} \in \Lambda$. The set Λ' of such matrices is an n-dimensional vector space, which will be shown also to be a Lie algebra. The matrices I_α are called the <u>generators</u> of Λ'.

It will now be shown that $I_\beta I_\gamma - I_\gamma I_\beta$ is also in Λ' and is, in fact, $c^\alpha{}_{\beta\gamma} I_\alpha$ where the $c^\alpha{}_{\beta\gamma}$ are the structure constants of Λ. This is shown by applying equation (2) directly to G, with $\mathbf{p}(s)$ and $\mathbf{q}(t)$ assumed to be one-parameter subgroups:

$$A(\mathbf{r}(s,t)) = A(\mathbf{p}(s))A(\mathbf{q}(t))A(\mathbf{p}(-s))A(\mathbf{q}(-t)). \tag{4.12}$$

The desired result can be obtained by evaluating the second derivative, with respect to s and t, of this identity, at $s = t = 0$. It is simpler, however, to expand each side to second order in s and t and equate the coefficients of st on each side. Since we have seen that terms in s^2 and t^2 do not appear in equation (3b), it is sufficient to expand $A(\mathbf{p}(s))$ and $A(\mathbf{q}(t))$ to first order in s and t, that is,

$$A(\mathbf{p}(s)) = I + \frac{\partial A}{\partial p^\beta}(0)a^\beta s + \ldots = I + I_\beta a^\beta s + \ldots.$$

Similarly, $A(\mathbf{q}(t)) = I + I_\gamma b^\gamma t + \ldots.$

To first order in s and t, $A(\mathbf{p}(-s)) = I - I_\beta a^\beta s$, and $A(\mathbf{q}(-t)) = I - I_\gamma b^\gamma t$. In the desired approximation we can also write $r^\alpha(s,t) = c^\alpha{}_{\beta\gamma} a^\beta b^\gamma\, st$ and therefore $A(\mathbf{r}(s,t)) = I + I_\alpha c^\alpha{}_{\beta\gamma} a^\beta b^\gamma\, st$. Equation (12) is therefore, in second order,

$$I + c^\alpha{}_{\beta\gamma} I_\alpha a^\beta b^\gamma st = (I + I_\beta a^\beta s)(I + I_\gamma b^\gamma t)(I - I_\beta a^\beta s)(I - I_\gamma b^\gamma t)$$

$$= I + (I_\beta I_\gamma - I_\gamma I_\beta)a^\beta b^\gamma st.$$

Equating the coefficient of st on each side shows that

$$c^\alpha{}_{\beta\gamma} I_\alpha a^\beta b^\gamma = (I_\beta I_\gamma - I_\gamma I_\beta)a^\beta b^\gamma.$$

The numbers a^β and b^γ can be chosen arbitrarily, and therefore

$$(I_\beta I_\gamma - I_\gamma I_\beta) = c^\alpha{}_{\beta\gamma} I_\alpha. \tag{4.13}$$

Comparison of this result with (5b) shows that the basis vectors I_α in Λ' satisfy the same relations, under the product defined by (9), as the basis vectors $\mathbf{e}_\alpha$ in Λ. Furthermore, the product in (9) is linear in the factors A and B so that if $a^\alpha I_\alpha$ and $b^\beta I_\beta$ correspond to **a** and **b** respectively, $(a^\alpha I_\alpha)(b^\beta I_\beta) - (b^\beta I_\beta)(a^\alpha I_\alpha)$ corresponds to $[\mathbf{a}, \mathbf{b}]$. Explicitly,

$$(a^\alpha I_\alpha)(b^\beta I_\beta) - (b^\beta I_\beta)(a^\alpha I_\alpha) = a^\alpha b^\beta (I_\alpha I_\beta - I_\beta I_\alpha)$$
$$= a^\alpha b^\beta c^\gamma{}_{\alpha\beta} I_\gamma = [\mathbf{a}, \mathbf{b}]^\gamma I_\gamma.$$

We can conclude:

THEOREM 4-2. The Lie algebra Λ' spanned by matrices I_α defined by equation (11) with multiplication defined by (9), is isomorphic to the Lie algebra Λ defined by equations (1) and (5a).

It should be remarked that equations (11) and (13) depend on the possibility of differentiating the matrices with respect to their parameters; this in turn is based on the possibility of taking linear combinations (which are not defined in an arbitrary Lie group) of matrices. The resulting matrices, the I_α, are not, in general, group elements.

4-3 AN EXAMPLE

Before discussing further properties of Lie algebras, the rather abstract considerations of the last two sections will be illustrated by an example. We choose for this the affine group in one dimension, consisting of matrices of the form

$$A(p^1, p^2) = \begin{pmatrix} e^{p^1} & p^2 \\ 0 & 1 \end{pmatrix}, \tag{4.14}$$

The law of group multiplication is given by

$$f^1(p^1, p^2; q^1, q^2) = p^1 + q^1$$
$$f^2(p^1, p^2; q^1, q^2) = p^2 + e^{p^1} q^2. \tag{4.15}$$

The elements of the Lie algebra in the abstract sense are two-dimensional vectors $\mathbf{a} = (a^1, a^2)$. It can be verified directly that the subgroup associated with this vector consists of the matrices

$$A(s) = \begin{pmatrix} e^{a^1 s} & \frac{a^2}{a^1}\left(e^{a^1 s} - 1\right) \\ 0 & 1 \end{pmatrix} \tag{4.16}$$

The element a(s, t) can be obtained by a bit of computation.

$$a(s,t) = \begin{pmatrix} 1 & \left(\frac{a^2}{a^1} - \frac{b^2}{b^1}\right)\left(e^{a^1 s} + e^{b^1 t} - e^{a^1 s + b^1 t} - 1\right) \\ 0 & 1 \end{pmatrix}$$

The parameters of a(s, t) can be obtained by comparison with (14):

$$p^1 = 0 \tag{4.17a}$$

$$p^2 = \left(\frac{a^2}{a^1} - \frac{b^2}{b^1}\right)\left(e^{a^1 s} + e^{b^1 t} - e^{a^1 s + b^1 t} - 1\right)$$
$$\sim (a^1b^2 - a^2b^1)st \tag{4.17b}$$

The last line in (17b) give p^2 correctly up to second-order terms in s and t. By equations (3c) and (5a) we conclude that

$$[\mathbf{a}, \mathbf{b}]^1 = 0, \ [\mathbf{a}, \mathbf{b}]^2 = a^1b^2 - a^2b^1. \tag{4.18}$$

The one-parameter subgroup associated with this element of the Lie algebra is obtained from (16) by substituting 0 for a^1 and $a^1b^2 - a^2b^1$ for a^2. It is, taking the limit $a^1 \to 0$,

$$A(s) = \begin{pmatrix} 1 & (a^1b^2 - a^2b^1)s \\ 0 & 1 \end{pmatrix}$$

The commutator could also have been obtained by calculating the structure constants from equation (4b). For this purpose only c^1_{12} and c^2_{12} are needed; the remainder are either zero or can be obtained from equation (6). From equation (15) it is seen that

$$\frac{\partial^2 f^1}{\partial p^1 \partial q^2} = 0 = \frac{\partial^2 f^1}{\partial q^1 \partial p^2}$$

and hence that $c^1_{12} = 0 = -c^1_{21}$. Also,

$$\frac{\partial^2 f^2}{\partial p^1 \partial q^2} = e^{p^1}, \ \frac{\partial^2 f^2}{\partial q^1 \partial p^2} = 0$$

so that $c^2_{12} = -c^2_{21} = 1 - 0 = 1$. From (5a) it is found therefore that

$$[\mathbf{a},\mathbf{b}]^1 = 0 \qquad [\mathbf{a},\mathbf{b}]^2 = c^2{}_{\alpha\beta}\, a^\alpha b^\beta = a^1 b^2 - a^2 b^1,$$

in agreement with the previous calculation. We have used the fact also that $c^1{}_{11} = c^1{}_{22} = c^2{}_{11} = c^2{}_{22} = 0$.

The "more concrete" form of the Lie algebra makes use of the matrices $I_\alpha = \partial A / \partial p^\alpha(0)$. These are, from (14),

$$I_1 = \begin{pmatrix} 1 & 0 \\ 0 & 0 \end{pmatrix} \quad I_2 = \begin{pmatrix} 0 & 1 \\ 0 & 0 \end{pmatrix}.$$

The general element of the algebra is

$$a^1 I_1 + a^2 I_2 = \begin{pmatrix} a^1 & a^2 \\ 0 & 0 \end{pmatrix}$$

These matrices form a 2-dimensional vector space and

$$[a^1 I_1 + a^2 I_2, b^1 I_1 + b^2 I_2] = \begin{pmatrix} a^1 & a^2 \\ 0 & 0 \end{pmatrix}\begin{pmatrix} b^1 & b^2 \\ 0 & 0 \end{pmatrix} - \begin{pmatrix} b^1 & b^2 \\ 0 & 0 \end{pmatrix}\begin{pmatrix} a^1 & a^2 \\ 0 & 0 \end{pmatrix}$$

$$= \begin{pmatrix} 0 & a^1 b^2 - a^2 b^1 \\ 0 & 0 \end{pmatrix},$$

which corresponds to the $[\mathbf{a},\mathbf{b}]$ of (18). Evidently the construction of the Lie algebra is most straightforward from the matrix definition. However, the definition in terms of tangent vectors is more natural for abstract groups and also permits a simpler discussion of some of the relations between Lie algebras and Lie groups. These relations will be discussed in Section 6 of this chapter.

4-4 THE JACOBI IDENTITY

It has been seen that the commutation operation in a Lie algebra satisfies the antisymmetry and linearity properties of equations (6) and (7). These are not in themselves sufficient to define a Lie algebra; a third property, the Jacobi identity, must also be satisfied. The identity is:

THEOREM 4-3

$$[\mathbf{a}, [\mathbf{b},\mathbf{c}]] + [\mathbf{c}, [\mathbf{a},\mathbf{b}]] + [\mathbf{b}, [\mathbf{c},\mathbf{a}]] = 0. \qquad (4.19)$$

The identity is a reflection of the associative law of group multiplication, although this fact is not obvious.

If the Lie group is a matrix group, the **a**, **b**, **c** are matrices and the commutators in (19) can be evaluated from equation (9). In this case equation (19) is a consequence of the associative law of matrix multiplication as one finds by writing out the $3\times2\times2 = 12$ terms explicitly. Inasmuch as there is a matrix group locally isomorphic to any Lie group (though we have not proved this and will prove it in Chapter 6 only for groups that have a center consisting only of e), equation (19) is a consequence of the simple proof for matrix Lie groups. Equation (19) can, however, be proved directly from the associative law (3.2) of group multiplication. The method of proof is to differentiate (3.2) three times, with respect to p^β, q^γ, and r^δ, and evaluate the result at $\mathbf{p} = \mathbf{q} = \mathbf{r} = 0$. The resulting identity can be rearranged to demonstrate (19). The calculation is, however, tedious and not instructive, and will not be given here. It should be noted that although the Jacobi identity is closely connected with the associative law of the group, the associative law need not be valid for the multiplication law of the algebra.

Equation (19) provides a restriction on the structure constants. If **a**, **b**, **c** are basis vectors $\mathbf{e}_\beta$, $\mathbf{e}_\gamma$, $\mathbf{e}_\delta$ and equation (5b) is taken into account, the result is

$$c^\alpha{}_{\beta\mu} c^\mu{}_{\gamma\delta} + c^\alpha{}_{\delta\mu} c^\mu{}_{\beta\gamma} + c^\alpha{}_{\gamma\mu} c^\mu{}_{\delta\beta} = 0. \tag{4.20}$$

This is the αth component of the identity. In (20) the indices α, β, γ, δ are free and μ is a summation index; the three terms are generated by cyclic permutations of β, γ, and δ. If any two of these are equal, (20) reduces to an identity as a result of the antisymmetry relation (6). Hence in the previous example of a 2-dimensional Lie algebra, the Jacobi relations are automatically satisfied. Equation (20) is actually the result that is derived from the group associative law (3.2), rather than (19).

An n-dimensional linear vector space with a product defined that satisfies the linearity, antisymmetry and Jacobi identities is also said to be a Lie algebra, whether or not it can be constructed from a Lie group. It was shown by Lie that for every such Lie algebra, there is a local Lie group that has that Lie algebra. A local Lie group is essentially a set of functions **f** defined in some neighborhood of the origin that satisfy equation (3.1) and (3.2) and therefore define, for points **p** and **q** in the neighborhood of the origin, a product. The local Lie group may not be a Lie group, however, since **f**(**p**, **q**) may be outside the domain of the product functions, so that multiplication by **f**(**p**, **q**) is not defined. The proof of this result is quite involved and will not be given here.

It is, furthermore, true that groups that have the same Lie

algebra are locally isomorphic. It is from this fact that the Lie algebra obtains its importance; it determines all the properties of the elements of a Lie group in the neighborhood of the identity, that is, all the local properties. This is a consequence of the proof of Lie's theorem, in which the functions **f** are constructed in canonical coordinates as solutions of partial differential equations, and the uniqueness of the solutions of these equations can be demonstrated.

4-5 SUBALGEBRAS AND FACTOR ALGEBRAS

It is possible to define, in analogy to group theory, a subalgebra of a Lie algebra. An m-dimensional linear subspace M of a Lie algebra Λ is a subalgebra if, for each pair **a** and **b** in M, [**a**, **b**] is also in M. It is possible to formulate the existence of a subalgebra in terms of the structure constants. The basis vectors $\{\mathbf{e}_\lambda\}$ could, if M is a subalgebra, be chosen so that $\mathbf{e}_1, \mathbf{e}_2, \ldots, \mathbf{e}_m$ are in M. The condition that $[\mathbf{e}_i, \mathbf{e}_j] \in M$ if $\mathbf{e}_i$ and $\mathbf{e}_j$ are in M can be seen to be

$$c^{\alpha}_{\beta\gamma} = 0, \quad \alpha > m, \quad \beta \leq m, \quad \gamma \leq m. \tag{4.21}$$

It is apparent that M is a subalgebra if there is a transformation of the form (8) such that the transformed structure constants have the property (21).

A subalgebra M is said to be an ideal if, for each $\mathbf{a} \in \Lambda$ and $\mathbf{x} \in M$, $[\mathbf{a}, \mathbf{x}] \in M$. It will be seen that the ideal is the analogue of the normal subgroup of group theory and could perhaps be more suitably called a normal subalgebra. In the coordinate system in which the first m basis vectors are in M, the structure constants satisfy

$$c^{\alpha}_{\beta\gamma} = 0, \quad \alpha > m, \quad \beta \leq m \tag{4.22}$$

for all γ. Again we remark that Λ contains an ideal if the structure constants can be transformed to have property (22).

If a Lie algebra Λ contains an ideal M, it is possible to define a factor algebra Λ/M as follows. We consider the set **a** + M of all elements of the form **a** + **m**, $\mathbf{m} \in M$. This set is in fact a group theoretic coset of M where M is a normal subgroup of Λ under the group operation of vector addition. Two elements **a** and **a'** are in the same coset if and only if $\mathbf{a} - \mathbf{a}' \in M$. The family of all cosets **a** + M is defined to be the factor algebra Λ/M. It is necessary to define the linear and commutation operations in Λ/M. These are given by

$$c(\mathbf{a} + M) = c\mathbf{a} + M, \tag{4.23}$$

$$(\mathbf{a} + M) + (\mathbf{b} + M) = (\mathbf{a} + \mathbf{b}) + M, \tag{4.24}$$

$$[\mathbf{a} + M, \mathbf{b} + M] = [\mathbf{a}, \mathbf{b}] + M. \tag{4.25}$$

In order that these definitions be consistent, it is necessary to verify that they are independent of the choice of $\mathbf{a}$ and $\mathbf{b}$ from their respective cosets. We will do this for (25) and leave to the reader the corresponding arguments for (23) and (24). If $\mathbf{a}'$ and $\mathbf{b}'$ are arbitrary elements from $\mathbf{a} + M$ and $\mathbf{b} + M$, we can write $\mathbf{a}' = \mathbf{a} + \mathbf{m}_1$ and $\mathbf{b}' = \mathbf{b} + \mathbf{m}_2$ where $\mathbf{m}_1$ and $\mathbf{m}_2$ are in M. In terms of $\mathbf{a}'$ and $\mathbf{b}'$, (25) becomes

$$[\mathbf{a}' + M, \mathbf{b}' + M] = [\mathbf{a}', \mathbf{b}'] + M = [\mathbf{a} + \mathbf{m}_1, \mathbf{b} + \mathbf{m}_2] + M$$

$$= [\mathbf{a}, \mathbf{b}] + M,$$

since $[\mathbf{a}, \mathbf{m}_2]$, $[\mathbf{m}_1, \mathbf{b}]$, and $[\mathbf{m}_1, \mathbf{m}_2]$ are all in M and $\mathbf{m} + M = M$ if $\mathbf{m} \varepsilon$ M. It is here that the property that M is an ideal is used. The zero

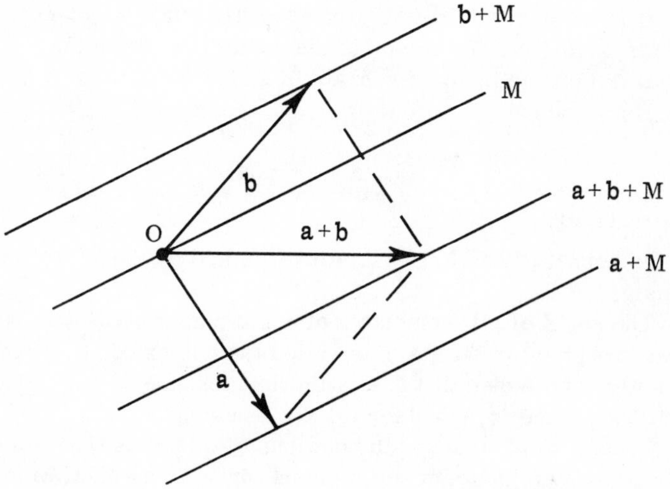

Fig. 4-1

A 2-dimensional Lie algebra with ideal M. The elements of Λ/M are lines parallel to M. In this case Λ/M is Abelian, since it is one-dimensional.

element of Λ/M is the coset M. It is easy to verify from (25) that antisymmetry and Jacobi conditions are satisfied in Λ/M. In Fig. 4-1 we show Λ as a plane and M as a line through the origin; the factor algebra Λ/M consists of all lines parallel to M.

A Lie algebra Λ is said to be homomorphic to a Lie algebra Λ' if there is a linear function f mapping Λ onto Λ' with the property that for any pair of elements **a** and **b** in Λ

$$[f(\mathbf{a}), f(\mathbf{b})] = f([\mathbf{a}, \mathbf{b}]). \tag{4.26}$$

We note for completeness that a linear function is one with the property that

$$f(\alpha\mathbf{a} + \beta\mathbf{b}) = \alpha f(\mathbf{a}) + \beta f(\mathbf{b}), \tag{4.27}$$

and that this implies $f(0) = 0$.

If a Lie algebra Λ is homomorphic to a Lie algebra Λ', the set K of elements of Λ that map into the zero element of Λ' is called the kernel of the homomorphism. That is, $\mathbf{a} \in K$ if and only if $f(\mathbf{a}) = 0$. The set K is a linear subspace of Λ and is, furthermore, an ideal since if $\mathbf{x} \in K$, $\mathbf{a} \in \Lambda$, $f([\mathbf{x}, \mathbf{a}]) = [f(\mathbf{x}), f(\mathbf{a})] = [0, f(\mathbf{a})] = 0$, and hence $[\mathbf{x}, \mathbf{a}] \in K$. To complete the analogy to group theory, we remark that the factor algebra Λ/K is isomorphic to Λ' by the correspondence

$$\mathbf{a} + K \longleftrightarrow f(\mathbf{a}). \tag{4.28}$$

If the kernel of f is 0, f has an inverse and is, therefore, an isomorphism.

The set Z of all elements **z** of a Lie algebra with the property that $[\mathbf{z}, \mathbf{a}] = 0$ for all $\mathbf{a} \in \Lambda$ is called the center of Λ. It can be readily established that Z is a linear subspace of Λ and that Z is an ideal, since $[\mathbf{z}, \mathbf{a}] = 0$ for all $\mathbf{a} \in \Lambda$ and $0 \in Z$.

The set of all linear combinations of elements that can be expressed as commutators of elements in Λ is an ideal which is called the derived subalgebra of Λ and is denoted by Λ'; Λ' is an ideal since for any $\mathbf{x} \in \Lambda'$ and $\mathbf{a} \in \Lambda$, $[\mathbf{a}, \mathbf{x}] \in \Lambda'$ by the definition. The derived subalgebra has the property that Λ/Λ' is Abelian. The proof of this fact is analogous to the proof of the similar result in the theory of groups and will be omitted.

If the center of a Lie algebra Λ consists only of 0, it is possible to obtain a Lie algebra of matrices isomorphic to Λ. Suppose $\mathbf{e}_1, \mathbf{e}_2, \ldots, \mathbf{e}_n$ are basis vectors in Λ in satisfying $[\mathbf{e}_\beta, \mathbf{e}_\gamma] = c^\alpha{}_{\beta\gamma}\,\mathbf{e}_\alpha$. We consider $n \times n$ matrices $I_1, I_2, \ldots, I_n$ defined by

$$(I_\mu)_{\alpha\beta} = c^\alpha{}_{\mu\beta}. \tag{4.29}$$

It can be verified by direct calculation using the antisymmetry and Jacobi identities that $[I_\beta, I_\gamma] = c^\alpha{}_{\beta\gamma} I_\alpha$.

$$[I_\beta, I_\gamma]_{\rho\sigma} = (I_\beta)_{\rho\tau}(I_\gamma)_{\tau\sigma} - (I_\gamma)_{\rho\tau}(I_\beta)_{\tau\sigma}$$
$$= c^\rho{}_{\beta\tau} c^\tau{}_{\gamma\sigma} - c^\rho{}_{\gamma\tau} c^\tau{}_{\beta\sigma} = -c^\rho{}_{\sigma\tau} c^\tau{}_{\beta\gamma} = c^\tau{}_{\beta\gamma}(I_\tau)_{\rho\sigma}.$$

The set Λ' of all linear combinations of the I_μ is a Lie algebra, and Λ is homomorphic to Λ' by the mapping

$$a^\mu \mathbf{e}_\mu \rightarrow a^\mu I_\mu.$$

It is not difficult to see that the kernel of this mapping is the center Z of Λ. Suppose $Z \neq 0$ and is of dimension m; it is convenient to choose the basis vectors so that $\mathbf{e}_\alpha \in Z, \alpha \leq m$. The condition $[\mathbf{e}_\alpha, \mathbf{a}] = 0$, $\alpha \leq m$, requires that $c^\gamma{}_{\alpha\beta} = 0$ for all β and γ and hence that $I_\alpha = 0$. This demonstrates that Z maps into 0 in Λ'. Conversely if an I_μ, or a linear combination of I_μ, is zero, the corresponding element in Λ is in Z. We can conclude that the mapping is an isomorphism if and only if $Z = 0$. The Lie algebra Λ' is called the adjoint representation of Λ. In Chapter 6 a similar matrix representation for a Lie group will be constructed.

4-6 RELATIONS BETWEEN LIE GROUPS AND THEIR ALGEBRAS

The relation of various properties of groups to the corresponding algebras will now be discussed briefly. The first remark is rather obvious and is that if G is Abelian, Λ is also Abelian. This is an immediate consequence of (3) and (5), since if G is Abelian, $r(s,t) = 0$ and $a_{12}{}^\alpha = 0$.

We consider now the homomorphic relation. Suppose that G and G' are Lie groups with corresponding Lie algebras Λ and Λ' and suppose that f is a homomorphic mapping of G onto G'. It is to be expected that f should generate a homomorphic mapping $\tilde{f}$ of Λ onto Λ' and it will now be shown that this is indeed the case. It is natural to define $\tilde{f}(\mathbf{a})$ to be the tangent at the origin to the curve $\mathbf{p}'(s) = f(\mathbf{p}(s))$ where $\mathbf{p}(s)$ is a curve in G with tangent $\mathbf{a}$; this is possible since, according to the remarks at the end of Section 3-6, f is a differentiable function of the parameters $\mathbf{p}$. The components of $\tilde{f}(\mathbf{a})$ are then given by

$$\tilde{f}^{\alpha}(\mathbf{a}) = \frac{\partial f^{\alpha}}{\partial p^{\beta}}(0)\,\dot{p}^{\beta}(0) = \frac{\partial f^{\alpha}}{\partial p^{\beta}}(0)a^{\beta}.$$

It is observed from this that $\tilde{f}(\mathbf{a})$ is a linear function of $\mathbf{a}$. If $[\mathbf{a}, \mathbf{b}]$ is tangent to $\mathbf{r}(s) = \mathbf{p}(\theta)\mathbf{q}(\theta)\mathbf{p}(-\theta)\mathbf{q}(-\theta)$, $\theta = s^{1/2}$, then $\tilde{f}([\mathbf{a}, \mathbf{b}])$ is tangent to $f(\mathbf{r}(s)) = f(\mathbf{p}(\theta))f(\mathbf{q}(\theta))f(\mathbf{p}(-\theta))f(\mathbf{q}(-\theta))$; the tangent to the latter curve can be expressed as $[\tilde{f}(\mathbf{a}), \tilde{f}(\mathbf{b})]$, which is therefore the same as $\tilde{f}([\mathbf{a}, \mathbf{b}])$. The mapping $\tilde{f}$ is therefore a homomorphism.

If a Lie group G contains a subgroup H that is also a Lie group, the Lie algebra M of H is a subalgebra of the Lie algebra Λ of G. This is a simple consequence of the fact that a one-parameter subgroup of H is also a one-parameter subgroup of G. Therefore, a tangent in M is also a tangent in Λ and M is a subset of Λ. Since the linear operations and commutator can be defined in terms of group operations, which are the same in G and H, it follows readily that M is a subalgebra of Λ.

If N is a normal Lie subgroup of G, it can be seen that the Lie algebra M of G is an ideal in Λ, the Lie algebra of G. Suppose $\mathbf{a} \in \Lambda$ and $\mathbf{m} \in M$ are tangent respectively to curves $\mathbf{p}(s) \in G$ and $\mathbf{n}(s) \in N$. Then $[\mathbf{a}, \mathbf{m}]$ is tangent to $\mathbf{r}(s) = \mathbf{p}(\theta)\mathbf{n}(\theta)\mathbf{p}(\theta)^{-1}\mathbf{n}(\theta)^{-1}$, $\theta = s^{1/2}$. Since N is normal, $\mathbf{p}(\theta)\mathbf{n}(\theta)\mathbf{p}(\theta)^{-1} = \mathbf{n}'(\theta) \in N$ and hence $\mathbf{r}(s) = \mathbf{n}'(\theta)\mathbf{n}(\theta)^{-1} \in N$. It follows that $\dot{\mathbf{r}}(0) = [\mathbf{a}, \mathbf{m}] \in M$, and hence it is true that M is an ideal.

If G/N is also a Lie group, it is reasonable to expect that the Lie algebra Λ' of G/N should be isomorphic to Λ/M. To prove this we consider the natural homomorphism f of G onto G/N. Corresponding to this there is a homomorphism $\tilde{f}$ of Λ onto Λ'. If it can be shown that the kernel K of $\tilde{f}$ is M, the result will be proved, since it is known that Λ' is isomorphic to Λ/K. We wish to show that M is the set of all $\mathbf{a} \in \Lambda$ such that $\tilde{f}(\mathbf{a}) = 0$. Suppose first that $\mathbf{a} \in M$. Then $\mathbf{a}$ is tangent to a curve $\mathbf{n}(t) \in N$. Since $f(\mathbf{n}(t)) = e'$, the identity of G/N, the definition of $\tilde{f}(\mathbf{a})$ as the tangent to $f(\mathbf{n}(t))$ shows that $\tilde{f}(\mathbf{a}) = 0$. Suppose, conversely, that $\tilde{f}(\mathbf{a}) = 0$. We wish to show that $\mathbf{a} \in M$. There is a one-parameter subgroup $\mathbf{p}(t) \in G$ with $\mathbf{a}$ as its tangent vector. (In canonical coordinates $\mathbf{p}(t) = \mathbf{a}t$.) Since f is a homomorphism, $f(\mathbf{p}(t))$ is a one-parameter subgroup of G/N, and since $\tilde{f}(\mathbf{a}) = 0$, the tangent to $f(\mathbf{p}(t))$ at e' is 0. The one-parameter subgroup $\mathbf{p}'(t) = e'$ also has this property, and by the uniqueness property of the solution of ordinary differential equations, we can argue that $f(\mathbf{p}(t)) = e'$. This implies that $\mathbf{p}(t) \in N$ and hence that $\mathbf{a}$, the tangent to $\mathbf{p}(t)$, is in M. We conclude that M is the kernel of $\tilde{f}$ and that Λ/M is isomorphic to Λ'.

4-7 SOME IMPORTANT LIE ALGEBRAS

In this section we will calculate the Lie algebras of the important matrix groups that are denoted by L(n), SL(n), O(n), U(n), and SU(n). The definition of each group will be given when it is discussed.

The group L(n) (linear group in n dimensions) is the set of all $n \times n$ real matrices with positive determinant. (The corresponding group with complex matrix elements is usually denoted by L(n), C).) If A is any $n \times n$ real matrix, the curve e^{At} defined by (3.24) is in L(n). This follows because e^{At} has an inverse e^{-At} and therefore $|e^{At}| \neq 0$; the determinant $|e^{At}|$ is a continuous function of t and therefore $|e^{At}| > 0$. The tangent to e^{At} at $t = 0$ is A; it can be concluded, therefore, that the Lie algebra of L(n) is composed of all $n \times n$ real matrices.

It may be worthwhile to note that in this case the one-parameter subgroups do not cover the whole group. The eigenvalues λ_1 and λ_2 of a real matrix A are either real or $\lambda_2 = \lambda_1{}^*$. Then either e^{λ_1} and e^{λ_2} are both positive, or $e^{\lambda_1} = (e^{\lambda_2})^*$, that is, the eigenvalues of e^A cannot be real, negative, and distinct and therefore the matrix

$$Q = \begin{pmatrix} -a & 0 \\ 0 & -b \end{pmatrix},$$

a, b > 0 and distinct cannot be expressed in the form e^A, although it is an element of L(2). The one-parameter subgroups do not even cover a subgroup of L(2), since $Q = (-Q)(-I) = e^A e^{i\pi\sigma_y}$, where

$$A = \begin{pmatrix} \ln a & 0 \\ 0 & \ln b \end{pmatrix} \qquad \sigma_y = \begin{pmatrix} 0 & i \\ -i & 0 \end{pmatrix}.$$

We have assumed that the eigenvalues of e^A are e^{λ_i} where λ_i are the eigenvalues of A. This is certainly true if A is Hermitian and is also true if the eigenvalues of A are distinct since, if $A\mathbf{u} = \lambda\mathbf{u}$, $e^A\mathbf{u} = e^\lambda\mathbf{u}$, as can be seen by operating on $\mathbf{u}$ with equation (3.24). If the eigenvalues of A are not distinct, it is possible to regard A as a limit of matrices A_α, whose eigenvalues are distinct. Since the eigenvalues are continuous functions of the matrix elements, and the elements of e^A are continuous functions of the elements of A, as $A_\alpha \to A$ the eigenvalues $e^{\lambda\alpha}$ of e^{A_α} approach eigenvalues of e^A, and therefore, if λ is a multiple eigenvalue of A, e^λ is an eigenvalue of e^A of the same multiplicity.

It will now be shown that

$$|e^A| = e^{\operatorname{Tr} A} \tag{4.30}$$

$$\operatorname{Tr} A = a_{11} + a_{22} + \dots + a_{nn}. \tag{4.31}$$

The eigenvalues of e^A satisfy the secular equation $|e^A - \lambda I| = (e^{\lambda_1}-\lambda)(e^{\lambda_2}-\lambda)\dots(e^{\lambda_n}-\lambda) = 0$, where $\lambda_1, \lambda_2, \dots, \lambda_n$ are the eigenvalues of A, not necessarily distinct. Putting $\lambda = 0$ shows that $|e^A| = e^{\lambda_1 + \lambda_2 + \dots + \lambda_n}$. The eigenvalues of A satisfy $|A - \lambda I| = (\lambda_1 - \lambda) \times (\lambda_2 - \lambda)\dots(\lambda_n - \lambda)$. The coefficient of λ^{n-1} on the right-hand side of this identity is $-(\lambda_1 + \lambda_2 + \dots + \lambda_n)$. A term in λ^{n-1} in $|A - \lambda I|$ can only arise from the product $(a_{11} - \lambda)(a_{22} - \lambda)\dots(a_{nn} - \lambda)$ of the diagonal elements of $A - \lambda I$ since all other terms in the determinant contain at most $n-2$ factors from the diagonal. The coefficient of λ^{n-1} is therefore seen to be $-(a_{11} + a_{22} + \dots + a_{nn})$, and hence (30) is valid. This argument can be replaced by a simpler one if A is Hermitian, but we require the result for a general matrix.

The group SL(n) (special linear group) is the subgroup of L(n) composed of all matrices of unit determinant. Such a matrix is said to be unimodular. The determinantal rule $|AB| = |A|\,|B|$ ensures that this is a group. It will now be shown that the Lie algebra of SL(n) is composed of all $n \times n$ matrices with zero trace. A one-parameter subgroup of SL(n), since it is also a one-parameter subgroup of L(n), can be written in the form e^{At}; equation (30) implies that $e^{At} \in SL(n)$ if and only if $\operatorname{Tr} A = 0$. Therefore, an element of the Lie algebra of SL(n) must have zero trace, and any traceless matrix A is in the Lie algebra since it is tangent to the curve $e^{At} \in SL(n)$.

The group O(n) (orthogonal group) is the set of all orthogonal $n \times n$ matrices, that is, matrices satisfying

$$M^T M = I \tag{4.32}$$

where M^T is the transpose of M. Since $|M^T|$, the determinant of M^T, is equal to that of M, it follows from (32) that $|M| = \pm 1$. The subgroup of O(n) of unimodular matrices is of the greatest interest for our purposes; this is often denoted by SO(n), $O(n)^+$, or R_n. It is easy to see that SO(n) is isomorphic to the factor group $O(n)/Z_2$ where Z_2 consists of $\pm I$.

It will now be shown that the Lie algebra of SO(n) is composed of all $n \times n$ skew-symmetric matrices. We again consider a one-parameter subgroup expanded in the form $I + At + Bt^2 + \dots$ where A is an element of the Lie algebra. This expansion is possible since a one-parameter subgroup of SO(n) is also a one-parameter subgroup of L(n). Equation (32) requires $I = (I + A^T t + B^T t^2 + \ldots) \times (I + At + Bt^2 + \ldots)$ or $0 = (A^T + A)t + (B^T + A^T A + B)t^2 + \ldots$ The coefficient of each power of t must vanish and, in particular, $A^T -A$.

This does not show that all skew-symmetric matrices are in the algebra. To prove this, consider a curve e^{At} where $A^T = -A$. Then $I = e^{-At}e^{At} = e^{ATt}\, e^{At} = (e^{At})^T e^{At}$. It follows that $e^{At} \; \varepsilon \; SO(n)$, and since its tangent at $t = 0$ is A, that A is in the Lie algebra.

It can be seen in a similar way that the Lie algebra of the group U(n) of n-dimensional unitary matrices satisfying

$$U^\dagger U = I \tag{4.33}$$

is the set of all n-dimensional skew-Hermitian matrices, that is, matrices with the property $A^\dagger = -A$. It is also evident that the group SU(n) of unitary unimodular matrices is the set of all skew-Hermitian matrices with zero trace.

It should be remarked that these two groups are somewhat outside the theory that has been developed, since the parameters are apparently complex numbers. This difficulty can be avoided by the rather artificial device of regarding each complex parameter as a pair of real parameters. The corresponding Lie algebra, which consists of all matrices of the form A + Bi, where A is skew-symmetric and B is symmetric can be rendered real by considering the set of all 2n-dimensional real matrices of the form

$$\begin{pmatrix} A & B \\ -B & A \end{pmatrix}$$

where B is symmetric and A is skew-symmetric. It is easy to show that this set of matrices is isomorphic to the Lie algebra of U(n).

4-8 LIE ALGEBRAS OF DIMENSION 1, 2, AND 3

In order to illustrate more fully the concept and some properties of Lie algebras we will calculate those algebras whose dimension is less than four. The algebras will be expressed by giving the commutators of linearly independent vectors which will be selected to provide canonical forms with a minimum of arbitrary structure constants.

There is only one one-dimensional Lie algebra with one unit vector $\mathbf{1}$ satisfying $[\mathbf{1}, \mathbf{1}] = 0$. We shall call the n-dimensional Abelian

Lie algebra A_n; the present one is then A_1. There are two essentially different Lie groups with this Lie algebra. They are the groups U(1) and R defined in Section 3-3; one of these is compact and the other is not, but locally they are of course the same.

There are two essentially different two-dimensional Lie algebras. One of these is A_2, the Abelian algebra in which $[\mathbf{i}, \mathbf{j}] = 0$ for any pair of vectors in the algebra. The other algebra is not Abelian. There is, therefore, a pair of linearly independent vectors $\mathbf{a}$ and $\mathbf{b}$ such that $[\mathbf{a}, \mathbf{b}] = \mathbf{i} \neq 0$. Any pair of vectors can be written in the form $\alpha_1 \mathbf{a} + \beta_1 \mathbf{b}$ and $\alpha_2 \mathbf{a} + \beta_2 \mathbf{b}$; because of the linearity of commutator and since $[\mathbf{a}, \mathbf{a}] = [\mathbf{b}, \mathbf{b}] = 0$, the commutator of these two vectors is $(\alpha_1 \beta_2 - \beta_1 \alpha_2)\mathbf{i}$. It follows that all commutators are proportional to $\mathbf{i}$ so that the derived algebra is one-dimensional. We will choose $\mathbf{i}$ to be one of the basis vectors. If $\mathbf{k}$ is any vector linearly independent of $\mathbf{i}$, we can write $[\mathbf{i}, \mathbf{k}] = c\,\mathbf{i}$ where $c \neq 0$, since the algebra is non-Abelian. If we put $\mathbf{k} = c\mathbf{j}$ we obtain the canonical form for the algebra $[\mathbf{i}, \mathbf{j}] = \mathbf{i}$. An example of this algebra is provided by all 2×2 matrices with the second row zero; the elements $\mathbf{i}$ and $\mathbf{j}$ are then given by

$$\mathbf{i} = \begin{pmatrix} 1 & 0 \\ 0 & 0 \end{pmatrix} \qquad \mathbf{j} = \begin{pmatrix} 0 & 1 \\ 0 & 0 \end{pmatrix}. \tag{4.34}$$

It is apparent that this algebra is that of the affine group in one dimension discussed in Section 3. This group, which is denoted $\mathcal{A}_1$ is not compact.

The three-dimensional algebras can be analyzed on the basis of the dimension of their derived subalgebras. For example, if the dimension of the derived algebra is zero, the algebra is A_3, the three-dimensional Abelian algebra.

There are two inequivalent algebras in which the derived algebra, which will be denoted by Λ', is one-dimensional. This is shown by choosing a vector $\mathbf{i} \in \Lambda'$ and any two other linearly independent vectors $\mathbf{j}$ and $\mathbf{k}$. The commutators can then be written

$$[\mathbf{i}, \mathbf{j}] = \alpha \mathbf{i}, \qquad [\mathbf{i}, \mathbf{k}] = \beta \mathbf{i}, \qquad [\mathbf{j}, \mathbf{k}] = \gamma \mathbf{i}. \tag{4.35}$$

We distinguish two cases. The first is $\alpha = \beta = 0$, in which case γ must be nonzero since the algebra is assumed not Abelian. It is possible to scale $\mathbf{i}$ so that $\gamma = 1$ and the canonical form

$$[\mathbf{i}, \mathbf{j}] = [\mathbf{i}, \mathbf{k}] = 0 \quad [\mathbf{j}, \mathbf{k}] = \mathbf{i} \tag{4.36}$$

is obtained. An example of this algebra is provided by the matrices

$$\mathbf{i}=\begin{pmatrix}0&0&0\\0&0&1\\0&0&0\end{pmatrix}\ \mathbf{j}=\begin{pmatrix}0&0&1\\0&0&0\\0&0&0\end{pmatrix}\ \mathbf{k}=\begin{pmatrix}0&0&0\\-1&0&0\\0&0&0\end{pmatrix}. \qquad (4.37)$$

Another realization of (36) is given by the Born-Jordan operators $\mathbf{j} = q$, $\mathbf{k} = p$, and $\mathbf{i}$ multiplication with $i\hbar$.

The second case is that in which α or β is nonzero. It is then possible to form a linear combination of $\mathbf{j}$ and $\mathbf{k}$ that commutes with $\mathbf{i}$; we assume that this was done initially and the result chosen for the vector $\mathbf{j}$ so that $\alpha = 0$. We now put $\mathbf{j}' = \gamma\mathbf{i} - \beta\mathbf{j}$; $\mathbf{j}'$ is linearly independent of $\mathbf{i}$, since by assumption $\beta \neq 0$, and one can verify that $\mathbf{j}'$ commutes with both $\mathbf{i}$ and $\mathbf{k}$. Finally, $\mathbf{k}$ can be scaled so that $\beta = 1$. This gives the canonical form for the commutators

$$[\mathbf{i},\mathbf{j}'] = 0 \quad [\mathbf{i},\mathbf{k}] = \mathbf{i} \quad [\mathbf{j}',\mathbf{k}] = 0. \qquad (4.38)$$

An example of this algebra is given by the matrices

$$\mathbf{i}=\begin{pmatrix}0&1\\0&0\end{pmatrix}\ \mathbf{j}'=\begin{pmatrix}1&0\\0&1\end{pmatrix}\ \mathbf{k}=\begin{pmatrix}0&0\\0&1\end{pmatrix}. \qquad (4.39)$$

The two algebras can be seen to be inequivalent, since $\mathbf{i}$ is in the center of the first algebra, but not of the second. The algebra of (39) is the direct sum of the affine algebra $\mathfrak{A}_1$ and the Abelian algebra A_1.

We consider now the case in which Λ' is two-dimensional. We will let $\mathbf{i}$ and $\mathbf{j}$ be vectors in Λ' and assume that Λ' is in canonical form, that is, either $[\mathbf{i},\mathbf{j}]=0$, or $[\mathbf{i},\mathbf{j}]=\mathbf{i}$. It will be shown first that the second case is impossible. If $\mathbf{k}$ is any other vector linearly independent of $\mathbf{i}$ and $\mathbf{j}$ we can write $[\mathbf{i},\mathbf{j}]=\mathbf{i}$, $[\mathbf{i},\mathbf{k}] = \alpha\mathbf{i}+\beta\mathbf{j}$, $[\mathbf{j},\mathbf{k}] = \mu\mathbf{i}+\nu\mathbf{j}$. Substitution of these commutators into the Jacobi identity

$$[\mathbf{i}, [\mathbf{j},\mathbf{k}]] + [\mathbf{k}, [\mathbf{i},\mathbf{j}]] + [\mathbf{j}, [\mathbf{k},\mathbf{i}]] = 0 \qquad (4.40)$$

gives, after a straightforward calculation, $\nu\mathbf{i} - \beta\mathbf{j} = 0$. Since $\mathbf{i}$ and $\mathbf{j}$ are assumed linearly independent this implies $\nu = \beta = 0$, which in turn implies that Λ' is one-dimensional, contrary to assumption. Hence we can assume that Λ' is Abelian, so that the commutators can be written in the form $[\mathbf{i},\mathbf{j}] = 0$, $[\mathbf{i},\mathbf{k}] = \alpha\mathbf{i} + \beta\mathbf{j}$, $[\mathbf{j},\mathbf{k}] = \mu\mathbf{i} + \nu\mathbf{j}$. We wish now to choose suitable linear combinations to eliminate as many as possible of the parameters α, β, μ, ν. We remark first that adding any linear combination of $\mathbf{i}$ and $\mathbf{j}$ to $\mathbf{k}$ does not affect the commutators, so that the only significant change which can be made in **k** is in its scale. We investigate now the possibility of choosing linear combinations of **i** and **j** to simplify the form of the commutators. For this purpose we look for elements **m** ε Λ' that satisfy [**m**,**k**] = λ**m**; **m** can be expressed in the form a**i** + b**j**, leading to the eigenvalue equation

$$\begin{pmatrix} \alpha & \mu \\ \beta & \nu \end{pmatrix}\begin{pmatrix} a \\ b \end{pmatrix} = \lambda \begin{pmatrix} a \\ b \end{pmatrix}. \tag{4.41}$$

The eigenvalues of this equation must be nonzero; otherwise Λ' would be one-dimensional. We can now consider three possibilities. Equation (41) may have two nonzero real eigenvalues λ_1 and λ_2 with corresponding eigenvectors **m** and **n**. If this is the case, **k** can be scaled so that $\lambda_1 = 1$; this gives the commutation relations

$$[\mathbf{m},\mathbf{n}] = 0, \quad [\mathbf{m},\mathbf{k}] = \mathbf{m}, \quad [\mathbf{n},\mathbf{k}] = \lambda \mathbf{n}. \tag{4.42}$$

Each value of λ gives an inequivalent Lie algebra. An example of this algebra is given by the matrices

$$\mathbf{m} = \begin{pmatrix} 0 & 0 & 1 \\ 0 & 0 & 0 \\ 0 & 0 & 0 \end{pmatrix} \; \mathbf{n} = \begin{pmatrix} 0 & 0 & 0 \\ 0 & 0 & 1 \\ 0 & 0 & 0 \end{pmatrix} \; \mathbf{k} = \begin{pmatrix} -1 & 0 & 0 \\ 0 & -\lambda & 0 \\ 0 & 0 & 0 \end{pmatrix}. \tag{4.43}$$

If the eigenvalue equation has only one nonzero root λ and corresponding eigenvector **m**, we can write [**m**,**k**] = λ**m**, [**n**,**k**] = α**m** + β**n** where **n** is any other vector linearly independent of **m** and **k**. The scale of **k** can be chosen so that $\lambda = 1$ and the scale of **m** can be chosen so that $\alpha = 1$. (If $\alpha = 0$, the algebra is that of equation (42).) The condition that the two eigenvalues be equal then requires $\beta = 1$. This gives the commutators

$$[\mathbf{m},\mathbf{n}] = 0, \quad [\mathbf{m},\mathbf{k}] = \mathbf{m}, \quad [\mathbf{n},\mathbf{k}] = \mathbf{m} + \mathbf{n}. \tag{4.44}$$

An example of this algebra is provided by the matrices

$$\mathbf{m} = \begin{pmatrix} 0 & 0 & 1 \\ 0 & 0 & 0 \\ 0 & 0 & 0 \end{pmatrix} \; \mathbf{n} = \begin{pmatrix} 0 & 0 & 0 \\ 0 & 0 & 1 \\ 0 & 0 & 0 \end{pmatrix} \; \mathbf{k} = \begin{pmatrix} -1 & -1 & 0 \\ 0 & -1 & 0 \\ 0 & 0 & 0 \end{pmatrix}. \tag{4.45}$$

If equation (41) has two complex roots, we proceed by expressing one root as $\lambda_r + i\lambda_i$ and the corresponding eigenvector as **m** + i**n**. The eigenvalue equation can be written [**m** + i**n**,**k**] = $(\lambda r + i\lambda_i)$(**m** + i**n**). It is possible, since $\lambda_i \neq 0$, to scale **k** so that $\lambda_i = 1$. If we take the real and imaginary parts of the eigenvalue equation and replace λ_r by λ, we obtain the canonical form for the commutators

$$[\mathbf{m}, \mathbf{n}] = 0, \quad [\mathbf{m}, \mathbf{k}] = \lambda \mathbf{m} - \mathbf{n}, \quad [\mathbf{n}, \mathbf{k}] = \mathbf{m} + \lambda \mathbf{n}. \tag{4.46}$$

The matrices

$$\mathbf{m} = \begin{pmatrix} 0 & 0 & 1 \\ 0 & 0 & 0 \\ 0 & 0 & 0 \end{pmatrix} \quad \mathbf{n} = \begin{pmatrix} 0 & 0 & 0 \\ 0 & 0 & 1 \\ 0 & 0 & 0 \end{pmatrix} \quad \mathbf{k} = \begin{pmatrix} -\lambda & -1 & 0 \\ 1 & -\lambda & 0 \\ 0 & 0 & 0 \end{pmatrix} \tag{4.47}$$

provide an example of this algebra. We will discover that the particular case $\lambda = 0$ is of special geometric and physical interest.

The case in which Λ' is three-dimensional is somewhat more difficult to analyze. It will be shown first that there exists a pair of vectors whose commutator is linearly independent of them. We suppose that this is not the case. Then any pair of vectors spans a two-dimensional subalgebra and there is one such subalgebra that is not Abelian, since otherwise Λ would be Abelian. This subalgebra can be taken in canonical form so that there exist vectors $\mathbf{i}$ and $\mathbf{j}$ such that $[\mathbf{i}, \mathbf{j}] = \mathbf{i}$. If $\mathbf{k}$ is any other linearly independent vector, we can, according to our assumption, write $[\mathbf{j}, \mathbf{k}] = \alpha_1 \mathbf{j} + \alpha_2 \mathbf{k}$ and $[\mathbf{k}, \mathbf{i}] = \beta_1 \mathbf{k} + \beta_2 \mathbf{i}$. Substituting these commutators into the Jacobi identity (40) gives

$$[\mathbf{i}, \alpha_1 \mathbf{j} + \alpha_2 \mathbf{k}] + [\mathbf{j}, \beta_1 \mathbf{k} + \beta_2 \mathbf{i}] + [\mathbf{k}, \mathbf{i}] = 0$$

$$\text{or} \qquad (\alpha_1 - \alpha_2 \beta_2)\mathbf{i} + \alpha_1 \beta_1 \mathbf{j} + \beta_1 \mathbf{k} = 0.$$

Since $\mathbf{i}$, $\mathbf{j}$, and $\mathbf{k}$ are linearly independent, this implies $\beta_1 = 0$; this is impossible, however, since if $\beta_1 = 0$, the vectors $\mathbf{i}$ and $\alpha_1 \mathbf{j} + \alpha_2 \mathbf{k}$ span Λ' which would consequently be two-dimensional.

We consider now three linearly independent vectors $\mathbf{i}, \mathbf{j}$, and $\mathbf{k}$ such that $[\mathbf{i}, \mathbf{j}] = \mathbf{k}$. It should be noted that any multiple of $\mathbf{i}$ can be added to $\mathbf{j}$ without affecting the form of this commutator. We can now write the other two commutators as

$$[\mathbf{j}, \mathbf{k}] = \alpha_1 \mathbf{i} + \alpha_2 \mathbf{j} + \alpha_3 \mathbf{k} \qquad [\mathbf{k}, \mathbf{i}] = \beta_1 \mathbf{i} + \beta_2 \mathbf{j} + \beta_3 \mathbf{k}.$$

It will be assumed for the present that $\beta_2 \neq 0$. Since interchanging $\mathbf{i}$ and $\mathbf{j}$ and changing the sign of $\mathbf{k}$ effectively interchanges α_1 and β_2, it is also sufficient that $\alpha_1 \neq 0$. The coefficient α_2 can be transformed to zero by replacing $\mathbf{j}$ by $\mathbf{j} + (\alpha_2/\beta_2)\mathbf{i}$. This transformation may change the coefficients α_i and β_i, but leaves the commutator

$[\mathbf{i},\mathbf{j}]$ invariant. If the Jacobi identity is again employed, the result is

$$[\mathbf{i}, \alpha_1\mathbf{i} + \alpha_3\mathbf{k}] + [\mathbf{j}, \beta_1\mathbf{i} + \beta_2\mathbf{j} + \beta_3\mathbf{k}] + [\mathbf{k},\mathbf{k}] = 0$$

$$\text{or} \quad -\alpha_3(\beta_1\mathbf{i} + \beta_2\mathbf{j} + \beta_3\mathbf{k}) - \beta_1\mathbf{k} + \beta_3(\alpha_1\mathbf{i} + \alpha_3\mathbf{k}) = 0.$$

The coefficient of each of $\mathbf{i}$, $\mathbf{j}$, and $\mathbf{k}$ must vanish. This implies that β_1, the coefficient of $\mathbf{k}$, is zero. We can also write $\beta_3\alpha_1 = -\alpha_3\beta_2 = 0$ since these are the coefficients of $\mathbf{i}$ and $\mathbf{j}$. It can be argued that $\alpha_1 \neq 0$ since if $\alpha_1 = 0$, Λ' is spanned by $\mathbf{k}$ and $[\mathbf{k},\mathbf{i}]$ and is therefore two-dimensional. By assumption $\beta_2 \neq 0$. It can be concluded that $\beta_3 = \alpha_3 = 0$ and that the commutators can be written in the form

$$[\mathbf{i}, \mathbf{j}] = \mathbf{k}, \quad [\mathbf{j},\mathbf{k}] = \alpha_1\mathbf{i}, \quad [\mathbf{k},\mathbf{i}] = \beta_2\mathbf{j}.$$

The possibility of changing the scale of the basis vectors remains. If we make the substitution

$$\mathbf{i} = |\beta_2|^{1/2}\mathbf{i}', \quad \mathbf{j} = |\alpha_1|^{1/2}\mathbf{j}', \quad \mathbf{k} = |\alpha_1\beta_2|^{1/2}\mathbf{k}'$$

the commutation relations become $[\mathbf{i}',\mathbf{j}'] = \mathbf{k}'$, $[\mathbf{j}',\mathbf{k}'] = \pm\mathbf{i}'$, $[\mathbf{k}',\mathbf{j}'] = \pm\mathbf{j}'$. There are apparently four different cases but only two of these are essentially different because of the possibility of permuting and changing the signs of the basis vectors. The two cases can be expressed by

$$[\mathbf{i},\mathbf{j}] = \mathbf{k}, \quad [\mathbf{j},\mathbf{k}] = \mathbf{i}, \quad [\mathbf{k},\mathbf{i}] = \mathbf{j} \tag{4.48}$$

$$[\mathbf{i},\mathbf{j}] = \mathbf{k}, \quad [\mathbf{j},\mathbf{k}] = -\mathbf{i}, \quad [\mathbf{k},\mathbf{i}] = -\mathbf{j}. \tag{4.49}$$

We return now to the case $\beta_2 = \alpha_1 = 0$. The Jacobi identity is now

$$[\mathbf{i}, \alpha_2\mathbf{j} + \alpha_3\mathbf{k}] + [\mathbf{j}, \beta_1\mathbf{i} + \beta_3\mathbf{k}] + [\mathbf{k},\mathbf{k}] = 0$$

$$\text{or} \quad \alpha_2\mathbf{k} - \alpha_3(\beta_1\mathbf{i} + \beta_3\mathbf{k}) - \beta_1\mathbf{k} + \beta_3(\alpha_2\mathbf{j} + \alpha_3\mathbf{k}) = 0.$$

This requires that $\alpha_3\beta_1 = 0, \beta_3\alpha_2 = 0, \alpha_2 - \beta_1 = 0$. If $\beta_1 = 0$, A' is spanned by $\mathbf{k}$ and $[\mathbf{j},\mathbf{k}]$ and is two-dimensional; therefore $\beta_1 \neq 0$ and $\alpha_3 = 0$. Similarly, it follows that $\beta_3 = 0$. The commutators can therefore be written $[\mathbf{i},\mathbf{j}] = \mathbf{k}$, $[\mathbf{j},\mathbf{k}] = \alpha_2\mathbf{j}$, $[\mathbf{k},\mathbf{i}] = \alpha_2\mathbf{i}$. Putting $\mathbf{i}' = \mathbf{i} + \mathbf{j}$, $\mathbf{j}' = \mathbf{i} - \mathbf{j}$, we find $[\mathbf{i}', \mathbf{j}'] = -2\mathbf{k}$, $[\mathbf{j}',\mathbf{k}] = -\alpha_2\mathbf{i}'$, $[\mathbf{k}, \mathbf{i}'] = \alpha_2\mathbf{j}'$. It is observed that these commutators can be reduced to the form (49).

We will find that equation (48) describes the Lie algebra of the three-dimensional rotation group and of SU(2). Equation (49) describes the algebra of the group of Lorentz transformations and rotations of a plane into itself. The two algebras can be represented by the sets of matrices

$$\mathbf{i} = \begin{pmatrix} 0 & 0 & 0 \\ 0 & 0 & -1 \\ 0 & 1 & 0 \end{pmatrix} \quad \mathbf{j} = \begin{pmatrix} 0 & 0 & 1 \\ 0 & 0 & 0 \\ -1 & 0 & 0 \end{pmatrix} \quad \mathbf{k} = \begin{pmatrix} 0 & -1 & 0 \\ 1 & 0 & 0 \\ 0 & 0 & 0 \end{pmatrix} \tag{4.50}$$

$$\mathbf{i} = \begin{pmatrix} 0 & 0 & 0 \\ 0 & 0 & 1 \\ 0 & 1 & 0 \end{pmatrix} \quad \mathbf{j} = \begin{pmatrix} 0 & 0 & 1 \\ 0 & 0 & 0 \\ 1 & 0 & 0 \end{pmatrix} \quad \mathbf{k} = \begin{pmatrix} 0 & -1 & 0 \\ 1 & 0 & 0 \\ 0 & 0 & 0 \end{pmatrix} \tag{4.51}$$

respectively.

The algebra of equation (49) contains the subalgebra consisting of $\mathbf{i}$ and $\mathbf{j} + \mathbf{k}$ which, since $[\mathbf{i}, \mathbf{j} + \mathbf{k}] = \mathbf{j} + \mathbf{k}$, is isomorphic to $\mathcal{A}_1$. Hence, the corresponding group cannot be compact.

Since it has been possible to give matrix representations for all the algebras, it is unnecessary to verify the Jacobi identity for any of them.

Chapter 5

INVARIANT INTEGRATION

The present and subsequent chapters will be concerned with properties of functions defined on a group. The functions of principal interest are real or complex; if Φ is such a function, its domain is the group and its range is either the set of real numbers or that of the complex numbers. Our aim in this chapter is to define an "invariant" integral over the group.. This means that the integral of a function Φ over the group should be the same as that of the function Φ_a where Φ_a is defined by $\Phi_a(g) = \Phi(ag)$, a and g being arbitrary group elements. The requirement of invariance of the integral is quite natural because the functions Φ and Φ_a assume exactly the same values on the group, but at different group elements.

5-1 INTEGRATION ON A FINITE GROUP

A finite group of order n provides a very simple example, although the integral is not what one usually thinks of as an integral. In this case, the function Φ is specified by a finite set of numbers, $\Phi(g_1)$, $\Phi(g_2), \ldots, \Phi(g_n)$. It is natural to define the "integral" of Φ over the group to be the sum of the values that Φ assumes on the group. Thus we set

$$\int \Phi(g)\, dg = \sum_{g \varepsilon G} \Phi(g). \tag{5.1}$$

With this definition, the integral indeed has the property that

$$\int \Phi_a(g)\, dg = \int \Phi(ag)\, dg = \int \Phi(g) dg. \tag{5.2a}$$

This property is termed the left invariance property of the integral. It is an immediate consequence of the fact that the sum over the group of $\Phi(ag)$ includes each value of Φ exactly once, since multiplication of the group with a has only the effect of permuting the group elements. It is worth mentioning that equation (2a) depends on the fact that the summation is over the whole group; the result would certainly not be valid if the sum were over only a subset of the group.

It will be noted that the integral is also right invariant: the function Φ^a defined by $\Phi^a(g) = \Phi(ga)$ satisfies, for the same reasons that imply (2a),

$$\int \Phi^a(g)\ dg = \int \Phi(ga)\ dg = \int \Phi(g)\ dg. \tag{5.2b}$$

Moreover, for similar reasons,

$$\int \hat{\Phi}(g)\ dg = \int \Phi(g^{-1})\ dg = \int \Phi(g)\ dg \tag{5.2c}$$

where $\hat{\Phi}$ is defined by $\hat{\Phi}(g) = \Phi(g^{-1})$.

We note further the trivial but important facts that the integral is linear and positive-definite; that is,

$$\int [a\Phi(g) + b\Psi(g)]\ dg = a\int \Phi(g)\ dg + b\int \Psi(g)\ dg \tag{5.3}$$

$$\int |\Phi(g)|\ dg \geq 0, \tag{5.4}$$

with the equality valid only if Φ is identically zero.

5-2 INTEGRATION ON A COMPACT LIE GROUP. THE HURWITZ INTEGRAL

The invariance of the integration over a finite group is rather trivial. We turn now to the case in which the group G is an n parameter Lie group.

It is natural to attempt to define the integral as a definite integral over the group parameters. In doing this we meet immediately the problem that the various parameter domains may overlap, whereas the integral can hardly be expected to be invariant unless there is a 1-1 correspondence between group elements and coordinate points. To this end, we can delete from some of the parameter domains their intersection with others, so that the points of the resulting domains are in 1-1 correspondence with the group elements. As previously mentioned, the resulting domains may not be open, but this does not matter for defining the integral. Some of the domains may be of lower dimension than n; the volume of such regions is zero. Actually, in all cases with which we shall be concerned, the original regions in parameter space can be chosen so that a single one, which will be described in all examples, covers the entire group except for a set of lower dimensionality. The integral can then be expressed as the integral over one parameter domain, with the set of lower dimension ignored.

It is convenient in the discussion of invariant integration not to distinguish between points in the parameter space and group elements; this does not cause any mathematical difficulty if the assumptions of the previous paragraph are valid, and it leads to a simpler notation.

We attempt, therefore, to define the group integral in the form

$$\Phi(g)\, dg = \int \Phi(\mathbf{p})\, w(\mathbf{p})\, d\mathbf{p}\,, \tag{5.5}$$

the integral being over a single parameter domain. The function $w(\mathbf{p})$ is a weight function that is included to give different weights to various regions of the parameter space. It can be seen that such a function is required, since if the group parameters are changed to $\mathbf{p}'$, the integral on the right hand side of (5) becomes

$$\int \Phi(\mathbf{p}(\mathbf{p}'))\, w(\mathbf{p}(\mathbf{p}'))\, \frac{\partial \mathbf{p}}{\partial \mathbf{p}'}\, d\mathbf{p}' = \int \Phi'(\mathbf{p}')\, w'(\mathbf{p}')\, d\mathbf{p}' \tag{5.6a}$$

where

$$\int w'(\mathbf{p}') = w(\mathbf{p}(\mathbf{p}'))\, \frac{\partial \mathbf{p}}{\partial \mathbf{p}'}. \tag{5.6b}$$

The notation $\partial\mathbf{p}/\partial\mathbf{p}'$ is used to denote the Jacobian

$$\frac{\partial(p^1, p^2, \ldots, p^n)}{\partial(p'^1, p'^2, \ldots, p'^n)}.$$

Equations (6) show that even if the weight function were not present in one parametrization, it would be necessary to include it is another parametrization. The problem of constructing an invariant integral is, in fact, a problem of finding a suitable weight function.

The weight function can be multiplied by an arbitrary constant without affecting the invariance property. It is customary to "normalize" w either so that $w(e) = 1$, or so that the total group volume is 1. We will choose the former normalization.

It is possible to evaluate the weight function by considering the left invariance requirement for a particular function E which will be defined shortly. It is then possible to demonstrate that, because of the group associativity, the integral is left invariant.

Let us consider a volume element ΔV in the neighborhood of the identity, or the origin in the parameter space. The function E is defined by $E(\mathbf{p}) = 1$, $\mathbf{p} \varepsilon \Delta V$, and $E(\mathbf{p}) = 0$ otherwise; E is sometimes called the <u>characteristic function</u> of ΔV.

The left invariance requirement is

$$\int E(\mathbf{p})\, w(\mathbf{p})\, d\mathbf{p} = \int E(\mathbf{ap})\, w(\mathbf{p})\, d\mathbf{p}. \tag{5.7}$$

The integrand on the left hand side is nonzero only in ΔV; if it is assumed that $w(\mathbf{p}) = w(0) = 1$ in ΔV, and this is a good approximation if ΔV is small, the left hand integral is the volume of ΔV, which will be denoted by $|\Delta V|$.

We consider now the right hand integral. The integrand is nonzero only if $\mathbf{ap} \in \Delta V$, that is, only if $\mathbf{p} \in \mathbf{a}^{-1}\Delta V$. We will denote the volume element $\mathbf{a}^{-1}\Delta V$ by $\Delta V'$. We again make the assumption of constant w; this time over $\Delta V'$. Since $\mathbf{a}^{-1} \in \Delta V'$, we can take $w(\mathbf{p}) = w(\mathbf{a}^{-1})$. The right hand integral in (7), which is over only $\Delta V'$, is therefore $w(\mathbf{a}^{-1})\,|\Delta V'|$ where $|\Delta V'|$ is the volume of $\Delta V'$. Equation (7) therefore leads to

$$w(\mathbf{a}^{-1}) = \frac{|\Delta V|}{|\Delta V'|} = \left(\frac{|\Delta V'|}{|\Delta V|}\right)^{-1} \tag{5.8}$$

This argument is illustrated in Fig. 5-1.

The ratio of the two volume elements can be expressed as a Jacobian. A point $\mathbf{p} \in \Delta V$ is mapped into a point $\mathbf{p}' = \mathbf{a}^{-1}\mathbf{p} = \mathbf{f}(\mathbf{a}^{-1}, \mathbf{p}) \in \Delta V'$. The quotient of the volume elements is

$$\frac{|\Delta V'|}{|\Delta V|} = \frac{\partial \mathbf{p}'}{\partial \mathbf{p}} = \left| \frac{\partial f^{\alpha}}{\partial q^{\beta}} (\mathbf{a}^{-1}, \mathbf{p}) \right| .$$

Since ΔV is located at e, this should be evaluated at $\mathbf{p} = 0$. We obtain therefore, replacing $\mathbf{a}^{-1}$ by $\mathbf{a}$,

$$w(\mathbf{a}) = \left| \frac{\partial f^{\alpha}}{\partial q^{\beta}} (\mathbf{a}, 0) \right|^{-1} \tag{5.9}$$

It is observed that w is the inverse of the determinant of the functions $v^{\alpha}{}_{\beta}$ defined by (3.8). It was shown in Section 3-4 that this determinant is nonzero. It follows that $w(\mathbf{a})$ exists and, being continuous, is positive.

The quotient $|\Delta V|/|\Delta V'|$ can also be expressed as a Jacobian. The coordinates of a point $\mathbf{p} \in \Delta V$ are given in terms of those of $\mathbf{p}' \in \Delta V'$ by $\mathbf{p} = \mathbf{f}(\mathbf{a}, \mathbf{p}')$. Therefore,

$$\frac{|\Delta V|}{|\Delta V'|} = \left| \frac{\partial f^{\alpha}}{\partial q^{\beta}} (\mathbf{a}, \mathbf{p}') \right| .$$

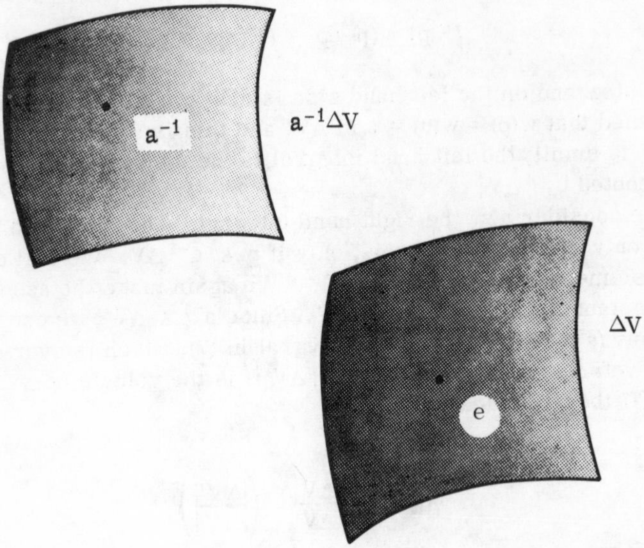

Fig. 5-1

If $E(\mathbf{p})$ is nonzero only for $\mathbf{p} \varepsilon \Delta V$, $E(\mathbf{ap})$ is nonzero only for $\mathbf{p} \varepsilon \mathbf{a}^{-1} \Delta V$. To ensure left invariance, the "volume" of $\mathbf{a}^{-1} \Delta V$ must be reduced by the weight function to be that of ΔV.

This is to be evaluated at $\mathbf{p} = 0$ or at $\mathbf{p}' = \mathbf{a}^{-1}$. We obtain, therefore, again replacing $\mathbf{a}^{-1}$ by $\mathbf{a}$,

$$w(\mathbf{a}) = \left| \frac{\partial f^{\alpha}}{\partial q^{\beta}} (\mathbf{a}^{-1}, \mathbf{a}) \right| \tag{5.10}$$

as an alternate expression for w.

It is possible to give a heuristic argument that the integral defined with the weight function w is left invariant. Let Φ be a continuous function defined on G. We can approximate Φ arbitrarily closely by a function that is constant over small regions of G. This amounts to writing Φ as a sum $c_1 E_1 + c_2 E_2 + \ldots + c_n E_n$, where E_i is the characteristic function of one of the small regions in which Φ is constant. Because of the linearity of the integral (5), it is sufficient to demonstrate the invariance of the integral for the functions E_i. Let ΔV_i

be the volume element whose characteristic function is E_i and let $\mathbf{b}$ be an element of ΔV_i.

We can express ΔV_i as $\mathbf{b}\Delta V'$ where $\Delta V' = \mathbf{b}^{-1}\Delta V_i$ is a volume element containing e. We can write $E_i(\mathbf{p}) = E(\mathbf{b}^{-1}\mathbf{p})$ where E is the characteristic function of $\Delta V'$, since $E(\mathbf{b}^{-1}\mathbf{p}) = 1$ or 0 depending on whether $\mathbf{b}^{-1}\mathbf{p} \in \Delta V'$, that is, whether $\mathbf{p} \in \mathbf{b}\Delta V' = \Delta V_i$. We can, therefore, write

$$\int E_i(\mathbf{p})\, w(\mathbf{p})\, d\mathbf{p} = \int E(\mathbf{b}^{-1}\mathbf{p})\, w(\mathbf{p})\, d\mathbf{p} = \int E(\mathbf{p})\, w(\mathbf{p})\, d\mathbf{p} \qquad (5.11)$$

where the second equality stems from the fact that we have constructed $w(\mathbf{p})$ to ensure the left invariance of the integral of functions like $E(\mathbf{p})$, namely characteristic functions of volume elements at e. On the other hand,

$$\int E_i(\mathbf{ap})\, w(\mathbf{p})\, d\mathbf{p} = \int E(\mathbf{b}^{-1}(\mathbf{ap}))\, w(\mathbf{p})\, d\mathbf{p} =$$
$$\int E((\mathbf{b}^{-1}\mathbf{a})\mathbf{p})\, w(\mathbf{p})\, d\mathbf{p} = \int E(\mathbf{p})\, w(\mathbf{p})\, d\mathbf{p}.$$

Comparison with (11) demonstrates the desired left invariance of the integral of E_i. The first step in the above calculation stems from the fact that $E_i(\mathbf{ap})$ and $E(\mathbf{b}^{-1}(\mathbf{ap}))$ are each characteristic functions of $\mathbf{a}^{-1}\Delta V_i$ since each of these is 1 for $\mathbf{p} \in \mathbf{a}^{-1}\Delta V_i$ and 0 elsewhere. It is important to observe that the associative law is necessary in the proof in equating $E(\mathbf{b}^{-1}(\mathbf{ap}))$ and $E((\mathbf{b}^{-1}\mathbf{a})\mathbf{p})$. The "geometry" underlying the argument is illustrated in Fig. 5-2.

These rather intuitive arguments will now be converted into a formal theorem that may also satisfy those who doubt the transition from the quotient of volume elements to Jacobians of equations (9) and (10).

THEOREM 5-1. If $w(\mathbf{p})$ is defined by equation (9)

$$\int \Phi(\mathbf{p})\, w(\mathbf{p})\, d\mathbf{p} = \int \Phi(\mathbf{ap})\, w(\mathbf{p})\, d\mathbf{p} \qquad (5.12)$$

for any continuous function Φ and any group element $\mathbf{a}$, if the integral is taken over the whole group. The integral so defined is linear and positive-definite.

Proof. We again consider equation (3.9). If we take the determinant of each side of (3.9) and use the result that the determinant of the product of two matrices is the product of their determinants, we obtain

$$w(\mathbf{f}(\mathbf{p}, \mathbf{q}))^{-1} = \left| \frac{\partial f^{\alpha}}{\partial q^{\beta}}(\mathbf{p}, \mathbf{q}) \right| w(\mathbf{q})^{-1}$$

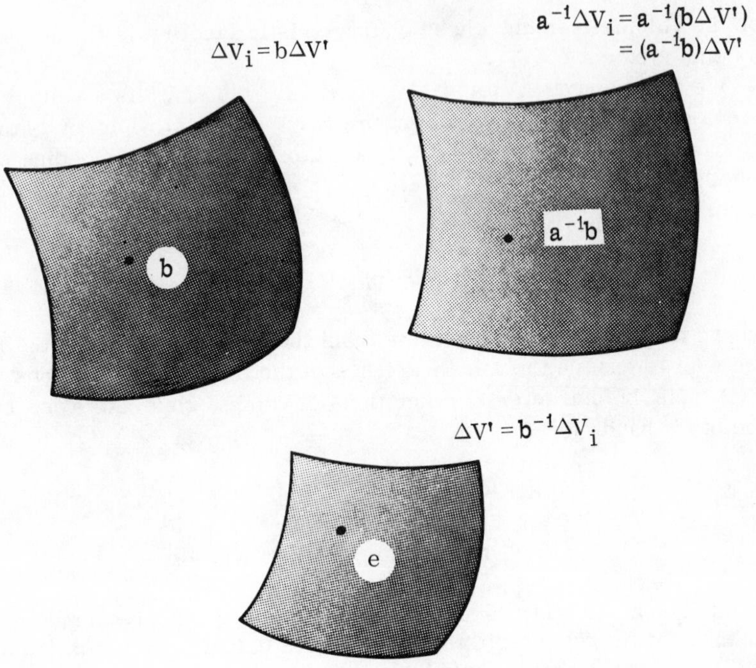

Fig. 5-2

If $E_i(\mathbf{p})$ is nonzero only in ΔV_i, $E_i(\mathbf{ap})$ is nonzero only in $\mathbf{a}^{-1}\Delta V_i$. The "group" volume of these two regions is the same, each being the volume of $\Delta V'$.

or, replacing $\mathbf{p}$ by $\mathbf{a}^{-1}$,

$$w(\mathbf{q}) = \left| \frac{\partial f^{\alpha}}{\partial q^{\beta}} (\mathbf{a}^{-1}, \mathbf{q}) \right| w(\mathbf{f}(\mathbf{a}^{-1}, \mathbf{q})). \tag{5.13}$$

It is at this point that the associative law is used, since (3.9) was derived from it.

We now change the variables of integration in the right-hand side of (12) to $\mathbf{q} = \mathbf{ap} = \mathbf{f}(\mathbf{a}, \mathbf{p})$; then $\mathbf{p} = \mathbf{a}^{-1}\mathbf{q} = \mathbf{f}(\mathbf{a}^{-1}, \mathbf{q})$. The right-hand side of (12) becomes, including the Jacobian $\partial\mathbf{p}/\partial\mathbf{q}$,

$$\int \Phi(\mathbf{q})\, w(\mathbf{f}(\mathbf{a}^{-1}, \mathbf{q})) \left| \frac{\partial f^{\alpha}}{\partial q^{\beta}} (\mathbf{a}^{-1}, \mathbf{q}) \right| d\mathbf{q} = \int \Phi(\mathbf{q})\, w(\mathbf{q})\, d\mathbf{q},$$

according to (13). This is, however, the left-hand side of (12). In changing variables in the multiple integral, it is necessary also to change the integration domain. Since the integral is over the whole group, the domain is not essentially changed when $\mathbf{p}$ is replaced by $\mathbf{f}(\mathbf{a}^{-1}, \mathbf{p})$ but is merely rearranged. It can be concluded, therefore, that (12) is valid. It is important to note, though, that this again depends on the integral's being extended over the whole group.

The integral defined is obviously linear in the function Φ and, since we have argued that $w(\mathbf{p}) > 0$, the integral satisfies the positive definiteness condition of equation (4). If we put $\mathbf{q} = \mathbf{a}$ in equation (13), we find equation (10) as a suitable alternate expression for $w(\mathbf{a})$, since $w(\mathbf{f}(\mathbf{a}^{-1}, \mathbf{a})) = w(e) = 1$.

The above calculation of w and the ensuing argument is valid for any Lie group. The integral (5) may not always exist, however, so that the argument applies only if the integral is finite. If the group is compact, however, the integral must exist for all continuous Φ since the integration is over a bounded region in the parameter space, and the functions Φ and w must be bounded since they are continuous on a compact set.

As an example, the weight function for the non-Abelian affine group considered in Section 4-3 will be calculated. The functions $v^{\alpha}{}_{\beta}$ for this group can be calculated from equations (3.8) and (4.15). They are

$$v^1{}_1 = 1 \quad v^1{}_2 = 0 \quad v^2{}_1 = 0 \quad v^2{}_2 = e^{p^1}.$$

The invariant weight function is therefore e^{-p^1}. The affine group is not compact, so that even for continuous Φ, the integral over the group may not converge. If, however, a function Φ is such that the integral

$$\int_{-\infty}^{\infty} e^{-p^1}\, dp^1 \int_{-\infty}^{\infty} dp^2\ \Phi(p^1, p^2)$$

exists, it is left invariant.

5-3. RIGHT INVARIANT INTEGRATION

It is clear that a right invariant integral over a compact Lie group can also be defined. If the procedure of the previous section is carried through, one obtains a right invariant weight function w_r; the result analogous to equation (9) is

$$w_r(\mathbf{a}) = \left| \frac{\partial f^\alpha}{\partial p^\beta}(0, \mathbf{a}) \right|^{-1} \tag{5.14}$$

and the result analogous to equation (10) is

$$w_r(\mathbf{a}) = \left| \frac{\partial f^\alpha}{\partial p^\beta}(\mathbf{a}, \mathbf{a}^{-1}) \right| . \tag{5.15}$$

In general, the weight function w_r for right invariant integration may differ from the weight function w. For example, in the affine group considered previously,

$$w_r(\mathbf{a}) = \begin{vmatrix} 1 & 0 \\ q^2 & 1 \end{vmatrix}^{-1} = 1 \neq w(\mathbf{a}).$$

It is obvious that the left and right invariant weight functions must be the same in any Abelian group. It is also true, but far from obvious, that the two weight functions are equal in any compact Lie group. This result will now be proved. We will first sketch the idea of the proof and then give a formal theorem.

We suppose first that for some group element $\mathbf{a}$, $w_r(\mathbf{a}) = \lambda w(\mathbf{a})$ where $\lambda \neq 1$. It has been seen that if ΔV is a volume element containing e, $|\Delta V| = w(\mathbf{a}) \, |\mathbf{a}\Delta V|$. Similarly, for any ΔU we have $|\Delta U| = w_r(\mathbf{a}) \, |\Delta U\mathbf{a}|$. This is true in particular for $\Delta U = \mathbf{a}\,\Delta V\,\mathbf{a}^{-1}$, so that $|\mathbf{a}\,\Delta V\,\mathbf{a}^{-1}| = w_r(\mathbf{a}) \, |\mathbf{a}\Delta V| = \lambda w(\mathbf{a}) \, |\mathbf{a}\Delta V| = \lambda |\Delta V|$. It follows that transforming any volume element ΔV to $\mathbf{a}\,\Delta V\,\mathbf{a}^{-1}$ changes its volume by a factor λ. The set $\mathbf{a}\,\Delta V\,\mathbf{a}^{-1}$ is again a volume element containing e, and hence $|\mathbf{a}(\mathbf{a}\,\Delta V\,\mathbf{a}^{-1})\mathbf{a}^{-1}| = \lambda^2 |\Delta V|$. It follows that transforming ΔV to $\mathbf{a}^2\,\Delta V\,\mathbf{a}^{-2}$ changes its volume by a factor λ^2. It can easily be proved inductively that transforming ΔV to $\mathbf{a}^n\,\Delta V\,\mathbf{a}^{-n}$ transforms its volume by a factor λ^n.

The set of elements $\mathbf{a}^n$, n = 1, 2, ... is infinite and, since the group is compact, must have at least one limit element $\mathbf{c} \in G$. The transformation of ΔV to $\mathbf{c}\,\Delta V\,\mathbf{c}^{-1}$ must change the volume of ΔV by a factor that is either zero or infinite, because of the continuity of the group operations. On the other hand, the transformation $\mathbf{a}' = \mathbf{c}\,\mathbf{a}\,\mathbf{c}^{-1}$ is an invertible mapping of the group onto itself, so that the corresponding coordinate transformation must have a finite Jacobian. The resolution of this contradiction is that λ is necessarily 1 and $w(\mathbf{a}) = w_r(\mathbf{a})$. We will now attempt to put these considerations into a precise form.

THEOREM 5-2. If G is a compact Lie group, $w_r(\mathbf{a}) = w(\mathbf{a})$.

Proof. We consider, for each $\mathbf{a} \varepsilon$ G, a transformation $q_{\mathbf{a}}(\mathbf{p})$ defined by $q_{\mathbf{a}}(\mathbf{p}) = \mathbf{apa}^{-1} = \mathbf{f}(\mathbf{f}(\mathbf{a}, \mathbf{p}), \mathbf{a}^{-1})$. It will be shown that the value at e of the Jacobian of this transformation is the quotient λ discussed above. The value of the Jacobian at e will be denoted by $M(\mathbf{a})$. Then

$$M(\mathbf{a}) = \left| \frac{\partial f^{\alpha}}{\partial p^{\gamma}} (\mathbf{f}(\mathbf{a}, \mathbf{p}), \mathbf{a}^{-1}) \frac{\partial f^{\gamma}}{\partial q^{\beta}} (\mathbf{a}, \mathbf{p}) \right|_{\mathbf{p}=0}$$

$$= \left| \frac{\partial f^{\alpha}}{\partial p^{\gamma}} (\mathbf{a}, \mathbf{a}^{-1}) \right| \left| \frac{\partial f^{\gamma}}{\partial q^{\beta}} (\mathbf{a}, 0) \right| = \frac{w_r(\mathbf{a})}{w(\mathbf{a})}, \tag{5.16}$$

where we have made use of (9) and (15). It is observed that $M(\mathbf{a}) = \lambda$, and we therefore wish to show that $M(\mathbf{a}) = 1$.

It will first be shown that $M(\mathbf{a})\, M(\mathbf{b}) = M(\mathbf{ab})$. For this purpose, we consider the composition transformation $q_{\mathbf{a}}(q_{\mathbf{b}}(\mathbf{p})) = q_{\mathbf{a}}(\mathbf{bpb}^{-1}) = \mathbf{a}(\mathbf{bpb}^{-1})\mathbf{a}^{-1}$. This is the same as $(\mathbf{ab})\mathbf{p}(\mathbf{ab})^{-1} = q_{\mathbf{ab}}(\mathbf{p})$, so that

$$q_{\mathbf{a}}(q_{\mathbf{b}}(\mathbf{p})) = q_{\mathbf{ab}}(\mathbf{p}). \tag{5.17}$$

The value of the Jacobian of $q_{\mathbf{ab}}$ at e is $M(\mathbf{ab})$. The Jacobian of $q_{\mathbf{a}}(q_{\mathbf{b}}(\mathbf{p}))$ is the product of the Jacobians of $q_{\mathbf{a}}$ and $q_{\mathbf{b}}$; at $\mathbf{p}$ = e the Jacobian of $q_{\mathbf{b}}$ is $M(\mathbf{b})$ and, since $q_{\mathbf{b}}(e) = e$, the Jacobian of $q_{\mathbf{a}}$ is $M(\mathbf{a})$. We can conclude that $M(\mathbf{a})\, M(\mathbf{b}) = M(\mathbf{ab})$. From this it follows that $M(\mathbf{a}^n) = [M(\mathbf{a})]^n$.

The above considerations apply in any Lie group. In a compact Lie group, however, the sequence of elements $\mathbf{a}, \mathbf{a}^2, \mathbf{a}^3, \ldots$ has a limit element $\mathbf{c} \varepsilon$ G; that is, there is a subsequence $\mathbf{a}^{n_1}, \mathbf{a}^{n_2}, \ldots$ that converges to $\mathbf{c}$. In view of the continuity of the group operations, the Jacobians $M(\mathbf{a}^{n_j}) = [M(\mathbf{a})]^{n_j}$ must converge to $M(\mathbf{c})$, which must, however be a finite number ($M(\mathbf{c}) \neq 0$ and $M(\mathbf{c}) \neq \infty$) since $q_{\mathbf{c}}$ is an invertible transformation. If $M(\mathbf{a})^{n_j}$ converges to a finite number, $M(\mathbf{a})$ is necessarily 1, showing that $w(\mathbf{a}) = w_r(\mathbf{a})$.

It can be shown as a corollary to Theorem 5-2 that in a compact group

$$\int \Phi(\mathbf{q}^{-1})\, w(\mathbf{q})\, d\mathbf{q} = \int \Phi(\mathbf{q})\, w(\mathbf{q})\, d\mathbf{q}. \tag{5.18}$$

That is, the invariant integral over a compact group also has the invariance property of equation (2c). To show this we put $\mathbf{p} = \mathbf{q}^{-1}$ in the left-hand side of (18) to obtain

$$\int \Phi(\mathbf{q}^{-1})\, w(\mathbf{q})\, d\mathbf{q} = \int \Phi(\mathbf{p})\, w(\mathbf{q}) \left| \frac{\partial \mathbf{q}}{\partial \mathbf{p}} (\mathbf{p}) \right| d\mathbf{p}, \tag{5.19}$$

where the integral is again the whole group. It is necessary to take the absolute value of the Jacobian, since it will be found that this particular Jacobian is negative. We now recall equation (3.7) which can be written in the present notation as

$$\frac{\partial q^\gamma}{\partial p^\beta}(\mathbf{p}) = -\frac{\partial f^\gamma}{\partial p^\alpha}(0, \mathbf{q})\frac{\partial f^\alpha}{\partial q^\beta}(\mathbf{p}^{-1}, \mathbf{p}). \tag{5.20}$$

Taking the Jacobian of each side of (20), and using (10) and (14), we find

$$\frac{\partial \mathbf{q}}{\partial \mathbf{p}}(\mathbf{p}) = -\frac{w(\mathbf{p})}{w_r(\mathbf{q})} = -\frac{w(\mathbf{p})}{w(\mathbf{q})},$$

provided the group is compact. Substituting this result into (19) shows that

$$\int \Phi(\mathbf{q}^{-1})\, w(\mathbf{q})\, d\mathbf{q} = \Phi(\mathbf{p})\, w(\mathbf{p})\, d\mathbf{p}.$$

Chapter 6

GROUP REPRESENTATIONS

Since the study of special functions in this book is based for the most part on their properties as matrix elements of group representations, it is necessary to study group representations in some detail and this will be done in this and the following chapter.

A group representation is a group of matrices to which the group is homomorphic, although for many purposes it is more convenient to view the representation as a group of linear operators. The relation between the two viewpoints will be described in some detail in the first section.

The representations of most interest for finite and compact Lie groups are finite-dimensional. It will be shown, in fact, that any infinite-dimensional representation of such a group can be expressed in terms of the finite-dimensional representations. The situation is not so satisfactory for the noncompact groups, which provide three of the interesting examples for the present work. The important representations of such groups are infinite-dimensional. The theory of such representations is involved, and the representations of these groups will be discussed here very much on an ad hoc basis, without recourse to the general theory.

The first extensive investigation of group representations was carried out in a series of articles by Frobenius [1], who developed much of the theory of the representations of finite groups, and in particular, of the symmetric groups. Frobenius introduced the group character function, which is important for the classification of representations. The methods developed by Frobenius were clarified by I. Schur [2], who made use of the lemma that bears his name, and which will be proved in Section 5. Much of the Frobenius theory of representations was also obtained independently by Burnside [3].

6–1 GROUP REPRESENTATIONS

In this section we consider an abstract group G, which may be finite or a Lie group, and a linear vector space L which may be real or complex, n-dimensional or a Hilbert space ($n = \infty$). If $n = \infty$ there are certain convergence considerations that will be ignored in this chapter, but that will be treated more carefully when the need arises in the applications. Elements of L will be denoted by boldface letters $\mathbf{u}$, $\mathbf{v}$, and so on.

An operator representation of G in L is a group Γ of linear operators on L, together with a homomorphic mapping of G onto Γ. That is, for each a, b ε G, there is an element D(a) ε Γ such that

$$D(a)\,D(b) = D(ab). \qquad (6.1)$$

D therefore denotes the homomorphism and D(a) is a linear operator in L. It is further assumed that

$$D(e) = I \qquad (6.2)$$

where I is the identity operator defined by $I\mathbf{u} = \mathbf{u}$ for all $\mathbf{u}$ ε L. This assumption is made to exclude representations by singular operators like

$$\begin{pmatrix} a & 0 \\ 0 & 0 \end{pmatrix}$$

which, for $a \neq 0$ would otherwise be a representation of the multiplicative group of the real numbers. Conditions (1) and (2) together imply that

$$D(a^{-1}) = [D(a)]^{-1}, \qquad (6.3)$$

so that the operators D(a) are invertible.

If the mapping D of G onto Γ is an isomorphism, the representation is said to be faithful; certain of the groups to be studied are matrix groups, so that they provide faithful representations of themselves.

The operator representations of G can be classified into equivalence classes such that any representation is equivalent to all the representations in the same class and inequivalent to all other representations. The definition of equivalence is as follows. Let D(a) and D'(a) be operator representations of G in vector spaces L and L' respectively. The representations are equivalent if there is an isomorphism between L and L' such that under the isomorphism, D'(a) operates in L' in the same way that D(a) operates in L. By an isomorphism between L and L' we mean a linear 1-1 correspondence between L and L'. There is then an invertible mapping S of L onto L' with the property that $S(a\mathbf{u} + b\mathbf{v}) = aS\mathbf{u} + bS\mathbf{v}$.

The condition that D'(a) operate in L' in the same way that D(a) operates in L is that if $\mathbf{u} \leftrightarrow \mathbf{u}'$, then, for all $a \in G$, $D(a)\mathbf{u} \leftrightarrow D'(a)\mathbf{u}'$. This can be expressed in terms of S by putting $\mathbf{u}' = S\mathbf{u}$, $D'(a)\mathbf{u}' = SD(a)\mathbf{u}$, so that $SD(a)\mathbf{u} = D'(a)S\mathbf{u}$. Since this must hold for all $\mathbf{u} \in L$, S satisfies

$$S\,D(a) = D'(a)\,S. \tag{6.4}$$

It is apparent that although equivalent representations may differ in their definition, they will be essentially the same in all their properties as representations.

It remains to show that the relation so defined is an equivalence relation. It will be recalled that a relation $\sim$ among a, b, c, and so on is an equivalence relation if $a \sim a$, $a \sim b$ implies $b \sim a$, and $a \sim b$ and $b \sim c$ implies $a \sim c$. It is obvious that a representation is equivalent to itself by the mapping I, and that if D'(a) is equivalent to D(a) under the mapping S, D(a) is equivalent to D'(a) under S^{-1}. Finally, if D'(a) is equivalent to D(a) by $SD(a) = D'(a)S$ and D''(a) is equivalent to D'(a) by $TD'(a) = D''(a)T$, then $D''(a)TS = TD'(a)S = TSD(a)$ so that D''(a) is equivalent to D(a). This proves the assertion that the representations can be classified so that any two in the same class are equivalent and any two in different classes are inequivalent.

An operator representation D(a) of G gives rise to a matrix representation of G, that is, a set of matrices satisfying equations (1)-(3). This will be shown explicitly. Let $\mathbf{e}_1, \mathbf{e}_2, \ldots, (\mathbf{e}_n)$ be a basis of linearly independent vectors in L. We define a matrix $\widetilde{D}(a)$ to have matrix elements given by

$$D(a)\mathbf{e}_j = \sum_{i=1}^{n} \widetilde{D}(a)_{ij}\mathbf{e}_i; \tag{6.5}$$

that is, $\widetilde{D}(a)_{ij}$ is the coefficient for the expansion of $D(a)\mathbf{e}_j$ in terms of the $\mathbf{e}_i$. Equation (5) is important for much of what follows; we draw attention particularly to the order of subscripts in the definition of $\widetilde{D}(a)$.

It will now be shown that the matrices $\widetilde{D}(a)$ constitute an explicit representation; that is, that they satisfy equations (1) - (3). This is proved by calculating

$$D(a)\,D(b)\mathbf{e}_k = D(a)\sum_{j=1}^{n} \widetilde{D}(b)_{jk}\mathbf{e}_j = \sum_{j=1}^{n} \widetilde{D}(b)_{jk}[D(a)\mathbf{e}_j]$$

$$= \sum_{j=1}^{n}\sum_{i=1}^{n} \widetilde{D}(b)_{jk}[\widetilde{D}(a)_{ij}\mathbf{e}_i] = \sum_{i=1}^{n}[\sum_{j=1}^{n} \widetilde{D}(a)_{ij}\widetilde{D}(b)_{jk}]\mathbf{e}_i.$$

On the other hand,

$$D(a)\,D(b)\mathbf{e}_k = D(ab)\mathbf{e}_k = \sum_{i=1}^{n} \tilde{D}(ab)_{ik}\mathbf{e}_i.$$

Equating coefficients of $\mathbf{e}_i$ shows that

$$\sum_{j=1}^{n} \tilde{D}(a)_{ij}\tilde{D}(b)_{jk} = \tilde{D}(ab)_{ik}, \tag{6.6}$$

which is the matrix form of equation (1). The calculation $D(e)\mathbf{e}_j = \mathbf{e}_j = \sum_{i=1}^{n} \delta_{ij}\mathbf{e}_i$ shows that the matrix elements of $\tilde{D}(e)$ are δ_{ij} and that $\tilde{D}(e)$ is the unit matrix. Since (1) and (2) are satisfied by the $\tilde{D}(a)$, (3) must also be satisfied.

Conversely, a matrix representation of G gives rise to a group of linear transformations in the familiar vector space whose vectors are sets of n ordered numbers.

We consider now the matrix representations corresponding to two equivalent operator representations D(a) and D'(a) in vector spaces L and L'. Let $\{\mathbf{e}_j\}$ and $\{\mathbf{e}_i'\}$ be linearly independent basis vectors in L and L' respectively. Since L and L' are isomorphic, the vectors $S^{-1}\mathbf{e}_i'$ are basis vectors in L. It is therefore possible to expand the basis vectors $\mathbf{e}_j$ in terms of $S^{-1}\mathbf{e}_i'$. We introduce a matrix $\tilde{S}$ whose elements $\tilde{S}_{ij}$ are defined by

$$\mathbf{e}_j = \sum_{i=1}^{n} \tilde{S}_{ij}(S^{-1}\mathbf{e}_i'). \tag{6.7}$$

The matrix $\tilde{S}$ has an inverse whose elements give the expansion of $\mathbf{e}_i'$ in terms of the vectors $S\mathbf{e}_j$:

$$\mathbf{e}_i' = \sum_{j=1}^{n} (\tilde{S}^{-1})_{ji}(S\mathbf{e}_j). \tag{6.8}$$

The operator equation $D'(a)S = SD(a)$ can be shown without difficulty to give rise to the corresponding matrix equation, or to

$$\tilde{D}'(a) = \tilde{S}\tilde{D}(a)\tilde{S}^{-1}. \tag{6.9}$$

Equation (9) provides an equivalence classification of matrix representations in the same way as does (4); that is matrix representations are <u>equivalent</u> if there is a nonsingular matrix $\tilde{S}$ such that equation (9) is satisfied. The matrix $\tilde{S}$ is said to <u>transform</u> $\tilde{D}(a)$ to $\tilde{D}'(a)$.

Each matrix representation gives rise to a family of equivalent representations corresponding to all possible choices of the nonsingular matrix $\tilde{S}$. As we have noted, each matrix representation corresponds to an operator representation; these operator representations are equivalent under a mapping S that can be defined through equation (7), multiplied by S.

It can of course be verified quite independently of the above discussion that $\widetilde{D}'(a)$ defined by (9) is a representation, by direct substitution in (1) - (3).

We can sum up this discussion as follows. Both matrix and operator representations can be grouped into equivalence classes, and to each operator equivalence class there corresponds one matrix equivalence class. All the representation properties of all representations in a particular class are determined by any one representation in the class.

Because of the complete correspondence between operator and matrix representations we will no longer distinguish between them notationally. The type of representation being discussed will usually be clear from the context, but any argument pertaining to one type of representation will apply equally well to the other.

An additional requirement that will be made on representations of Lie groups is that they should be continuous in the group parameters. For a matrix representation, this is that the matrix elements $D(a)_{ij}$ should be continuous functions of the parameters of a. Continuity of an operator representation means that it should be possible to make $|D(a')\mathbf{u} - D(a)\mathbf{u}|$ arbitrarily small by making the parameters of a and a' sufficiently close together. The two conditions are equivalent for finite-dimensional representations. For infinite-dimensional representations the latter one is stronger, and is the correct one.

It would be natural to impose also a differentiability requirement and this will be done for finite-dimensional representations. In fact, it will be shown in Chapter 7 that if a compact Lie group has one faithful differentiable matrix representation, then any continuous representation is differentiable. The situation is more complex for the infinite-dimensional representations of noncompact groups. The derivatives of these representations can be unbounded operators that are not defined for all vectors in the Hilbert space; this means that the representation is not differentiable acting on all vectors in the Hilbert space.

6-2 UNITARY REPRESENTATIONS

An important special type of representation is the unitary representation whose matrices satisfy $D(a)^\dagger D(a) = 1$. The unitary property cannot be defined for an operator representation unless there is an inner product defined on the vector space, in which case the representation is unitary if $(D(a)\mathbf{u}, D(a)\mathbf{v}) = (\mathbf{u}, \mathbf{v})$ for all $\mathbf{u}, \mathbf{v}$ in the vector space and all $a \in G$. Unitary representations have particular important properties so that the following theorem is quite significant.

THEOREM 6-1. Any representation of a finite group or a compact Lie group is equivalent to a unitary representation.

PROOF. The proof will be given for an explicit matrix representation. We consider the matrix X defined by

$$X = \int D(g)^\dagger D(g) dg. \tag{6.10}$$

We understand X to be the matrix obtained by integrating each element of $D(g)^\dagger D(g)$ over the group. The matrix X is obviously Hermitian and is also positive-definite since

$$(\mathbf{u}, X\mathbf{u}) = \int (\mathbf{u}, D(g)^\dagger D(g)\mathbf{u}) dg = \int |D(g)\mathbf{u}|^2 dg,$$

which is nonnegative and can vanish only if $\mathbf{u} = 0$ since $D(g)\mathbf{u} \neq 0$ for any $\mathbf{u} \neq 0$. The matrix X has the further property that

$$D(a)^\dagger X D(a) = X \tag{6.11}$$

for all $a \in G$ since

$$D(a)^\dagger X D(a) = \int D(a)^\dagger D(g)^\dagger D(g) D(a) dg = \int D(ga)^\dagger D(ga) dg$$
$$= \int D(g)^\dagger D(g) dg = X.$$

We have used successively the linearity property of the group integral, the representation property, and the right invariance of the integral. Since X is Hermitian and positive-definite, there exists a nonsingular Hermitian matrix S with the property that $S^2 = X$. Equation (11) can therefore be written

$$D(a)^\dagger S^2 D(a) = S^2$$
$$[S^{-1} D(a)^\dagger S][S D(a) S^{-1}] = I.$$

or,

If we put $D'(a) = S D(a) S^{-1}$, we find that

$$D'(a)^\dagger D'(a) = S^{-1} D(a)^\dagger S][S D(a) S^{-1}] = I$$

so that the representation $D'(a)$ is unitary.

In an operator representation by operators D(a) in a vector space L, it is possible to define a new inner product in L by $(\mathbf{u}, \mathbf{v})' = (\mathbf{u}, X\mathbf{v})$. This new inner product has all the necessary properties of an inner product, and furthermore $(D(a)\mathbf{u}, D(a)\mathbf{v})' = (D(a)\mathbf{u}, XD(a)\mathbf{v}) = (\mathbf{u}, X\mathbf{v}) = (\mathbf{u}, \mathbf{v})'$. The representation is therefore unitary with respect to this inner product. A difficulty with this argument is that the meaning of equation (10) is rather obscure since we have not defined an integral over the group of linear operators; it is, therefore, necessary to evaluate X in a particular basis.

It is evident that the argument for Theorem 6-1 may fail if the group is not compact, since the integral for X may not exist. For example, the group R of real numbers can be represented by the one-dimensional matrices $D(x) = e^x$. This matrix is unchanged under any transformation of the form (9) and so cannot be transformed to unitary form. More generally, any group of matrices containing a matrix whose determinant is not of unit modulus cannot be transformed to a unitary form since the determinant is invariant under the transformation (9) and the determinant of a unitary matrix has modulus one.

6-3 REDUCIBILITY OF REPRESENTATIONS

If two representations of a group G by matrices $D^1(a)$ and $D^2(a)$ are known, it is possible to form a new representation, the direct sum of D^1 and D^2, composed of matrices

$$D(a) = \begin{pmatrix} D^1(a) & 0 \\ 0 & D^2(a) \end{pmatrix}. \tag{6.12}$$

A simple calculation shows that $D(a)D(b) = D(ab)$, so that D is a representation. The dimension of D is obviously the sum of the dimensions of D^1 and D^2.

The direct sum of operator representations $D^1(a)$ and $D^2(a)$ in vector spaces L_1 and L_2 is defined in the direct sum $L_1 \oplus L_2$ of L_1 and L_2; $L_1 \oplus L_2$ is defined to be the set of all pairs $(\mathbf{u}_1, \mathbf{u}_2)$, $\mathbf{u}_1 \in L_1$, $\mathbf{u}_2 \in L_2$. The linear operations and inner product in $L_1 \oplus L_2$ are defined by

$$a(\mathbf{u}_1, \mathbf{u}_2) + b(\mathbf{v}_1, \mathbf{v}_2) = (a\mathbf{u}_1 + b\mathbf{v}_1, a\mathbf{u}_2 + b\mathbf{v}_2) \tag{6.13a}$$

$$((\mathbf{u}_1, \mathbf{u}_2), (\mathbf{v}_1, \mathbf{v}_2)) = (\mathbf{u}_1, \mathbf{v}_1) + (\mathbf{u}_2, \mathbf{v}_2) \tag{6.13b}$$

respectively. The direct sum $D^1 \oplus D^2(a)$ of $D^1(a)$ and $D^2(a)$ is defined in $L_1 \oplus L_2$ by

$$D^1 \oplus D^2(a)(\mathbf{u}_1, \mathbf{u}_2) = (D^1(a)\mathbf{u}_1, D^2(a)\mathbf{u}_2). \tag{6.14}$$

It will be left to the reader to show that $D^1 \oplus D^2(a)$ is linear, a representation, and corresponds to the matrix representation (12).

The possibility of expressing a given representation as the direct sum of two other representations is of greater interest than the direct sum itself. If a representation is equivalent to the direct sum of two other representations, that is, can be transformed to the form (12), it is said to be completely reducible. The interesting properties of a completely reducible representation are limited to those of the representations that compose it.

It is implied that a reducible representation should also be defined. A reducible representation is one that can be transformed to the block form

$$D(a) = \begin{pmatrix} D^1(a) & C(a) \\ 0 & D^2(a) \end{pmatrix}. \tag{6.15}$$

Although this is not a direct sum, it can be verified that $D^1(a)$ and $D^2(a)$ do constitute representations. A representation that is not reducible is said to be irreducible.

The equation

$$\begin{pmatrix} D^1(a) & C(a) \\ 0 & D^2(a) \end{pmatrix}\begin{pmatrix} \mathbf{u}_1 \\ 0 \end{pmatrix} = \begin{pmatrix} D^1(a)\mathbf{u}_1 \\ 0 \end{pmatrix}$$

shows that any vector with the last n_2 components zero (n_2 being the dimension of D^2) is transformed into a similar vector by the reduced representation. This observation leads to the following definitions. A linear subspace (a subset of L that is also a linear space with the same law of linear combination) M of L is invariant under D(a) if, for each $\mathbf{u} \in M$, $D(a)\mathbf{u}$ is also in M. An operator representation D(a) in a vector space L is reducible if L contains a proper (neither L nor $\{0\}$) linear subspace M that is invariant under all D(a). In the above example, the set of all vectors whose last n_2 components are zero constitutes the invariant subspace.

Since M is a linear vector space, it must contain linearly independent basis vectors $\mathbf{e}_1, \mathbf{e}_2, \ldots, \mathbf{e}_p$ where $p < n$, the dimension of L. (If $p = n$, M would be the same as L.) It is possible to construct $n - p$ more linearly independent basis vectors, $\mathbf{e}_{p+1}, \mathbf{e}_{p+2}, \ldots, \mathbf{e}_n$ which are not in M, such that the $\mathbf{e}_i$, $i = 1, 2, \ldots, n$ span L. If these vectors are used to construct a matrix representation, through equation (5), the result is in the reduced form (15). Suppose that $j \leq p$. Then $\mathbf{e}_j \in M$ and, by definition, $D(a)\mathbf{e}_j \in M$. This means that the only terms that contribute to the sum in (5) are those for which $i \leq p$. It follows that $\tilde{D}(a)_{ij} = 0$ for $j \leq p$, $i > p$, which means that $\tilde{D}(a)$ is in the reduced form (15). This argument is meaningful only if D(a) is finite-dimensional. However, the definition of reducibility in terms of invariant subspaces applies equally well to infinite-dimensional representations.

It may be possible to choose the vectors $\mathbf{e}_{p+1}, \mathbf{e}_{p+2}, \ldots, \mathbf{e}_n$ so that the subspace N that they span is also invariant under D(a). If this is the case, the matrix representation arising from D(a) and the $\mathbf{e}_i$ is in the completely reduced form (12). An operator representation is therefore defined to be completely reducible if the space L can be written as the direct sum of subspaces M and N, each of which is invariant under all the D(a).

It is important to note that if a unitary representation is reducible, it is necessarily completely reducible. Let D(a) be a unitary operator representation in a space L and let M be an invariant subspace of L. The set $M^{\perp}$ composed of all vectors that are orthogonal to every vector in M is also an invariant subspace. It is first clear that any linear combination of vectors in $M^{\perp}$ is again in $M^{\perp}$, since if $\mathbf{u}$ and $\mathbf{v}$ are each orthogonal to all vectors in M, $a\mathbf{u} + b\mathbf{v}$ is also. To show the invariance of $M^{\perp}$, consider $\mathbf{v} \in M^{\perp}$ and $D(a)\mathbf{v}$. Then for any $\mathbf{u} \in M$, $(D(a)\mathbf{v}, \mathbf{u}) = (\mathbf{v}, D(a)^{\dagger}\mathbf{u}) = (\mathbf{v}, D(a)^{-1}\mathbf{u}) = (\mathbf{v}, D(a^{-1})\mathbf{u})$. However, because of the invariance of M, $D(a^{-1})\mathbf{u} \in M$ if $\mathbf{u}$ is and hence $(\mathbf{v}, D(a^{-1})\mathbf{u}) = 0$, since $\mathbf{v}$ is orthogonal to all vectors in M. Therefore $D(a)\mathbf{v} \in M^{\perp}$ and $M^{\perp}$ is invariant. Any vector $\mathbf{w} \in L$ can be expressed uniquely as a sum $\mathbf{u} + \mathbf{v}$, where $\mathbf{u} \in M$ and $\mathbf{v} \in M^{\perp}$. It is then easy to show that L is isomorphic to the direct sum of M and $M^{\perp}$, which therefore effect the complete reduction of D(a).

It follows from this and Theorem 6-1 that any reducible representation of a finite or compact Lie group is completely reducible. This is not, in general, the case; for example, the matrices

$$\begin{pmatrix} a & b \\ 0 & 1 \end{pmatrix}$$

constitute a group and therefore a representation. This representation is reducible, but not completely reducible.

We will be concerned for the most part with unitary representations so that the distinction between reducibility and complete reducibility disappears.

6-4 EXAMPLES OF REPRESENTATIONS

In order to clarify some of the preceding material a few examples of group representations will be given. A rather trivial example is that in which D(a) = 1 for all a ε G.

A somewhat more interesting example can be given for the group of transformations of an equilateral triangle into itself. Rotations of the triangle through $2\pi/3$ and $4\pi/3$ are denoted by C_3 and C_3^2 respectively. The transformations that leave the top, lower left, and lower right vertices fixed are denoted by C_2, C_2', C_2'' respectively. Then, for example, $C_2'C_2'' = C_3$ where the right hand of the two factors is taken to operate first. This group has the faithful unitary representation

$$D(e) = \begin{pmatrix} 1 & 0 \\ 0 & 1 \end{pmatrix} \quad D(C_3) = \frac{1}{2}\begin{pmatrix} -1 & -\sqrt{3} \\ \sqrt{3} & -1 \end{pmatrix} \quad D(C_3^2) = \frac{1}{2}\begin{pmatrix} -1 & \sqrt{3} \\ -\sqrt{3} & -1 \end{pmatrix} \tag{6.16}$$

$$D(C_2) = \begin{pmatrix} 1 & 0 \\ 0 & -1 \end{pmatrix} \quad D(C_2') = \frac{1}{2}\begin{pmatrix} -1 & -\sqrt{3} \\ -\sqrt{3} & 1 \end{pmatrix} \quad D(C_2'') = \frac{1}{2}\begin{pmatrix} -1 & \sqrt{3} \\ \sqrt{3} & 1 \end{pmatrix}.$$

The compact Lie group of rotations of a plane into itself has the real unitary representation

$$D(\theta) = \begin{pmatrix} \cos\theta & -\sin\theta \\ \sin\theta & \cos\theta \end{pmatrix} \tag{6.17}$$

where θ is the rotation angle. This representation is not irreducible, but rather is transformed to $SD(\theta)S^{-1}$ =

$$D'(\theta) = \begin{pmatrix} e^{i\theta} & 0 \\ 0 & e^{-i\theta} \end{pmatrix} \tag{6.18a}$$

by

$$S = \frac{1}{\sqrt{2}}\begin{pmatrix} 1 & i \\ i & 1 \end{pmatrix}. \tag{6.18b}$$

An example of the representation of a Lie group by a set of linear operators will now be given. This representation is analogous to the adjoint representation of a Lie algebra defined by equation (4.29). Let G be a Lie group with Lie algebra Λ. The adjoint representation of G is a set of linear operators D(g) with domain Λ defined as follows. Suppose $\mathbf{a} \in \Lambda$ and is tangent to the parameters of the curve $x(t) \in G$. We define $D(g)\mathbf{a}$ to be tangent to the curve $gx(t)g^{-1}$.

It is necessary to prove that $D(g)$ is a linear operator and that $D(g)D(g') = D(gg')$. It is evident that $kD(g)a = D(g)(ka)$ since each of these is tangent to the curve $gx(kt)g^{-1}$. Suppose $\mathbf{a}$ and $\mathbf{b}$ are tangent to $x(t)$ and $y(t)$ respectively. Then $\mathbf{a} + \mathbf{b}$ is tangent to $x(t)y(t)$ and $D(g)(\mathbf{a}+\mathbf{b})$ is tangent to $gx(t)y(t)g^{-1} = [gx(t)g^{-1}][gy(t)g^{-1}]$. The tangent to this curve is, however, $D(g)\mathbf{a} + D(g)\mathbf{b}$, and we can conclude that $D(g)$ is linear.

To prove that $D(g)$ is a representation, we again consider $\mathbf{a}$ and a curve $x(t)$ to which $\mathbf{a}$ is tangent. Then $D(g')\mathbf{a}$ is tangent to $g'x(t)g'^{-1}$ and $D(g)[D(g')\mathbf{a}]$ is tangent to $g(g'x(t)g'^{-1})g^{-1} = (gg')x(t)(gg')^{-1}$. Since $D(gg')\mathbf{a}$ is also tangent to this curve, we have $D(g)D(g') = D(gg')$.

A straightforward calculation shows that the matrix elements of the adjoint representation are given by

$$D(g)_{\mu\nu} = \frac{\partial f^{\mu}}{\partial q^{\beta}}(g, g^{-1}) \frac{\partial f^{\beta}}{\partial p^{\nu}}(0, g^{-1}).$$

From this it is possible to show that

$$\frac{\partial D_{\mu\nu}}{\partial p^{\lambda}}(0) = c^{\mu}{}_{\lambda\nu} = (I_{\lambda})_{\mu\nu}$$

where I_{λ} is defined by (4.29). This shows that the Lie algebra of the adjoint representation is the adjoint algebra of the Lie algebra Λ of G. If the center of G consists only of e, Λ has center $\{0\}$ and is isomorphic to its adjoint Lie algebra. This implies that G and its adjoint representation are at least locally isomorphic since they have the same Lie algebra.

6-5 SCHUR'S LEMMA

In this section two theorems on irreducible representations will be proved. These theorems together constitute Schur's lemma.

THEOREM 6-2. A unitary representation by operators $D(a)$ in a complex vector space is irreducible if, and only if, the only operators that commute with every $D(a)$ are of the form cI where c is a number and I is the identity operator.

PROOF. Suppose $D(a)$ is irreducible and X commutes with all $D(a)$, so that $XD(a) = D(a)X$ for all $a \in G$. We wish to prove that $X = cI$.

We consider the eigenvalue problem $X\mathbf{u} = \lambda\mathbf{u}$; it is known that in a complex vector space this has at least one solution, since the corresponding characteristic equation $|X-\lambda I| = 0$ has at least one root, λ_0. We consider the linear subspace M of all eigenvectors corresponding to this eigenvalue. We wish to show that M is an invariant subspace. Let $\mathbf{u} \varepsilon M$, that is, $X\mathbf{u} = \lambda_0\mathbf{u}$ and consider $D(a)\mathbf{u}$. We can write $XD(a)\mathbf{u} = D(a)X\mathbf{u} = \lambda_0 D(a)\mathbf{u}$; this shows that $D(a)\mathbf{u}$ is also an eigenvector of X with eigenvalue λ_0, and hence, $D(a)\mathbf{u} \varepsilon M$. It follows that M is invariant, and, since D(a) is irreducible, that M is the whole representation space. We can conclude that $X\mathbf{u} = \lambda_0\mathbf{u}$ for all $\mathbf{u}$, or that $X = \lambda_0 I$. This part of the theorem is valid whether or not D(a) is unitary.

If the representation is reducible, on the other hand, and also unitary, then it is completely reducible. The representation space is then the sum of invariant subspaces M and N. We can define an operator X by $X\mathbf{u} = \mathbf{u}$ if $\mathbf{u} \varepsilon M$, and $X\mathbf{u} = 0$ if $\mathbf{u} \varepsilon N$; (X is then the projection onto M). It is easy to see that X is a linear operator which commutes with all the D(a) but is not a multiple of I. In block form, X is

$$\begin{pmatrix} I & 0 \\ 0 & 0 \end{pmatrix},$$

which obviously commutes with the matrices of the block form (12). This result need not hold if the representation is reducible but not completely reducible.

It should be noted that the proof of Theorem 6-2 fails in a real vector space since the eigenvalue problem $X\mathbf{u} = \lambda\mathbf{u}$ may have no real solution. This is the only point at which the complex property of the vector space is used; all the other considerations are equally valid in a real vector space.

We will now prove the second part of Schur's lemma.

THEOREM 6-3. If $D^1(a)$ and $D^2(a)$ are irreducible group representations operating in vector spaces L_1 and L_2, and X is a linear mapping from L_1 to L_2 such that

$$D^2(a)X = XD^1(a), \tag{6.19}$$

for all a, then either $X = 0$ or X has an inverse so that $D^1(a)$ and $D^2(a)$ are equivalent. It is worth noting that the dimensions of L_1 and L_2 may be different; then X is not a square matrix. It is still a linear, but not 1-1, transformation.

PROOF. Each side of equation (19) is a mapping from L_1 to L_2. We consider the set M of elements $\mathbf{u} \in L_1$ such that $X\mathbf{u} = 0$; M is a linear subspace of L_1. If $X\mathbf{u} = 0$, $D^2(a)X\mathbf{u} = XD^1(a)\mathbf{u} = 0$, and therefore $D^1(a)\mathbf{u}$ is also in M. This implies that M is an invariant subspace of L_1 under all the $D^1(a)$, and hence, that M is either the whole of L_1 or the zero element of L_1, since $D^1(a)$ was assumed irreducible. In the former case $X\mathbf{u} = 0$ for all $\mathbf{u} \in L_1$ or $X = 0$. We now wish to show that in the latter case, in which $X\mathbf{u} \neq 0$ for any $\mathbf{u} \neq 0$, X has an inverse. It will first be shown that X maps L_1 into the whole of L_2. Let M_2 be the subset of L_2 composed of vectors of the form $X\mathbf{u}$, $\mathbf{u} \in L_1$ (M_2 is the range of X). The set M_2 is a linear subspace of L_2. Consider now a vector $\mathbf{v} \in M_2$; $\mathbf{v}$ can be written in the form $X\mathbf{u}$, $\mathbf{u} \in L_1$. The vector $D^2(a)\mathbf{v}$ can be written $D^2(a)X\mathbf{u} = XD^1(a)\mathbf{u} = X\mathbf{u}'$, $\mathbf{u}' \in L_1$. It follows that $D^2(a)\mathbf{v} \in M_2$ and that M_2 is an invariant subspace of L_2 and is either the whole of L_2 or the zero element in L_2, since L_2 is irreducible. In the latter case $X = 0$. In the former case, each element $\mathbf{v} \in L_2$ can be written in the form $X\mathbf{u}$, $\mathbf{u} \in L_1$; this representation is, moreover, unique since if $X\mathbf{u}_1 = X\mathbf{u}_2$, $X(\mathbf{u}_1 - \mathbf{u}_2) = 0$ which implies $\mathbf{u}_1 - \mathbf{u}_2 = 0$. We define the unique vector $\mathbf{u}$ such that $X\mathbf{u} = \mathbf{v}$ to be $X^{-1}\mathbf{v}$, giving a complete construction of the inverse mapping to X. It can be proved without difficulty that X^{-1} is linear.

This completes the proof of Schur's lemma. It should be remarked that at no point was the group property of the operators D(a) invoked. It can be seen that the theorems apply to any irreducible set of operators in a complex vector space, and that Theorem 6-3 applies as well in a real vector space. In particular, these theorems also apply to the irreducible representations of Lie algebras that will be considered shortly.

A useful consequence of Theorem 6-2 is that any irreducible representation in a complex vector space of an Abelian group must be one-dimensional. If D(a) is an irreducible representation, the matrices D(g) satisfy $D(g)D(a) = D(a)D(g)$, and hence, $D(g) = \lambda I$ for all $g \in G$. If D(a) is of dimension greater than one, it is obviously reducible, providing a contradiction.

6-6 ORTHOGONALITY PROPERTIES OF IRREDUCIBLE REPRESENTATIONS

In this section we will consider explicit unitary irreducible matrix representations of finite or compact Lie groups. It will be shown that the matrix elements $D(g)_{ij}$ of these representations are orthogonal functions defined on the group.

We consider, for an irreducible representation by matrices D(g) of a group G, the matrix

$$X = \int D(g)\, Z\, D(g^{-1}) dg, \tag{6.20}$$

where we understand the integral to be the integral of each element of the matrix $D(g)\, Z\, D(g^{-1})$ separately. This integral is well defined only for finite groups and compact Lie groups. Hence, the considerations of this chapter apply only for these groups. The matrix Z is to be, for the present, an arbitrary constant matrix. The matrix X satisfies $D(a)XD(a)^{-1} = X$, since

$$D(a)XD(a^{-1}) = D(a)\int D(g)\, Z\, D(g^{-1}) dg\, D(a)^{-1}$$

$$= \int D(a)\, D(g)\, Z\, D(g^{-1})\, D(a^{-1}) dg = \int D(ag)\, Z\, D((ag)^{-1})\, dg = X.$$

In deriving this result we have used the linearity and left invariance properties of the group integral and the representation properties of the D(a). It follows that $D(a)X = XD(a)$ for all $a \in G$, and from Theorem 6-2, that $X = \lambda I$.

It is also possible to obtain an expression for the constant λ. If the trace of X is evaluated, we can put $\lambda = \mathrm{Tr}\, X/n$, where n is the dimension of the representation, since $\mathrm{Tr}\, I = n$. We can write

$$\mathrm{Tr}\, X = \int \mathrm{Tr}[D(g) Z\, D(g^{-1})] dg = \int \mathrm{Tr}[D(g)^{-1} D(g) Z] dg$$

$$= \int \mathrm{Tr}\, Z\, dg = \Omega\, \mathrm{Tr}\, Z$$

where Ω is the group volume defined to be $\int dg$. We obtain the final result

$$\int D(g)\, Z\, D(g^{-1}) dg = \frac{\Omega\ \mathrm{Tr}\ Z}{n}\, I\,. \tag{6.21}$$

We now limit our attention to unitary representations so that $D(g^{-1}) = D(g)^{-1} = D(g)^{\dagger}$. Equation (21) can be written explicitly as

$$\int \sum_{kl} D(g)_{ik} Z_{kl} D(g)_{jl}^{*} dg = \frac{\Omega\ \mathrm{Tr}\ Z\ \delta_{ij}}{n}, \tag{6.22}$$

since $[D(g)^{\dagger}]_{lj} = D(g)_{jl}^{*}$. The matrix Z, which has been arbitrary to the present, will be chosen so that $z_{mn} = 1$ and all other elements are zero, that is, $z_{kl} = \delta_{km}\, \delta_{ln}$. The trace of Z is zero unless $m = n$, in which case it is 1 that is $\mathrm{Tr}\ Z = \delta_{mn}$. We substitute for Z in (22) and obtain, since the sum on k and l reduces to a single term,

$$\int D(g)_{im} D(g)_{jn}^{*} dg = \frac{\Omega}{n}\, \delta_{ij}\, \delta_{mn}. \tag{6.23}$$

We now consider two irreducible inequivalent representations by matrices $D^1(a)$ and $D^2(a)$ of dimension m and n respectively. According to Theorem 6-3, any matrix X that satisfies $XD^1(a) = D^2(a)X$ for all a must vanish. Such a matrix can be constructed in the form

$$X = \int D^2(g)\, Z\, D^1(g^{-1})dg, \tag{6.24}$$

where Z is an arbitrary matrix with m columns and n rows so that the matrix multiplication is meaningful. It can be shown exactly as before that $D^2(a)\, X\, D^1(a)^{-1} = X$ or that $D^2(a)\, X = X\, D^1(a)$ so that $X=0$. We again assume that the representations are unitary and that only one element of Z is nonzero. It can be seen that the result is analogous to equation (23) and is, for unitary representations,

$$\int D^2(g)_{im} D^1(g)_{jn}{}^* dg = 0. \tag{6.25}$$

These results can be summarized as a theorem.

THEOREM 6-4. Let $D^1(a)$, $D^2(a)$, ... be a family (finite or infinite) of inequivalent irreducible unitary representations of a finite or compact Lie group. The matrix elements of these representations satisfy the orthogonality relations

$$\int D^l(g)_{im} D^k(g)_{jn}{}^* dg = \frac{\Omega}{n_l}\, \delta_{lk}\, \delta_{ij}\, \delta_{mn} \tag{6.26}$$

where n_l is the dimension of $D^l(a)$.

If G is a finite group the integral in (26) reduces to a sum over G and the result is

$$\sum_{g \varepsilon G} D^l(g)_{im} D^k(g)_{jn}{}^* = \frac{N}{n_l}\, \delta_{lk} \delta_{ij} \delta_{mn} \tag{6.27}$$

where N is the order of the group. The functions $D^l(g)_{im}$ take on only a finite number N of values and could perhaps be more appropriately regarded as a set of vectors in an N-dimensional vector space. The functions $D^l(g)_{im}$ constitute a set of orthogonal vectors in this space; there are at most N such vectors so that it can be concluded that

$$\sum_l n_l{}^2 \leq N.$$

It will be shown in the next chapter that the equality sign must hold.

6-7 GROUP CHARACTERS

The problem of analyzing and classifying group representations is rendered much more tractable by considering the functions defined on the group known as the group characters. The character associated with a matrix representation is the function χ defined by

$$\chi(a) = \text{Tr } D(a) = \sum_{i=1}^{n} D(a)_{ii}. \tag{6.28}$$

An important invariance property of the character is that it is the same for all equivalent representations, since if $\chi'(a)$ is the character of $D'(a) = SD(a)S^{-1}$,

$$\chi'(a) = \text{Tr } [SD(a)S^{-1}] = \text{Tr } [S^{-1}SD(a)] = \text{Tr } D(a) = \chi(a).$$

It will also be shown that if two representations have the same character they are equivalent, so that the characters give a complete classification of the representations up to equivalences.

A second important property of the character is that it is an invariant function; that is, it is the same for all elements in an equivalence class of the group. This is a consequence of the fact that a and b are in the same class if there is an element t such that $b = tat^{-1}$. It follows that $D(b) = D(t)\, D(a)\, D(t)^{-1}$ and that $\text{Tr } D(b) = \text{Tr } D(a)$.

We consider now the problem of reducing an arbitrary unitary representation into a direct sum of irreducible representations. If a representation $D(a)$ is reducible into the direct sum of two other representations $D^1(a)$ and $D^2(a)$, it is apparent from (12) that

$$\chi(a) = \chi^1(a) + \chi^2(a), \tag{6.29}$$

where $\chi(a)$, $\chi^1(a)$, and $\chi^2(a)$ are the characters of $D(a)$, $D^1(a)$, and $D^2(a)$ respectively.

It may happen, however, that the subblocks on the diagonal of the reduced matrix are again reducible. The reduction process can then be continued and, if the representation is finite-dimensional, a point will be reached at which no further reduction is possible. One then obtains

$$SD(a)S^{-1} = \begin{pmatrix} D^{l_1}(a) & 0 & \cdots & 0 \\ 0 & D^{l_2}(a) & \cdots & 0 \\ \cdots & \cdot & & \\ 0 & 0 & \cdots & D^{l_p}(a) \end{pmatrix} \tag{6.30}$$

where the $D^l(a)$ on the diagonal are irreducible representations. Another view of this process of reduction is that the invariant subspaces of lowest possible dimension are sought out and the representation expressed as the direct sum of representations in these subspaces. It will be shown in the next chapter that this process of complete reduction can be carried out also for infinite-dimensional representations of compact Lie groups.

It is evident from equation (30) that

$$\chi(a) = \chi^{l_1}(a) + \chi^{l_2}(a) + \cdots + \chi^{l_p}(a)$$

since the trace of the large matrix is the sum of the traces of the small matrices on the diagonal. We can, therefore, write

$$\chi(a) = \sum \nu_l \chi^l(a) \tag{6.31}$$

where ν_l is the number of times the irreducible representation $D^l(a)$ occurs on the diagonal of the large matrix. We remark in passing that if the ν_l are either 0 or 1, the representation is said to be <u>simply reducible.</u>

It will now be shown that the numbers ν_l are completely determined by the character of the representation D(a). We consider a set of irreducible unitary representations $D^1(a)$, $D^2(a)$, ... such that there is one representation from each family of irreducible inequivalent representations. In other words, we assume that every irreducible representation is equivalent to one of the $D^l(a)$, but that $D^i(a)$ is not equivalent to $D^j(a)$ if $i \neq j$. The character of the representation $D^l(a)$ will be denoted by $\chi^l(a)$. The characters satisfy the orthogonality property

$$\int \chi^i(g)^* \chi^j(g) dg = \Omega\, \delta_{ij} \tag{6.32}$$

since, from equations (26) and (28),

$$\int \chi^i(g)^* \chi^j(g) dg = \sum_{kl} \int D^i(g)_{kk}{}^* D^j(g)_{ll} dg = \sum_k \frac{\Omega}{n_i} \delta_{ij} = \Omega\, \delta_{ij}.$$

If equation (31) is multiplied by $\chi^i(g)^*$ and the result integrated over the group, the result

$$\nu_i = \Omega^{-1} \int \chi^i(g)^* \chi(g) dg \tag{6.33}$$

is obtained. The numbers ν_i are, therefore, uniquely determined by the character $\chi(a)$.

We conclude that if an arbitrary unitary representation is completely reduced to the form of equation (30), the result is unique except that the various irreducible components may be permuted along the diagonal and each irreducible component may of course be transformed to an equivalent form.

It is also of interest to note from equations (31) and (32) that

$$\int |\chi(g)|^2 \, dg = \Omega \, \Sigma \nu_l^2 . \tag{6.34}$$

If a representation is irreducible, all the ν_l vanish except one which is unity; hence a representation with character $\chi(g)$ is irreducible if and only if

$$\int |\chi(g)|^2 \, dg = \Omega .$$

If two irreducible representations have the same character, their characters cannot be orthogonal, and therefore, the representations must be equivalent.

6-8 DIRECT PRODUCT OF REPRESENTATIONS

Given two representations, we have constructed a third representation, their direct sum. This is, however, of somewhat limited interest since the matrices of greatest importance are the irreducible representations. In this section a different, more useful, method of constructing new representations will be discussed. In keeping with the fact that it is more interesting, the construction is also more complicated.

We consider representations Γ_1 and Γ_2 by matrices $D^1(a)$ and $D^2(a)$ of dimension m and n respectively. The direct product is defined in the space L of all tensors A that have components a_{ij}, $1 \leq i \leq m$, $1 \leq j \leq n$. A linear combination $\alpha A + \beta B$ of tensors A and B is defined to be the tensor with components $\alpha a_{ij} + \beta b_{ij}$ where a_{ij} and b_{ij} are the components of A and B. The "tensors" A have mn components, and we shall regard these as components of a vector in a vector space of mn dimensions which is called the direct product space of the representation spaces of D^1 and D^2.

The <u>direct product</u> of Γ_1 and Γ_2 is defined to be the set of transformations D(a) in L defined by

$$[D(a)A]_{ij} = \sum_{k=1}^{m} \sum_{l=1}^{n} D^1(a)_{ik} D^2(a)_{jl} a_{kl} . \tag{6.35}$$

Since equation (35) is linear and homogeneous in the components of A the transformation it defines is certainly linear. It is easy to see that the transformations D(a) constitute a representation. We compute

$$[D(a)D(b)A]_{ij} = \sum_{k=1}^{m} \sum_{l=1}^{n} \sum_{s=1}^{m} \sum_{t=1}^{n} D^1(a)_{ik} D^2(a)_{jl} D^1(b)_{ks} D^2(b)_{lt} a_{st}$$

$$= \sum_{s=1}^{m} \sum_{t=1}^{n} D^1(ab)_{is} D^2(ab)_{jt} a_{st} = [D(ab)A]_{ij} \qquad (6.36)$$

where we have used the fact that $D^i(a)\, D^i(b) = D^i(ab)$.

The transformations D(a) can be regarded as matrices in which the indices are not single subscripts but pairs (ij), i = 1, ..., m, j = 1, ..., n. The matrix elements of D(a) can then be written

$$D(a)_{ij,kl} = D^1(a)_{ik} D^2(a)_{jl}$$

$$i, j = 1, \ldots, m \qquad k, l, = 1, \ldots, n. \qquad (6.37)$$

A shorthand notation for (37) is

$$D(a) = D^1(a) \times D^2(a) \qquad (6.38a)$$

and one says that the matrix D(a) is the direct product of the matrices $D^1(a)$ and $D^2(a)$. More generally, if

$$P_{ik,jl} = M_{ij}\, N_{kl}, \qquad (6.38b)$$

one writes $P = M \times N$ and says that P is the direct product of M and N. If equation (38a) holds for all elements of a group, and if $D^1(a)$ and $D^2(a)$ are representations of the group, one says that $D = D^1 \times D^2$ is the direct product representation of D^1 and D^2. The group representation property of $D^1 \times D^2$ is expressed by the equation

$$\sum_{s=1}^{n} \sum_{t=1}^{n} D(a)_{ij,st} D(b)_{st,kl} = D(ab)_{ik,jl}\, . \qquad (6.39)$$

It will be shown in the next chapter that every irreducible representation of a compact matrix group can be generated by taking repeated direct products of any faithful representation of the group with itself and reducing, if possible, the result. It is this property which renders the direct product of considerable importance.

The character of the direct product is again given by the sum of the diagonal elements;

$$\chi(a) = \sum_{ij} D(a)_{ij,ij} = \sum_i \sum_j D^1(a)_{ii} D^2(a)_{jj} = \chi^1(a)\chi^2(a). \tag{6.40}$$

The characters of the direct product of two representations is, therefore, the product of the characters of the representations. It follows that the direct products of equivalent representations are equivalent and that the irreducible components of $D^1 \times D^2$ and $D^2 \times D^1$ are the same.

It may be useful to write out the direct product $D^1 \times D^2$ in an explicit matrix form. This is the mn-dimensional matrix

$$D(a) = \begin{pmatrix} D^1(a)_{11}D^2(a), & D^1(a)_{12}D^2(a), & \ldots, & D^1(a)_{1m}D^2(a) \\ D^1(a)_{21}D^2(a), & D^1(a)_{22}D^2(a), & \ldots, & D^1(a)_{2m}D^2(a) \\ \cdot & \cdot & & \cdot \\ \cdot & \cdot & & \cdot \\ D^1(a)_{m1}D^2(a), & D^1(a)_{m2}D^2(a), & \ldots, & D^1(a)_{mm}D^2(a) \end{pmatrix} \tag{6.41}$$

In (41), the matrix D(a) is written in block form with m^2 blocks, each of which is of dimension $n \times n$. Each block of the matrix is the corresponding element of $D^1(a)$ multiplied by the whole of $D^2(a)$. It can be verified by direct calculation that the matrices D(a) provide a representation of the group. The trace of D(a) is given by

$$D^1(a)_{11}\chi^2(a) + D^1(a)_{22}\chi^2(a) + \ldots + D^1(a)_{mm}\chi^2(a) = \chi^1(a)\chi^2(a).$$

We suggest that the reader prove that the direct product of two unitary representations is again unitary.

6-9 REPRESENTATIONS IN FUNCTION SPACES

If a group G can be regarded as a set of transformations in some space S, it is possible to construct representations in the space of functions whose domain is S. For our purposes, S is usually a linear vector space, although this need not be the case. The points of S will be denoted by boldface letters **x**, **y**, and so on.

Let G be a group of continuous 1-1 transformations of S onto itself. The image of a point **x** under a transformation $a \in G$ will be denoted by a**x**; as a result of the 1-1 nature of the transformations, the equation $\mathbf{y} = a\mathbf{x}$, as an equation for x, has only one solution. The continuity of the transformation means that if $\mathbf{x}_i \to \mathbf{x}$, $a\mathbf{x}_i \to a\mathbf{x}$.

We consider the set H of all continuous complex functions f defined on S; H is a linear vector space (in general infinite-dimensional) in which linear combinations are defined by $[\alpha f + \beta g]\,(\mathbf{x}) = \alpha f(x) + \beta g(x)$. Linear operators D(a) can be defined in H as follows. For any function $f \varepsilon$ H, the function D(a)f is defined by

$$[D(a)f](\mathbf{x}) = f(a^{-1}\mathbf{x}); \tag{6.42}$$

that is, the function D(a)f evaluated at $\mathbf{x}\ \varepsilon$ S has the value of f at the point $a^{-1}\mathbf{x}$. Because of the continuous nature of the transformation a, the function D(a)f is continuous if f is. It can be shown that D(a) is linear, that is,

$$D(a)[\alpha f + \beta g] = \alpha D(a)f + \beta D(a)g. \tag{6.43}$$

It will now be verified that the operators D(a) satisfy $D(a)D(b) = D(ab)$ and, therefore, form a representation. We introduce the notation $D(b)f = f_b$. Then $D(a)f_b(\mathbf{x}) = f_b(a^{-1}\mathbf{x})$. On the other hand, $f_b(\mathbf{y}) = f(b^{-1}\mathbf{y})$ and hence, putting $\mathbf{y} = a^{-1}\mathbf{x}$, $f_b(a^{-1}\mathbf{x}) = f(b^{-1}a^{-1}\mathbf{x}) = f((ab)^{-1}\mathbf{x}) = [D(ab)f](\mathbf{x})$. It can be concluded that $[D(a)D(b)f](\mathbf{x}) = [D(a)f_b](\mathbf{x}) = [D(ab)f](\mathbf{x})$ and hence, that $D(a)D(b) = D(ab)$. Note that when operating on $f(b^{-1}x)$ with D(a) one obtains $f(b^{-1}a^{-1}x)$, not $f(a^{-1}b^{-1}x)$.

An example of the foregoing could be provided by an S that is the Euclidean plane, the group G being the group of all length-preserving transformations of S onto itself.

If we define $a_i \to a$ as meaning that $a_i\mathbf{x} \to a\mathbf{x}$ for all $\mathbf{x}$, then the representation (42) is also continuous. If G is a Lie group and the coordinates of $a\mathbf{x}$ are differentiable functions of the group parameters (as will always be the case), the representation will be differentiable, in the sense that if f is differentiable, D(a)f is a differentiable function of the parameters.

The representation D is infinite-dimensional if S has an infinite number of points. In general, however, H contains finite-dimensional subspaces invariant under D(a), so that D is reducible. A trivial example of an invariant subspace is the one-dimensional space of all constant functions on S; this obviously generates the identity representation since $D(a)f = f$ if f is constant. Any representation defined on a subspace H_1 of H will be said to be <u>projected</u> by D into H_1. The functions in H_1 are said to <u>carry</u> the projected representation or to be <u>partner functions</u> of the representation. If H_1 is finite-dimensional and is spanned by a set of linearly independent functions e^1, e^2,

..., e^n, an explicit matrix representation can be obtained by solving the analogue of (5)

$$e^j(a^{-1}\mathbf{x}) = \sum_i D(a)_{ij} e^i(\mathbf{x}) \tag{6.44}$$

for $D(a)_{ij}$.

As an example of a nontrivial invariant subspace of H, we suppose S to be a linear vector space and G to be a group of nonsingular linear operators in S. The subspace H_1 of linear functions defined on S is invariant under the mapping $f(\mathbf{x}) \rightarrow f(A^{-1}\mathbf{x})$. In fact, if an inner product is defined on S any linear function can be written in the form $(\mathbf{c}, \mathbf{x})$ for some $\mathbf{c} \in S$. Then

$$D(A)(\mathbf{c}, \mathbf{x}) = (\mathbf{c}, A^{-1}\mathbf{x}) = ((A^{-1})^\dagger \mathbf{c}, \mathbf{x})$$

which is again a linear function defined on S by the vector $(S^{-1})^\dagger \mathbf{c}$. This result indicates further that the operators $(A^{-1})^\dagger$ are also a representation of G, since D(A) transforms $\mathbf{c}$ into $(A^{-1})^\dagger \mathbf{c}$; $(A^{-1})^\dagger$ is called the matrix contragredient to A. It can also be verified directly that this is a representation: $((AB)^{-1})^\dagger = (B^{-1}A^{-1})^\dagger = (A^{-1})^\dagger (B^{-1})^\dagger$. If the matrices A are unitary, $(A^{-1})^\dagger = A$ and the contragredient representation is the original representation.

A more general invariant subspace of H is the set H_ν of all homogeneous functions of degree ν defined on S. A homogeneous function of degree ν is one with the property that $f(c\mathbf{x}) = c^\nu f(\mathbf{x})$. It is easy to verify that H_ν is a linear subspace of H and is invariant under D(A) if A is a linear operator in S. This method of constructing representations will be used to obtain the representation of certain groups.

Expression (42) for a representation can be generalized to functions of more than one variable. For example, if f is a function of variables $\mathbf{x}$ and $\mathbf{y}$, the domain of each of which is S, D(a)f can be defined by

$$[D(a)f](\mathbf{x}, \mathbf{y}) = f(a^{-1}\mathbf{x}, a^{-1}\mathbf{y}). \tag{6.45}$$

This type of representation is important in the discussion of the direct product. We suppose that $D^1(a)$ and $D^2(a)$ satisfy equations (44) for sets of functions e^i and f^j respectively; it will be assumed that these are finite sets of functions so that the representations are finite-dimensional. We consider the space H of functions of two variables defined by

$$h(\mathbf{x}, \mathbf{y}) = c_{ij} e^i(\mathbf{x}) f^j(\mathbf{y}),$$

where the c_{ij} are arbitrary constants. The representation defined in H by equation (45) is equivalent to $D^1 \times D^2$. In fact, $e^i(\mathbf{x})\, f^j(\mathbf{y})$ can be taken as basis vectors in H, and one has

$$e^m(a^{-1}\mathbf{x}) \quad e^n(a^{-1}\mathbf{y}) = \sum_m D^1(a)_{im}\, e^i(\mathbf{x}) \sum_n D^2(a)_{jn}\, f^j(\mathbf{y})$$

$$= \sum_{mn} [D^1 \times D^2(a)]_{ij,mn}\, e^i(\mathbf{x}) f^j(\mathbf{y}).$$

It is of interest to investigate whether the function space representation is unitary. This question is, however, meaningless since no inner product has thus far been defined on the vector space H or its subspaces. We consider an n-dimensional invariant subspace H_1 of H and a set of n linearly independent functions $e^1, e^2, \ldots, e^n$ contained in H_1 and define the inner product by defining $(e^i, e^j) = \delta_{ij}$. It will now be shown that the matrix representation generated by the e^i through equation (44) is unitary if the functions e^i satisfy the invariance property

$$\sum_{i=1}^{n} e^i(\mathbf{x})^* e\ (\mathbf{y}) = \sum_{i=1}^{n} e^i(a^{-1}\mathbf{x})^* e^i(a^{-1}\mathbf{y}) \tag{6.46}$$

for all a ε G. This is proved by writing (46) as

$$\sum_{i=1}^{n} \sum_{k=1}^{n} \sum_{l=1}^{n} D(a)_{ki}^* D(a)_{li} e^k(\mathbf{x})^* e^l(\mathbf{y}) = \sum_{i=1}^{n} e^i(x)^* e^i(\mathbf{y}).$$

This can also be written as

$$\sum_{k=1}^{n} \sum_{l=1}^{n} \left[\sum_{i=1}^{n} D(a)_{ki}^* D(a)_{li} - \delta_{kl} \right] e^k(\mathbf{x})^* e^l(\mathbf{y}) = 0.$$

The functions $e^k(\mathbf{x})^*\, e^l(\mathbf{y})$ are linearly independent, so that the unitary property

$$\sum_{i=1}^{n} D(a)_{ki}^* D(a)_{li} = \delta_{kl}$$

is proved.

6-10 REPRESENTATIONS OF LIE ALGEBRAS

It is natural to consider applying the concept of representation also to Lie algebras. A representation of a Lie algebra Λ can be defined to be a Lie algebra of n × n matrices, together with a homomorphic mapping J of Λ onto the matrix algebra. The homomorphic nature of J then implies that, for any pair of elements **a** and **b** in Λ,

$$J(\alpha\mathbf{a}+\beta\mathbf{b}) = \alpha J(\mathbf{a}) + \beta J(\mathbf{b}) \tag{6.47}$$

$$J(\mathbf{a})J(\mathbf{b}) - J(\mathbf{b})J(\mathbf{a}) = J([\mathbf{a},\mathbf{b}]). \tag{6.48}$$

It is clear that the representation can also be defined to be a set of linear operators that again satisfy equations (47) and (48).

In this section the relation between group representations and Lie algebra representations will be investigated. In particular, it appears plausible that a representation of a Lie group should give rise to a representation of the corresponding Lie algebra, and conversely it will be shown that to a certain extent this is true.

It was shown in Chapter 4 that the Lie algebra of the group U(n) of n × n unitary matrices is composed of all n × n skew-Hermitian matrices. The analogue of a unitary group representation is, therefore, a representation by skew-Hermitian matrices and these are of principal interest for the present work.

Two representations J(**a**) and K(**a**) of a Lie algebra are defined to be equivalent if there if a nonsingular matrix S such that

$$K(\mathbf{a}) = SJ(\mathbf{a})S^{-1} \tag{6.49}$$

for all **a** ε Λ. The matrices K(**a**) defined by (49) can be verified to constitute a representation for any S; K(**a**) need not be skew-Hermitian, however.

A representation of Λ is defined to be reducible, or completely reducible in exactly the same way as for a group representation. It is suggested that the reader show that a representation by skew-Hermitian matrices that is reducible is also completely reducible.

We consider now a matrix representation D(a) of a Lie group with corresponding Lie algebra Λ. If D(a) is again a Lie group, it gives rise to a matrix Lie algebra Λ'. It has been shown in Chapter 4 that a homomorphic mapping of a Lie group onto another generates a homomorphic mapping of the corresponding Lie algebras. It follows that Λ is homomorphic to Λ', or, Λ' is a representation of Λ. The question of whether D(a) is a Lie group remains, that is, whether the matrix elements $D(a)_{ij}$ are differentiable functions of the group parameters. As was remarked, the matrix representations of a compact Lie group are differentiable if there is one such differentiable representation. In the case of an infinite-dimensional representation of a noncompact group, the differentiability must be established for each special case.

If the representation D(a) is reducible, it is evident that J(**a**) derived from it is as well, since the matrices J(**a**) can be transformed to the block diagonal form (12) or (15) by the same matrix that reduces D(a).

The question of whether a representation of the Lie algebra can be used to construct a group representation is more difficult to resolve. A difficulty that can arise is that groups that are not isomorphic may be locally isomorphic, and therefore generate the same Lie algebra. It follows that a representation of the Lie algebra cannot be expected to produce a faithful representation of the group. It is possible, however, to construct a set of matrices which is at least locally isomorphic to the original group.

We consider now a representation spanned by matrices J_α of a Lie algebra Λ corresponding to a Lie group G. The matrix J_α is assumed to be a tangent vector along the coordinate axis α. We wish to discover whether there is a representation $D(\mathbf{p})$ of G such that

$$\frac{\partial D}{\partial p^\alpha}(0) = J_\alpha. \tag{6.50}$$

(For simplicity, the group parameters **p** rather than the group element will be used as the argument of D in this discussion.)

We will first derive a partial differential equation for $D(\mathbf{p})$. The group representation property requires that

$$D(\mathbf{p})D(\mathbf{q}) = D(\mathbf{f}(\mathbf{p},\mathbf{q})). \tag{6.51}$$

If D is a differentiable function of the group parameters, this can be differentiated with respect to q^β and evaluated at $\mathbf{q} = 0$. The result is

$$D(\mathbf{p}) \frac{\partial D}{\partial p^\beta}(0) = \frac{\partial D}{\partial p^\alpha}(\mathbf{p}) \frac{\partial f^\alpha}{\partial q^\beta}(\mathbf{p}, 0)$$

or, since $\partial f^\alpha / \partial q^\beta(\mathbf{p},0)$ was denoted by $v^\alpha{}_\beta(\mathbf{p})$,

$$v^\alpha{}_\beta(\mathbf{p}) \frac{\partial D}{\partial p^\alpha}(\mathbf{p}) = D(\mathbf{p})J_\beta. \tag{6.52}$$

We have adopted the convention of denoting the partial derivatives of D with respect to the αth argument by $\partial D/\partial p^{\alpha}$, regardless of the point at which the derivative is to be evaluated. Note that (52) gives n^2 equations, corresponding to the n^2 matrix elements of D, and that the right-hand side is the matrix product of $\mathbf{D(p)}$ and $\mathbf{J}_\beta$.

The theory of partial differential equations like (52) is by no means as simple as that of the ordinary differential equations which we have encountered before. These equations determine, implicitly, all the partial derivatives $\partial D/\partial p^{\alpha}$. These cannot be independent, but are subject to the integrability conditions

$$\frac{\partial}{\partial p^{\alpha}} \frac{\partial D}{\partial p^{\beta}} = \frac{\partial}{\partial p^{\beta}} \frac{\partial D}{\partial p^{\alpha}} \cdot \tag{6.53}$$

It is possible to show that the differential equations (52) do satisfy this condition and have a solution satisfying the initial condition $D(0) = I$, at least for $\mathbf{p}$ in some neighborhood of the origin.

The proof that solutions for these equations exist, for J_β and $v^{\alpha}{}_{\beta}(p)$ satisfying the necessary relations will not, however, be given here. This is not necessary anyway because the representations of the groups to be considered will be obtained explicitly.

If the existence of solutions of (52) is accepted, it can be shown that they are unique and satisfy (51), the group representation property. The uniqueness can be demonstrated by obtaining an ordinary differential equation for the representation, evaluated along a one-parameter subgroup. Let $\mathbf{p}(t)$ be a one-parameter subgroup, and consider the function $D(\mathbf{p}(t))$ where D is a representation, and therefore satisfies equation (52). We can write, using equation (3.13) for one-parameter subgroups,

$$\begin{aligned} \frac{d}{dt} D(\mathbf{p}(t)) &= \frac{\partial D}{\partial p^{\alpha}} (\mathbf{p}(t))\dot{p}^{\alpha}(t) = \frac{\partial D}{\partial p^{\alpha}} (\mathbf{p}(t)) v^{\alpha}{}_{\beta}(\mathbf{p}(t)) a^{\beta} \\ &= D(\mathbf{p}(t)) J_\beta a^{\beta}. \end{aligned} \tag{6.54}$$

The last line follows from equation (52). This equation has a unique solution for the initial condition $D(\mathbf{p}(0)) = I$:

$$D(\mathbf{p}(t)) = e^{(\mathbf{J}\cdot\mathbf{a})t} \tag{6.55}$$

where $\mathbf{J}\cdot\mathbf{a}$ denotes the matrix $a^{\beta} J_\beta$. Thus the representations of the one-parameter subgroups of G are obtained in a simple way from the generators J_β.

The fact that a solution of (52) satisfies also (51) is shown by proving that each side of (51), regarded as a function of $\mathbf{q}$, is a solution of (52), with the initial condition that at $\mathbf{q} = 0$ each side is $D(\mathbf{p})$. Since (52) is linear and homogeneous, if $D(\mathbf{q})$ is a solution, $D(\mathbf{p})D(\mathbf{q})$ is also a solution. To show that $D(\mathbf{f}(\mathbf{p},\mathbf{q}))$ is a solution, we calculate

$$v^{\alpha}{}_{\beta}(\mathbf{q}) \frac{\partial}{\partial q^{\alpha}} D(\mathbf{f}(\mathbf{p},\mathbf{q})) = v^{\alpha}{}_{\beta}(\mathbf{q}) \frac{\partial D}{\partial p^{\gamma}} (\mathbf{f}(\mathbf{p},\mathbf{q})) \frac{\partial f^{\gamma}}{\partial q^{\alpha}} (\mathbf{p},\mathbf{q})$$

$$= v^{\gamma}{}_{\beta}(\mathbf{f}(\mathbf{p},\mathbf{q})) \frac{\partial D}{\partial p^{\gamma}} (\mathbf{f}(\mathbf{p},\mathbf{q})) = D(\mathbf{f}(\mathbf{p},\mathbf{q}))J_{\beta}.$$

The first step follows from equation (3.9), and the second from replacing $\mathbf{p}$ by $\mathbf{f}(\mathbf{p},\mathbf{q})$ in (52). It is clear that each side of (51) is $D(\mathbf{p})$ at $\mathbf{q} = 0$. A solution of (52) satisfies the ordinary differential equation (54) along a one-parameter subgroup; it follows from the uniqueness property of solutions of ordinary differential equations that solutions of (52) are unique and, therefore, satisfy equation (51).

The preceding argument is incomplete because the existence of solutions of (52) has not been demonstrated. It should be recalled also that solutions of (52) may be restricted to a limited domain of $\mathbf{p}$ around $\mathbf{p} = 0$ and may, therefore, provide only a local representation. As a result, the solutions of (52) satisfy the group equations only for a limited range of the parameters. Moreover, the uniqueness proof applies only to points that can be reached by a one-parameter subgroup and these need not be the whole group.

The group of rotations in two dimensions gives an example of the breakdown of the argument. In this case $f(p, q) = p + q$ so that $v = 1$. Equation (52) is

$$\frac{dD}{dp} = DJ. \tag{6.56}$$

The solution of (56) with the initial condition $D(0) = 1$ is $D(p) = e^{Jp}$. This is not, however, a representation of the group, unless $J = ni$, where n is an integer. It is rather a representation of the locally isomorphic group of real numbers.

If a solution $D(\mathbf{p})$ of (52) exists and is a group representation, and if the matrices J_{β} are completely reducible, then the matrices $D(\mathbf{p})$ are also completely reducible, since if J_{β} is in diagonal block form

$$\begin{pmatrix} J_{\beta}' & 0 \\ 0 & J_{\beta}'' \end{pmatrix}$$

$e^{\mathbf{a}\cdot\mathbf{J}}$ is in the diagonal block form

$$\begin{pmatrix} e^{\mathbf{a} \cdot \mathbf{J}'} & 0 \\ 0 & e^{\mathbf{a} \cdot \mathbf{J}''} \end{pmatrix}.$$

Strictly speaking, this does not follow from the foregoing. It can be proved, however, by integrating (52) from the origin to any point in the group along a continuous path, the existence of which is the connectness postulate of the group.

Chapter 7

COMPLETENESS THEOREMS FOR GROUP REPRESENTATIONS

It was shown in the previous chapter that the matrix elements $D^l(g)_{mn}$ of the irreducible representations of a finite group or a compact Lie group constitute a set of orthogonal functions with respect to the invariant integral on the group. It is natural to investigate whether this set of functions is also a complete set of functions on the group. In this chapter it will be shown that this is the case for these groups; the demonstration for compact Lie groups is somewhat incomplete, however, since it will be assumed that the group considered is a matrix group or has a faithful representation by matrices. This is the case for the groups to be considered in this book.

The first section of this chapter will be devoted to the representations of finite groups. The completeness of the irreducible representations of compact Lie groups will be demonstrated and discussed in the second section. In the last section it will be shown an infinite-dimensional representation of a compact Lie group can be reduced to the direct sum of the finite-dimensional irreducible representations.

In this chapter we will denote by D^1, D^2, ..., D^l, ... a collection of irreducible, inequivalent representations of a finite or compact Lie group G. There may be either a finite or infinite number of such representations, depending on the nature of G.

7-1 COMPLETENESS THEOREMS FOR FINITE GROUPS

A function defined on a finite set of N elements is simply a finite set of numbers, the value of the function at each point, and can perhaps be more appropriately regarded as a vector in an N-dimensional vector space. The set of all complex-valued functions on the set is then just an N-dimensional vector space L.

The regular representation of a finite group G is defined as follows. We can associate with each element $a \in G$ a function v^a defined by

$$v^a(g) = \delta_{ag}; \tag{7.1}$$

that is $v^a(g)$ is zero unless $g = a$, in which case it is 1. The functions v^a can be taken as basis vectors in L; that is, for any function f,

$$f(g) = \sum_a f(a)\,\delta_{ag} = \sum_a f(a) v^a(g). \tag{7.2}$$

The functions v^a are used to construct the regular representation by defining, for any $r \in G$,

$$[D(r)v^a](g) = v^a(r^{-1}g). \tag{7.3}$$

It is now possible to use equation (6.44) to construct the explicit matrix representation:

$$v^a(r^{-1}g) = \delta_{a,r^{-1}g} = \sum_b D(r)_{ba} v^b(g) = \sum_b D(r)_{ba}\delta_{bg} = D(r)_{ga}, \tag{7.4}$$

or

$$D(r)_{mn} = \delta_{n,r^{-1}m} = \delta_{m,rn} \tag{7.5}$$

since $n = r^{-1}m$ if, and only if, $m = rn$ The matrix D(r) is an $N \times N$ matrix whose rows and columns are labeled by group elements rather than integers. A direct calculation,

$$\sum_n D(r)_{mn} D(s)_{np} = \sum_n \delta_{m,rn}\delta_{n,sp} = \delta_{m,rsp} = D(rs)_{mp}, \tag{7.6}$$

shows that D is a representation. The matrix D(r) multiplying an N-dimensional vector has the effect only of permuting its components. If the components of the vector are labeled by group elements, a component in position n is moved by D(r) to position rn.

Consider now the elements of D in the column labeled e; $D(r)_{me} = \delta_{mr}$. An arbitrary function f can be expressed in the form

$$f(g) = \sum_m f(m)\,\delta_{mg} = \sum_m f(m) D(g)_{me} \tag{7.7}$$

which indicates that the $D(g)_{me}$ constitute a complete set of function on G. Any other column of D(g) would have done as well for this argument.

Since there are N^2 matrix elements of D(g) and at most N orthogonal functions on the group, the representation D(g) must be reducible for N > 1. We suppose that $\bar{D}(g)$ is a completely reduced form of D(g);

$$\bar{D}(g) = \begin{pmatrix} D^{i_1}(g) & & \cdot & \cdot & \cdot & 0 \\ 0 & D^{i_2}(g) & \cdot & \cdot & \cdot & 0 \\ \cdot & \cdot & \cdot & \cdot & \cdot & \cdot \\ 0 & 0 & \cdot & \cdot & \cdot & D^{i_l}(g) \end{pmatrix} \tag{7.8}$$

where the $D^i(g)$ are irreducible representations. Since D(g) = $S^{-1}\bar{D}(g)S$, the elements of D(g) are expressible as linear combinations of the elements of the $D^i(g)$; we conclude that any function f can be expressed as a linear combination of the $D^i(g)$. It is interesting, but not essential for our purposes, to observe that the character $\chi(g)$ of the regular representation is $N\,\delta_{ge}$. Equation (6.33) shows then that $\nu_i = n_i$, the dimension of $D^i(g)$. Therefore, the number of times each inequivalent representation occurs on the diagonal of (8) is equal to its dimension.

It follows from the orthogonality property (6.27) of the irreducible representations that

$$f(g) = \sum_{imn} a^i{}_{mn} D^i(g)_{mn} \tag{7.9a}$$

where

$$a^i{}_{mn} = \frac{n_i}{N} \sum_h D^i(h)_{mn}{}^* f(h) \tag{7.9b}$$

where n_i is the dimension of $D^i(g)$. We note that, since there are exactly N elements in a complete set of orthogonal vectors in a vector space of N dimensions, $\sum n_i{}^2 = N$.

We consider now invariant functions on the group, that is, functions that are constant on a class, or that have the property $f(txt^{-1}) = f(x)$ for all $t \in G$. It has been observed that the characters of the representations are such functions. It will now be shown that the characters $\chi^i(g)$ of the irreducible representations are a complete set of invariant functions. Let f be an arbitrary invariant function. We introduce a matrix A^i whose elements are $a^i{}_{mn}{}^*$, that is,

$$A^i = \frac{n_i}{N} \sum_h D^i(h) f(h)^*. \tag{7.10}$$

We calculate, using the representation and invariance properties,

$$D^i(a)A^iD^i(a)^{-1} = \frac{n_i}{N}\sum D^i(a)D^i(h)D^i(a)^{-1}f(h)^*$$

$$= \frac{n_i}{N}\sum D^i(aha^{-1})f(h)^*$$

$$= \frac{n_i}{N}\sum D^i(h)f(a^{-1}ha)^* = A^i,$$

or $D^i(a)A^i = A^iD^i(a)$. It follows from Theorem 6-2 that $A^i = \lambda^i I$. The constant λ^i can be evaluated by calculating the trace of each side of (10); the result is

$$\lambda^i = \frac{1}{N}\sum \chi^i(h)f(h)^*.$$

We can, therefore, write

$$a^i{}_{mn} = c_i\delta_{mn} \tag{7.11a}$$

where

$$c_i = \frac{1}{N}\sum \chi^i(h)^*f(h). \tag{7.11b}$$

Substitution into (9a) gives the desired result:

$$f(g) = \sum_{imn} c^i\delta_{mn}D^i(g)_{mn} = \sum_i c^i\chi^i(g). \tag{7.12}$$

Since the maximum number of linearly independent invariant functions must equal the number of classes, we obtain the remarkable result that the number of inequivalent irreducible representations is equal to the number of classes.

7-2 THE PETER-WEYL THEOREM

This section is concerned with the possibility of approximating a function f on a compact set by a linear combination of functions ϕ_1, ϕ_2, ... that are mutually orthonormal on the domain of f. In general, the functions f and ϕ_i may be complex-valued. We consider functions

$$s_N(x) = \sum_{i=1}^{N} a_i\,\phi_i(x) \tag{7.13}$$

where the coefficients a_i are to be chosen to give a good approximation to f.

It is necessary to determine what is meant by a good approximation to the function f, and two different types of approximation will be considered. The first of these is uniform approximation. If, for any positive ϵ, the coefficients a_i and the number N of terms in (13) can be chosen so that

$$|f(x) - s_N(x)| < \epsilon \tag{7.14}$$

for all x, the function f can be *uniformly approximated* by functions of the form s_N. In other words, the maximum discrepancy between f(x) and $s_N(x)$ can be made arbitrarily small by a suitable choice of N and the a_i. Normally, for a fixed N, there will be a set of coefficients a_i that provide the best uniform approximation in the sense that max $|f(x) - s_N(x)|$ is a minimum. A complicating factor in uniform approximation is that these coefficients may vary as N increases.

Although the concept of uniform approximation appears quite natural, it is also somewhat naive, since important properties of f may be lost entirely in s_N. For example, the derivatives of f and s_N may be quite different even when s_N provides a good uniform approximation to f.

In the case of *approximation in the mean*, the coefficients a_i are chosen to minimize the nonnegative quantity

$$E_N = \int |f(x) - s_N(x)|^2 dx \tag{7.15}$$

where the integral is taken over the domain of the functions f and ϕ_i. If the functions f and s_N are continuous and $E_N = 0$, then $f(x) = s_N(x)$. Otherwise E_N is a measure of the average, or mean, square discrepancy between f and s_N.

A straightforward calculation, substituting (13) into (15) and using the orthonormality property of the ϕ_i, shows that

$$E_N = \int |f(x)|^2 dx - \sum_{i=1}^{N} [a_i c_i^* + a_i^* c_i] + \sum_{i=1}^{N} |a_i|^2$$

$$= \int |f(x)|^2 dx = \sum_{i=1}^{N} |c_i|^2 + \sum_{i=1}^{N} |a_i - c_i|^2 \tag{7.16}$$

where the c_i are the *Fourier coefficients* defined by

$$c_i = \int \phi_i(x)^* f(x) dx. \tag{7.17}$$

It is apparent by inspection of (16) that for fixed N, E_N is a minimum when the last term in (16) vanishes, that is, when $a_i = c_i$. Therefore, the Fourier coefficients minimize the mean square deviation between s_N and f.

The importance of approximation in the mean lies to a considerable extent in the facts that equation (17) provides an explicit expression for the optimum coefficients, and that these coefficients are independent of N. It should be emphasized that the best uniform approximation need not be the best approximation in the mean, and conversely. In particular, the coefficients for optimum uniform approximation may depend on N, while the Fourier coefficients do not.

The set of functions ϕ_i is usually infinite. Since $E_N \geq 0$, equation (16) with $a_i = c_i$ shows that

$$\sum_{i=1}^{N} |c_i|^2 \leq \int |f(x)|^2 \, dx, \tag{7.18}$$

a result known as Bessel's inequality. A bounded series of positive terms, such as the left-hand side of (18), must converge to a sum less than or equal to the bound; thus we can write

$$\sum_{i=1}^{\infty} |c_i|^2 \leq \int |f(x)|^2 \, dx$$

where the sum on the left necessarily exists.

If, for a particular function f,

$$\sum_{i=1}^{\infty} |c_i|^2 = \int |f(x)|^2 \, dx \tag{7.19}$$

the functions ϕ_i are said to be <u>complete</u> with respect to f. Equation (19) is then called the <u>completeness relation</u> for f.

A slight generalization of (19) will be required. Suppose f and g are two functions for which the ϕ_i are complete, and that c_i and d_i are their Fourier coefficients. If it is assumed that the ϕ_i are also complete with respect to f + g and f + ig, we can write

$$\sum_{i=1}^{\infty} [c_i^* d_i + d_i^* c_i] = \int [f(x)^* g(x) + g(x)^* f(x)] dx$$

$$i \sum_{i=1}^{\infty} [c_i^* d_i - d_i^* c_i] = i \int [f(x)^* g(x) - g(x)^* f(x)] dx$$

where the completeness relations for f and g have been applied. These two results can be combined to show that

$$\sum_{i=1}^{\infty} c_i^* d_i = \int f(x)^* g(x) \, dx. \tag{7.20}$$

If (20) is valid for a family of functions, (19) is clearly valid for the same family. Equation (19) implies (20), however, only if the family of functions for which it is valid is closed under linear combinations; this is always the case in practice.

We turn now to the case in which the domain of the function f is a compact Lie group G with unitary irreducible representations D^i. The approximating function s_N of (13) is now of the form

$$s_N(x) = \sum_{imn} a^i{}_{mn} D^i(x)_{mn} \tag{7.21}$$

where the $a^i{}_{mn}$ are arbitrary.

To simplify the discussion, the following two restriction will be placed on the s_N. The sum on m and n will be assumed to be only over complete representations; if one matrix element from a representation is included in (21), all the other matrix elements are to be included as well. The sum on i in (21) is to be over the first N irreducible representations. The coefficients $a^i{}_{mn}$ will also be restricted to be of the form

$$a^i{}_{mn} = \alpha_i \int D^i(y)^*_{mn} f(y)dy, \tag{7.22}$$

where the α_i are arbitrary. The coefficients $a^i{}_{mn}$ are, therefore, proportional to the Fourier coefficients, with the same proportionality constant for all matrix elements from a representation. The value $\alpha_i = n_i/\Omega$ corresponds to the choice of $a^i{}_{mn}$ as Fourier coefficients; the value is n_i/Ω rather than 1 to compensate for the fact that the $D^i(x)_{mn}$ are not normalized.

The following identity for unitary representations will be used frequently:

$$\begin{aligned} \sum_{mn} D(y)^*_{mn} D(x)_{mn} &= \sum_{mn} D(y^{-1})_{mn} D(x)_{mn} \\ &= \sum_n D(y^{-1}x)_{nn} \\ &= \chi(y^{-1}x). \end{aligned} \tag{7.23}$$

With the choice (22) of the coefficients $a^i{}_{mn}$, equation (21) becomes

$$\begin{aligned} s_N(x) &= \sum_{i=1}^{N} \alpha_i \sum_{mn} \int D^i(y)^*_{mn} f(y)dy D^i(x)_{mn} \\ &= \sum_{i=1}^{N} \alpha_i \int \chi^i(y^{-1}x) f(y)dy. \end{aligned} \tag{7.24}$$

Since the sum is finite, there is no difficulty in changing the order of summation and integration. Similarly, the completeness relation (20) that we wish to establish can be written

$$\sum_{i=1}^{\infty} \frac{n_i}{\Omega} \sum_{mn} \int D^i(x)_{mn} f(x)^* \, dx \int D^i(y)^*_{mn} g(y) \, dy = \int f(x)^* g(x) \, dx$$

or

$$\sum_{i=1}^{\infty} \frac{n_i}{\Omega} \int dx \quad dy \, f(x)^* \chi^i(y^{-1}x) \, g(y) = \int f(x)^* g(x) \, dx. \tag{7.25}$$

If it were true that

$$\sum_{i=1}^{\infty} n_i \chi^i(x) = \Omega \delta(x), \tag{7.26}$$

equation (25) would be valid, since the double integral on the left-hand side would reduce to a single integral. Similarly,

$$\lim_{N \to \infty} s_N(x) = f(x)$$

where $s_N(x)$ is defined through (24) with $\alpha_i = n_i/\Omega$. A relation such as (26) must be considerably qualified and cannot be in general valid; it will be shown, however, that if G has a faithful matrix representation D_f, it is possible to construct a linear combination of the characters χ^i of the irreducible representations that approximates (in a sense to be defined) a δ function arbitrarily closely. The coefficients in this linear combination need not be the Fourier coefficients n_i/Ω, however. This result will be formulated as a theorem.

THEOREM 7-1. Let G be a compact Lie group with a faithful matrix representation D_f. Then there is a sequence of nonnegative functions ψ_N with the properties

$$\psi_N(x) = \sum a_i^N \chi^i(x) \tag{7.27}$$

where the sum is over a finite number of terms,

$$\int \psi_N(x) \, dx = 1, \tag{7.28}$$

and for any open neighborhood U of e and any $\epsilon > 0$, there is an N such that $\psi_N(x) < \epsilon$ for all x outside U. This means that the ψ_N are an approximating sequence to a δ function peaked at e.

PROOF. It will be necessary to use the inequality

$$|\chi(x)| \leq \chi(e) \tag{7.29}$$

which is valid for any character and which can be proved by applying Schwarz' inequality to equation (23). One has

$$|\chi(y^{-1}x)|^2 = |\sum_{mn} D(y)^*_{mn} D(x)_{mn}|^2$$

$$\leq \sum_{mn} |D(y)_{mn}|^2 \sum_{mn} |D(x)_{mn}|^2 = \chi(e)^2.$$

The last line follows from (23) in the special case x = y.

The faithful representation D_f has the property that

$$\sum_{mn} [D_f(x)_{mn} - D_f(y)_{mn}]^* [D_f(x)_{mn} - D_f(y)_{mn}] > 0$$

for $x \neq y$, since if $D_f(x)_{mn} = D_f(y)_{mn}$ for all m and n, $D_f(x) = D_f(y)$ contrary to the assumption that D_f is faithful. This inequality can be written, from (23), as

$$2\chi_f(e) - \chi_f(y^{-1}x) - \chi_f(y^{-1}x)^* > 0, \; x \neq y. \tag{7.30}$$

The function $\chi_f + \chi_f^*$ is the character χ_r of the direct sum D_r of D_f and D_f^*. Then (29) and (30) together imply that, if $x \neq e$,

$$-\chi_r(e) \leq \chi_r(x) < \chi_r(e).$$

Let $m = \chi_r(e)$ be the dimension of D_r. Then the function χ given by $\chi(x) = m + \chi_r(x)$ is also a character, of the representation D that is the direct sum of D_r and m identity representations. Furthermore, $0 \leq \chi(x) < \chi(e)$ for $x \neq e$.

We can now define

$$\psi_N(x) = c_N \, [\chi(x)]^N$$

where c_N is to be chosen so that

$$\int \psi_N(x) \, dx = 1.$$

The function $[\chi(x)]^N$ is again a character, of the direct product of N factors of D, and therefore χ_N can be expressed through equation (6.31) as a linear combination of the characters χ^i of the irreducible representations so that (27) is valid.

Suppose now that U is an open neighborhood of e. The set G - U of all elements not in U is a compact set, and by a familiar theorem there is an element a in G - U for which χ is a maximum in G - U; that is, $\chi(a) \geq \chi(x)$ for all x in G - U. Since $a \neq e$, $\chi(e) > \chi(a) \geq \chi(x)$ for all x in G - U.

Since χ is continuous, there is an open neighborhood V of e such that

$$\chi(y) > \frac{\chi(e) + \chi(a)}{2}$$

for $y \in V$. Let $|V|$ denote the volume of V. Then

$$\int [\chi(y)]^N dy > |V| \left(\frac{\chi(e) + \chi(a)}{2}\right)^N$$

and hence

$$c_N < \frac{1}{|V|}\left[\frac{2}{\chi(e) + \chi(a)}\right]^N .$$

Then, for any $x \in G - U$,

$$\psi_N(x) < \frac{1}{|V|}\left[\frac{2\chi(x)}{\chi(e) + \chi(a)}\right]^N$$

$$\leq \frac{1}{|V|}\left[\frac{2\chi(a)}{\chi(e) + \chi(a)}\right]^N .$$

The last expression can be made arbitrarily small, independently of x, by choosing N sufficiently large.

It is now necessary to prove a theorem to the effect that if a function f is continuous on a compact Lie group, it is uniformly continuous. By this we mean that for any $\epsilon > 0$, there is an open neighborhood V of e such that if $y^{-1}x \in V$, $|f(x) - f(y)| < \epsilon$. This is a generalization of the definition for functions of a real variable which can be formulated as: for any $\epsilon > 0$, there is an interval $(-\delta, \delta)$, that contains 0, such that $|f(x) - f(y)| < \epsilon$ if $(x - y) \in (-\delta, \delta)$. The interval $(-\delta, \delta)$ corresponds to the open neighborhood V above.

THEOREM 7-2. If f is continuous on a compact Lie group G, f is uniformly continuous.

PROOF. Let $\epsilon > 0$ be given. Then for each a in G, there is an open neighborhood U_a of a such that $|f(x) - f(a)| < \epsilon/2$ for all $x \in U_a$. The identity ea = a, and the continuity of the group multiplication, which is implied by the differentiability, means that there are open neighborhoods V_a of e and W_a of a such that $V_a W_a \subset U_a$. Note that $W_a \subset U_a$. Each group element a is in its corresponding W_a, and therefore, the family of all W_a covers G. Since G is compact, it is possible to select a finite number of the W_a, $W_{a_1}, W_{a_2}, \ldots, W_{a_n}$ that still cover G. We consider now the corresponding neighborhoods of e, $V_{a_1}, V_{a_2}, \ldots, V_{a_n}$. Since these are finite in number and all contain e, their intersection V is also an open neighborhood of e; V is a subset of each of the V_{a_i}.

It will now be shown that V is the desired neighborhood of e. Suppose that $y^{-1}x \in V$. Now y must be in one of the sets W_{a_i}, and hence, in U_{a_i}. Therefore, $|f(y) - f(a_i)| < \epsilon/2$. Furthermore, $x = y(y^{-1}x) \in W_{a_i} V \subset W_{a_i} V_{a_i} \subset U_{a_i}$. Therefore, $|f(x) - f(a_i)| < \epsilon/2$, which implies that $|f(x) - f(y)| < \epsilon$.

It is now possible to prove the central result of this section, the Peter-Weyl theorem [1].

THEOREM 7-3. The Peter-Weyl Theorem. A continuous function f on a compact Lie group G can be uniformly approximated by a linear combination of the matrix elements $D^i(x)_{mn}$ of the unitary irreducible representations of G.

PROOF. Consider

$$\left|\int \psi_N(y^{-1}x)\, f(y)\,dy - f(x)\right| = \left|\int \psi_N(y^{-1}x)\, [f(y) - f(x)]\, dy\right|$$
$$\leq \int \psi_N(y^{-1}x)\, |f(y) - f(x)|\, dy, \qquad (7.31)$$

where ψ_N is one of the functions constructed in Theorem 7-1. The first step is a consequence of (28) and the invariance of the group integral under the substitution $y^{-1}x$ for y. Since f is continuous on a compact set, $|f(y) - f(x)|$ is bounded by some number A. Let $\epsilon > 0$ be given. From Theorem 7-2 it is possible to find a neighborhood V of e such that $|f(y) - f(x)| < \epsilon/2$ for $y^{-1}x \in V$. From Theorem 7-1, it is possible to find N such that $\psi_N(y^{-1}x) < \epsilon/2A\Omega$ for all $y^{-1}x$ outside V. The integral in the right-hand side of (31) can be separated into two integrals, one such that $y^{-1}x$ is in V and the other such that $y^{-1}x$ is outside of V. Each of these is bounded by $\epsilon/2$ from the above bounds on the integrands, and hence, for the above choice of N,

$$\int \psi_N(y^{-1}x)\, f(y)\, dy$$

differs from f(x) by less than ϵ. Equations (24) and (27) show that this is a linear combination of the $D^i(x)_{mn}$ so that the theorem is proved

It is now possible to establish the completeness of the functions $D^i(x)_{mn}$.

THEOREM 7-4. The functions $D^i(x)_{mn}$ are complete with respect to any continuous function f on the group.

PROOF. Consider equation (15). Since $|f(x) - s_N(x)|$ can be made arbitrarily small for all x by a suitable choice of s_N, E_N can be made arbitrarily small since the integral is over a compact domain. However, for fixed N, the Fourier coefficients minimize E_N, and hence, $E_N \to 0$ when s_N is chosen to be the Fourier series. Equations (19) and (20) follow.

The proof of Theorem 7-1 is essentially that given by Wigner [2] in his notes on this subject,except that the normalized functions $a_N e^{-N[\chi(e)-\chi(x)]^2}$ were used instead of ψ_N. These can be approximated arbitrarily closely by a finite linear combination of the $\chi^i(x)$. Another, somewhat similar, proof has been given by M. H. Stone [3]. This proof is based on an important generalization of the Weierstrass approximation theorem that has been proved by Stone and which is well described in the above reference.

The above proof of the Peter-Weyl theorem is based on the possibility of reduction of the repeated direct products of D_f and D_f^*, since this leads to the expression of ψ_N as a linear combination of the χ^i. In this process all (up to equivalences) the irreducible representations of the group can be generated. There can be no further irreducible representations, since if $D(x)_{ij}$ is a matrix element of such a representation, Theorem 6-4 indicates that all the Fourier coefficients of this function vanish. This contradicts the completeness relation, since the integral of $|D(x)_{ij}|^2$ over G is nonzero.

It follows from these remarks that if the matrix elements $D_f(x)_{ij}$ are differentiable functions of the group parameters, then the matrix elements of all the irreducible representations are also differentiable, since these are expressible as polynomials in the elements of D_f and D_f^*.

It should be mentioned that it is possible to prove Theorem 7-3 without assuming the existence of the faithful representation D_f [1].

This proof is quite complicated, however, and unnecessarily general for our purposes.

It is natural to ask whether, for a continuous function f, the Fourier series of f converges to f. The partial sums of the Fourier series can be written as

$$\begin{aligned} s_N(x) &= \sum_{i=1}^{N} \frac{n_i}{\Omega} \sum_{mn} \int D^i(y^{-1})_{nm}\, f(y)\, D^i(x)_{mn}\, dy \\ &= \sum_{i=1}^{N} \frac{n_i}{\Omega} \int \chi^i(y^{-1}x)\, f(y)\, dy \end{aligned} \tag{7.32}$$

where the sum is taken over the matrix elements of the first N irreducible representations. If equation (26) were valid, it would imply that $s_N(x) \to f(x)$ as $N \to \infty$. Unfortunately, it is known from the theory of trigonometric Fourier series that this is not always the case and that the series may not even converge for some values of x. It is, however, a consequence of the Riesz-Fischer theorem that there is a function to which the partial sums $s_N(x)$ converge in the mean and which must equal f except on a set of measure zero.

To guarantee that the series (32) converge to f, it is necessary to impose some further condition of smoothness on f. Many such conditions are known in the theory of trigonometric series, and some of these are quite complicated; they are described, for example, by Zygmund [4]. In the group theoretic case a simple condition on f is that it can be written in the integral form

$$f(x) = \int g(xz^{-1})\, h(z)\, dz, \tag{7.33}$$

where g and h are arbitrary continuous functions. If (33) is valid, one can write

$$\begin{aligned} s_N(x) &= \sum_{i=1}^{N} \frac{n_i}{\Omega} \iint \chi^i(y^{-1}x)\, g(yz^{-1})\, h(z)\, dy\, dz \\ &= \sum_{i=1} \frac{n_i}{\Omega} \iint \chi^i(z^{-1}y^{-1})\, g(xy)\, h(z)\, dy\, dz \end{aligned}$$

by making the substitution xyz for y. The completeness relation (25) shows that

$$\lim_{N\to\infty} s_N(x) = \int g(xz^{-1})\, h(z)\, dz = f(x).$$

In keeping with the simplicity of the derivation, this is a very weak result in that equation (33) is a very stringent condition on f. It may be of some interest to observe that any function arising in a physical problem must in principle satisfy (33), since any physical quantity must be determined by a detector of finite dimensions, which therefore averages the function over a finite region. If the function g in (33) is nonzero only in a small neighborhood of e, it can be interpreted as characterizing a detector averaging the function h being measured over a small region about the point x; the resultant average is then f(x).

If a function f is invariant on a compact Lie group, it is evident that the arguments that lead to equations (11) are still valid. The Fourier coefficients are then given by

$$c^{i}_{mn} = \delta_{mn} \frac{1}{\Omega} \int \chi^{i}(y^{-1})\, f(y)\, dy. \tag{7.34}$$

The partial sums of the Fourier series are given by

$$s_N(x) = \sum_{i=1}^{N} \frac{1}{\Omega} \int \chi^{i}(y^{-1})\, f(y)\, dy\, \chi^{i}(x). \tag{7.35}$$

It is apparent that the functions χ^i are complete with respect to any continuous invariant function on the group, and that if such a function satisfies condition (33), the partial sums of (35) converge to that function.

7-3 INFINITE-DIMENSIONAL REPRESENTATIONS OF A COMPACT LIE GROUP

It has been shown by Wigner [5] that a unitary infinite-dimensional representation of a compact Lie group can be expressed as a direct sum of the finite-dimensional irreducible representations, in the sense that, the Hilbert space H of the representation can be decomposed into the direct sum of finite-dimensional invariant subspaces. The proof of this result will be exhibited in this section.

According to the properties of the Hilbert space, a complete denumerable set of orthonormal vectors can be introduced into H. These vectors can be used to define a matrix representation of the group by matrices which are infinite-dimensional. We will denote their matrix elements by $\Delta(g)_{\mu\nu}$. In this discussion Greek letters will be used to denote indices which run over an infinite set and

Latin letters will be used for indices of finite matrices. The representation property requires

$$\sum_{\lambda} \Delta(a)_{\mu\lambda} \Delta(b)_{\lambda\nu} = \Delta(ab)_{\mu\nu}; \tag{7.36}$$

the sum on λ must converge if $\Delta(a)\Delta(b)\mathbf{v}$ is to be in H for all $\mathbf{v} \varepsilon$ H. It will be shown that the convergence is uniform in a and b. It can first be noted that

$$\begin{aligned} \sum_{\lambda} |\Delta(a)_{\mu\lambda}|^2 &= \sum_{\lambda} \Delta(a)^*_{\mu\lambda} \Delta(a)_{\mu\lambda} \\ &= \sum_{\lambda} \Delta(a)^*_{\mu\lambda} \Delta(a^{-1})^*_{\lambda\mu} \\ &= \Delta(e)^*_{\mu\mu} = 1. \end{aligned}$$

It is possible to show that if a series of positive continuous functions converges to a continuous function on a compact set, then the convergence is uniform [6]. From this it follows that

$$\sum_{\lambda=N}^{\infty} |\Delta(a)_{\mu\lambda}|^2 \rightarrow 0$$

uniformly on the group as $N \rightarrow \infty$. Now

$$\left| \sum_{\lambda=N}^{\infty} \Delta(a)_{\mu\lambda} \Delta(b)_{\lambda\nu} \right|^2 \leq \sum_{\lambda=N}^{\infty} |\Delta(a)_{\mu\lambda}|^2 \sum_{\lambda=N}^{\infty} |\Delta(b^{-1})_{\nu\lambda}|^2 \rightarrow 0$$

uniformly in a and b as $N \rightarrow \infty$. This shows that the convergence in (36) is uniform.

We now consider the Fourier coefficients of the functions $\Delta(a)_{\mu\nu}$ defined by

$$c^l(\mu\nu, mn) = n_l \int D^l(g)^*_{mn} \Delta(g)_{\mu\nu}\, dg. \tag{7.37}$$

It will be assumed for convenience that $\Omega = 1$

If (36) is multiplied by $n_l D^l(a)^*_{st}$ and integrated over a, the result is

$$\sum_\lambda c^l(\mu\lambda\,, st)\,\Delta(b)_{\lambda\nu} = n_l \int D^l(a)^*_{st}\,\Delta(ab)_{\mu\nu}\,da$$

$$= n_l \int D^l(ab^{-1})^*_{st}\;\Delta(a)_{\mu\nu}\;da$$

$$= n_l \sum_q \int D^l(a)^*_{sq}\;D^l(b)_{tq}\;\Delta(a)_{\mu\nu}\;da$$

$$= \sum_q c^l(\mu\nu,\ sq)\;D^l(b)_{tq}. \tag{7.38}$$

The integration of the left-hand side can be performed term by term, since the convergence is uniform in a. There is no difficulty in interchanging the integration and summation in the right-hand side, since the sum is finite.

The left-hand side of (38) can be shown by Schwarz' inequality to converge uniformly in b; we can, therefore, multiply by $n_j\ D^j(b)^*_{mn}$ and integrate over b to obtain, from (6.26)

$$\sum_\lambda c^l(\mu\lambda,\ st)\ c^j(\lambda\nu,\ mn) = \sum_q c^l(\mu\nu,\ sq)\ \delta_{lj}\ \delta_{tm}\ \delta_{qn}$$

$$= c^l(\mu\nu,\ sn)\ \delta_{lj}\ \delta_{tm}. \tag{7.39}$$

It is important to note that for $l = j$ and $t = m$, the left-hand side of (39) is independent of m.

A consequence of the unitarity of Δ and D^l is that

$$c^l(\alpha\beta,\ mn)^* = \int D^l(g)_{mn}\ \Delta(g)^*_{\alpha\beta}dg$$

$$= \int D^l(g^{-1})_{nm}\ \Delta(g^{-1})_{\beta\alpha}\ dg$$

$$= c^l(\beta\alpha,\ nm) \tag{7.40}$$

since the group integral is invariant under the substitution $g^{-1} \to g$.

It is now possible to give an explicit construction of the invariant subspaces of H. We consider, for each D^l, a fixed row, say row 0, and define a set of vectors $\mathbf{u}(\alpha, l,\ n)$ in H to be the vectors whose components in the particular representation chosen are given by

$$u(\alpha\,,\ l,\ n)_\beta = c^l(\alpha\beta,\ 0n). \tag{7.41}$$

It is necessary to verify that these vectors do belong to H, that is, have finite length. This can be shown, and the inner product of two such vectors calculated, by considering

$$(\mathbf{u}(\alpha, l, n), \mathbf{u}(\alpha', l', n')) = \sum_{\beta} c^{l}(\alpha\beta, 0n)^{*} c^{l'}(\alpha'\beta, 0n')$$

$$= c^{l}(\alpha'\alpha, 00)\, \delta_{ll'}\, \delta_{nn'}. \tag{7.42}$$

The last result is a consequence of equations (39) and (40). Equation (42) demonstrates that $\mathbf{u}(\alpha, l, n) \in H$ but that these vectors lack the desirable property of orthogonality.

It will now be shown that the vectors $\mathbf{u}$ are a complete set of vectors in H, in that any vector can be constructed from them. It is sufficient to show this for the original basis vectors $\mathbf{e}^{\rho}$, which have components given by

$$[e^{\rho}]_{\sigma} = \delta_{\rho\sigma}$$

in our representation. Consider the vector

$$v = \sum_{\alpha} \sum_{l n} c^{l}(\rho\alpha, n0)\, \mathbf{u}(\alpha, l, n) \tag{7.43}$$

which has σ component

$$v_{\sigma} = \sum_{\alpha} \sum_{l n} c^{l}(\rho\alpha, n0)\, c^{l}(\alpha\sigma, 0n)$$

$$= \sum_{\alpha} \sum_{l mn} n_l^{-1}\, c^{l}(\rho\alpha, nm)\, c^{l}(\alpha\sigma, mn). \tag{7.44}$$

The last step is justified since the sum on α has been shown to be independent of m. The sum on m is, therefore, equivalent to a sum over n_l terms, each of which is $c^{l}(\rho\alpha, n0)\, c^{l}(\alpha\sigma, 0n)$. Substitution of (37) into (44) gives

$$v_{\sigma} = \sum_{\alpha} \sum_{mn} n_l \iint D^{l}(x)_{nm}^{*}\, \Delta(x)_{\rho\alpha}\, D^{l}(y)_{mn}^{*}\, \Delta(y)_{\alpha\sigma}\, dx\, dy$$

$$= \sum_{\alpha} \sum_{l} n_l \iint \chi^{l}(x^{-1}y)\, \Delta(x)_{\rho\alpha}\, \Delta(y^{-1})_{\alpha\sigma}\, dx\, dy$$

where y has been replaced by y^{-1}. Equation (25) shows that

$$v_{\sigma} = \sum_{\alpha} \int \Delta(x)_{\rho\alpha} \Delta(x^{-1})_{\alpha\sigma} \, dx$$

$$= \int \sum_{\alpha} \Delta(x)_{\rho\alpha} \Delta(x^{-1})_{\alpha\sigma} \, dx$$

$$= \int \delta_{\rho\sigma} \, dx = \delta_{\rho\sigma}.$$

The interchange of the summation and integration can be justified since the sum has been shown to converge uniformly in x. The result shows that the sum (43) defining $\mathbf{v}$ is convergent in the order specified, and that $\mathbf{v}$ is the unit vector $\mathbf{e}^{\rho}$.

It is possible to construct from the vectors $\mathbf{u}(\alpha, l, n)$, for fixed l and n, an orthogonal set of vectors $\mathbf{w}(\beta, l, n)$ by means of the Schmidt orthogonalization procedure. The $\mathbf{w}(\beta, l, n)$ are defined to be a linear combination of the first β vectors $\mathbf{u}(\alpha, l, n)$, namely,

$$\mathbf{w}(\beta, l, n) = \sum_{\alpha=1}^{\beta} a^{l}_{\beta\alpha}{}^{*} \, \mathbf{u}(\alpha, l, n). \tag{7.45}$$

The coefficients $a^{l}_{\beta\alpha}$ are independent of n, since the inner product

$$(\mathbf{u}(\alpha, l, n), \mathbf{u}(\beta, l, n)) = c^{l}(\beta\alpha, 00)$$

which determines them, is independent of n. Since equation (45) can be inverted to express the $\mathbf{u}(\alpha, l, n)$ as a finite linear combination of the $\mathbf{w}(\beta, l, n)$, these vectors are also a complete set.

We now consider the vectors $\mathrm{w}(\beta, l, n)^{*}$ which are again a complete set. It will be shown that these vectors, for fixed β and l, span a finite-dimensional invariant subspace of H. Consider the vector $\Delta(g)\mathbf{w}(\beta, l, n)^{*}$ with λ component

$$[\Delta(g)\mathbf{w}(\beta, l, n)^{*}]_{\lambda} = \sum_{\mu} \Delta(g)_{\lambda\mu} \, w(\beta, l, n)_{\mu}^{*}$$

$$= \sum_{\mu\alpha} a^{l}_{\beta\alpha} \, \Delta(g)_{\lambda\mu} \, u(\alpha, l, n)_{\mu}^{*}$$

$$= \sum_{\mu\alpha} a^{l}_{\beta\alpha} \, \Delta(g^{-1})^{*}_{\mu\lambda} \, c^{l}(\alpha\mu, 0n)^{*}.$$

This can be rewritten, using (38) as

$$[\Delta(g)\mathbf{w}(\beta, l, n)^*]_\lambda = \sum_{\alpha q} a^l_{\beta\alpha} \, c^l(\alpha\lambda, 0q)^* \, D^l(g^{-1})^*_{nq}$$

$$= \sum_{\alpha q} D^l(g)_{qn} \, a^l_{\beta\alpha} \, \mathbf{u}(\alpha, l, q)^*_\lambda$$

$$= \sum_q D^l(g)_{qn} \, w(\beta, l, q)^*_\lambda \, .$$

This result shows that

$$\Delta(g)\mathbf{w}(\beta, l, n)^* = \sum_q D^l(g)_{qn} \, \mathbf{w}(\beta, l, q)^* \qquad (7.46)$$

and that the $\mathbf{w}(\beta, l, n)^*$ for fixed β and l span an invariant subspace with the dimension of D^l; comparison with (6.5) shows that Δ gives rise to the representation D^l in this subspace.

Chapter 8

THE GROUPS U(1) AND SU(2)

In this chapter the groups U(1) and SU(2) will be investigated. The former group is of limited interest since its structure is rather trivial, but it provides a simple example of much of the foregoing theory. The group SU(2) is of more interest and will be discussed in considerable detail.

The first section is concerned with U(1). In the second section a parametrization of SU(2) will be introduced, and the irreducible representations will be constructed by the method described in Section 6-9.

In Section 3 the theory of the reduction of the direct product of two representations of SU(2) will be reviewed. This theory will be applied in some of the later work. The elements of the matrix that reduces the direct product are related in a simple way to the numbers known as $3-j$ coefficients. These will be defined in Section 3, and some of their important properties will be demonstrated in Sections 3 and 4. Explicit expressions for a few $3-j$ coefficients that will be required are tabulated in Section 5.

In Section 6 a brief review of the theory of the reduction of the product of three irreducible representations of SU(2) will be given. This theory is very important in the quantum theory of angular momentum and will also be required in the discussion of the group O(4) and the Euclidean group in space.

8-1 ROTATIONS IN THE PLANE

We will denote by $R(\theta)$ a rotation by an angle θ, $0 \leq \theta < 2\pi$, of a plane into itself. The set of all such rotations constitutes the rotation group of the plane; the group multiplication law is

$$\begin{aligned} R(\theta)R(\phi) &= R(\theta+\phi), \quad \theta+\phi < 2\pi, \\ R(\theta)R(\phi) &= R(\theta+\phi-2\pi), \quad \theta+\phi \geq 2\pi \end{aligned} \tag{8.1a}$$

and the group product functions are given by

$$f(\theta,\phi) = \theta + \phi,\ \theta + \phi < 2\pi, \qquad (8.1b)$$

$$f(\theta,\phi) = \theta + \phi - 2\pi,\ \ \theta + \phi \geq 2\pi.$$

It is not difficult to see that the rotation group is isomorphic to the group R/Z defined in Section 3-3. Henceforth, when the sum of angles is written down, it will be assumed that it is reduced by a suitable multiple of 2π to bring it into the interval $[0, 2\pi)$.

A point with coordinates (x, y) in some coordinate system is transformed by a rotation $R(\theta)$ into the point whose coordinates are ($\cos\theta\ x - \sin\theta\ y$, $\sin\theta\ x + \cos\theta\ y$). This coordinate transformation is produced by the matrix

$$D(\theta) = \begin{pmatrix} \cos\theta & -\sin\theta \\ \sin\theta & \cos\theta \end{pmatrix} \qquad (8.2)$$

which, therefore, provides a faithful representation of the group. This cannot be an irreducible representation, since the group is Abelian, and hence, has only one-dimensional irreducible representations. It was shown in Section 6-4 that $D(\theta)$ can be reduced to

$$D'(\theta) = \begin{pmatrix} e^{i\theta} & 0 \\ 0 & e^{-i\theta} \end{pmatrix}.$$

It can be seen that the functions $e^{i\theta}$, $e^{-i\theta}$ are irreducible faithful representations of the group.

The direct product of the representation $e^{i\theta}$ with itself is the representation $e^{2i\theta}$; taking the direct product with $e^{i\theta}$ repeatedly generates a sequence of irreducible representations $e^{im\theta}$, $m = 1, 2, \ldots$. Similarly, taking the direct product of the representation $e^{-i\theta}$ with itself repeatedly generates a sequence of irreducible representations $e^{-im\theta}$, $m = 1, 2, \ldots$. These representations, together with the identity representation, exhaust the irreducible representations, since all the irreducible representations are generated by taking arbitrary direct products of $e^{i\theta}$ and its complex conjugate. Any such product generates a representation of the form $e^{in\theta}$, n an integer. It should perhaps be remarked that the representations $e^{2i\theta}$, and so on, are not faithful; for example, $e^{2i\pi} = 1$ while $R(\pi) \neq e$.

The weight function for invariant integration is, from (5.9) and (1b), given by $w(\theta) = 1$ and the group volume is 2π. The orthogonality property (6.26) of the representations $e^{in\theta}$ and $e^{im\theta}$ gives the familiar result

$$\int_0^{2\pi} e^{i(n-m)\theta}\,d\theta = 2\pi\,\delta_{nm}. \tag{8.3}$$

The Peter-Weyl theorem demonstrates the important result of Fourier series that the functions $e^{in\theta}$, n an integer, are a complete set on the interval $[0, 2\pi]$ for functions continuous on the group. It should be noted that continuity on the group requires that the function satisfy $f(0) = f(2\pi)$, since the point 2π is to be identified with 0.

The function $v^1{}_1(\theta)$, defined by (3.8), is 1. The differential equation (6.52) for the representations is, therefore,

$$\frac{dD}{d\theta} = DJ. \tag{8.4}$$

The matrix J constitutes a basis vector for the representation of the Lie algebra corresponding to D. If D is irreducible, J is simply a complex number. There is nothing in the algebra to indicate how J is to be selected, although in order that the corresponding group representation be unitary, it is necessary that J be skew-Hermitian, that is, imaginary. If $J = i$, the known representation $e^{i\theta}$ is generated by equation (4). If $J = ri$, r real, the function $e^{ir\theta}$ is generated; this function is not, in general, a group representation in the given parametrization, although the numbers $e^{ir\theta}$ do generate a group isomorphic to the rotation group and can be regarded as a representation under a suitable isomorphism. This illustrates the remark that a representation of the Lie algebra of a group can, in general, only generate a local representation of the group. A more serious breakdown occurs if J is not pure imaginary; in this case the representation is the group of numbers $e^{J\theta}$, which is a representation not of U(1) but of R, the noncompact group of real numbers.

8-2 REPRESENTATIONS OF THE GROUP SU(2)

The group of 2 × 2 unitary, unimodular matrices with complex coefficients is a three-parameter group. The matrix elements a_{ij} must satisfy the four conditions

$$|a_{11}|^2 + |a_{12}|^2 = 1 \tag{8.5a}$$

$$|a_{21}|^2 + |a_{22}|^2 = 1 \tag{8.5b}$$

$$a_{11}^* a_{21} + a_{12}^* a_{22} = 0 \tag{8.5c}$$

$$a_{11}a_{22} - a_{12}a_{21} = 1. \tag{8.5d}$$

Equation (5a) can be satisfied by writing $a_{11} = \cos\,\theta e^{i\phi}$, $a_{12} = i\,\sin\,\theta \times e^{i\psi}$, where $0 \leq \theta \leq \pi/2$, $0 \leq \phi < 2\pi$, $0 \leq \psi < 2\pi$. Equations (5b) and (5c) can be satisfied by writing $a_{21} = -a_{12}^{*}e^{i\alpha}$, $a_{22} = a_{11}^{*}e^{i\alpha}$, where α is an arbitrary real number. Equation (5d), the unimodular condition, can be seen to require that $e^{i\alpha} = 1$. The parametrization of the group is:

$$A(\theta, \phi, \psi) = \begin{pmatrix} \cos\,\theta\, e^{i\phi} & i\,\sin\,\theta\, e^{i\psi} \\ i\,\sin\,\theta\, e^{-i\psi} & \cos\,\theta\, e^{-i\phi} \end{pmatrix}. \tag{8.6}$$

Any element of SU(2) for which $\theta \neq 0$ or $\pi/2$ has a unique representation in the form (6). This parametrization has, however, the undesirable property that it is singular at $\theta = 0$ and $\pi/2$, since ψ is irrelevant at $\theta = 0$ and ϕ is irrelevant at $\theta = \pi/2$. The singularity at e is particularly unfortunate since it complicates the problem of finding the invariant weight function on the group.

The Lie algebra of the group SU(2) is known to be the set of all skew-Hermitian 2×2 matrices with trace zero. Such a matrix can be written in the form $xI_x + yI_y + zI_z$ where

$$I_x = \begin{pmatrix} 0 & i \\ i & 0 \end{pmatrix}, \quad I_y = \begin{pmatrix} 0 & -1 \\ 1 & 0 \end{pmatrix}, \quad I_z = \begin{pmatrix} i & 0 \\ 0 & -i \end{pmatrix}. \tag{8.7}$$

These matrices satisfy

$$[I_x, I_y] = 2I_z, \quad [I_y, I_z] = 2I_x, \quad [I_z, I_x] = 2I_y. \tag{8.8}$$

These are essentially the commutation relations of equation (4.48). It is of interest to note also that the matrices I are simply the Pauli spin matrices multiplied by i.

The character of the matrix $A(\theta, \phi, \psi)$ is $2\cos\,\theta\,\cos\,\phi$; since this is real the representation (6), which is a faithful representation, is equivalent to its complex conjugate. A matrix that transforms A to A^* is I_y.

The irreducible representations of SU(2) can be constructed by the method described in Section 6-9. Since the group is the group of unitary transformations in a 2-dimensional complex vector space, the irreducible representations can be constructed in the space of homogeneous polynomials of fixed degree defined on the vector space. To be explicit, consider a vector

$$\mathbf{z} = \begin{pmatrix} z_1 \\ z_2 \end{pmatrix}$$

and the set of functions

$$e^m(\mathbf{z}) = \frac{z_1^{j+m} z_2^{j-m}}{[(j+m)!\,(j-m)!\,]^{1/2}} \cdot \tag{8.9}$$

It will be shown that this choice of basis vectors generates a unitary representation. The functions e^m, $m = -j, -j+1, \ldots, j$ span the space of homogeneous polynomials of degree $2j$. The permitted values of j are $0, {}^1/_2, 1, \ldots$; it turns out that j can be used as an index for the irreducible representations. Since there are $(2j+1)$ possible values of the index m the representations generated are of this dimension. The representation matrices will be indexed on the values $-j, -j+1,$ j rather than on the integers $1, 2, \ldots, 2j+1$ as is usually the case.

The representations will now be calculated using equation (6.44), which in this case is

$$e^n(A^{-1}\mathbf{z}) = \sum_{m=-j}^{j} D^j(A)_{mn} e^m(\mathbf{z}). \tag{8.10}$$

Since $A^{-1} = A^\dagger$, $A^{-1}\mathbf{z}$ is the vector

$$\begin{pmatrix} \cos\theta\, e^{-i\phi} z_1 - i \sin\theta\, e^{i\psi} z_2 \\ -i \sin\theta\, e^{-i\psi} z_1 + \cos\theta\, e^{i\phi} z_2 \end{pmatrix}.$$

The function $e^n(A^{-1}\mathbf{z})$ is, therefore, using the binomial theorem,

$$\frac{(\cos\theta\, e^{-i\phi} z_1 - i \sin\theta\, e^{i\psi} z_2)^{j+n}(-i \sin\theta\, e^{-i\psi} z_1 + \cos\theta\, e^{i\phi} z_2)^{j-n}}{[(j+n)!\,(j-n)!]^{1/2}}$$

$$= \sum_{st} \frac{[(j+n)!\,(j-n)!\,]^{1/2}}{s!(j+n-s)!\,t!\,(j-n-t)!} (\cos\theta\, e^{-i\phi} z_1)^s (-i \sin e^{i\psi} z_2)^{j+n-s}$$

$$\times (-i \sin\theta\; e^{-i\psi} z_1)^t (\cos\theta\, e^{i\phi} z_2)^{j-n-t}$$

$$= \sum_{st} (-i)^{j+n-s+t} \frac{[(j+n)!\,(j-n)!\,]^{1/2}}{s!\,(j+n-s)!\,t!\,(j-n-t)!} \cos^{j-n+s-t}\theta \; \sin^{j+n-s+t}\theta$$

$$\times e^{i(j-n-s-t)\phi} e^{i(j+n-s-t)\psi} z_1^{s+t} z_2^{2j-s-t}.$$

The sums on s and t are over the values $0, 1, \ldots, j+n$ and $0, 1, \ldots,$

j−n respectively. It is observed that the sum is again, as expected, a homogeneous polynomial of degree 2j. The coefficient of $e^m(\mathbf{z})$ in the sum is the desired matrix element $D^j(A)_{mn}$. This can be obtained by putting s + t = j + m or s = j + m − t. This reduces the double sum to a single sum on t over values compatible with $0 \le j + m - t \le j + n$ and $0 \le t \le j - n$, or $m - n \le t \le j + m$, and $0 \le t \le j - n$. The final result is:

$$D^j(A)_{mn} = i^{m-n} \sum_t (-1)^t \frac{[(j+m)!(j-m)!(j+n)!(j-n)!]^{1/2}}{(j+m-t)!(t+n-m)!t!(j-n-t)!}$$
$$\times \cos^{2j+m-n-2t}\theta \sin^{2t+n-m}\theta \, e^{-i(m+n)\phi} e^{i(n-m)\psi}. \tag{8.11}$$

It should be observed that the values of t to be summed over are those for which the arguments of the factorial functions are nonnegative. It will now be shown that the representation obtained is unitary, irreducible, and exhaust the irreducible representations.

To demonstrate the unitarity it is sufficient, according to Section 6-9, to show that the function $f(\mathbf{w}, \mathbf{z})$ defined by

$$f(\mathbf{w}, \mathbf{z}) = \sum_{m=-j}^{j} e^m(\mathbf{w})^* e^m(\mathbf{z})$$

is invariant under the transformation to $f(A\mathbf{w}, A\mathbf{z})$. We calculate

$$f(\mathbf{w}, \mathbf{z}) = \sum_{m=-j}^{j} \frac{w_1^{*\,j+m} w_2^{*\,j-m} z_1^{j+m} z_2^{j-m}}{(j+m)!(j-m)!}$$
$$= \frac{[w_1^* z_1 + w_2^* z_2]^{2j}}{(2j)!} = \frac{(\mathbf{w}, \mathbf{z})^{2j}}{(2j)!}.$$

It follows from the unitary nature of A that

$$f(A\mathbf{w}, A\mathbf{z}) = \frac{(A\mathbf{w}, A\mathbf{z})^{2j}}{(2j)!} = \frac{(\mathbf{w}, \mathbf{z})^{2j}}{(2j)!} = f(\mathbf{w}, \mathbf{z}).$$

To prove that $D^j(A)$ is irreducible, we suppose that a matrix M commutes with $D^j(A)$ for all A. It is observed first that the commutator of a matrix A with a diagonal matrix B with elements $\delta_{ij}b_j$ has matrix elements $(b_k - b_l)a_{kl}$. If no two diagonal elements of B are equal, and A and B commute, it is apparent that A must also be diagonal.

Consider now the group elements for which $\theta = 0$. Since $A(0, \phi, \psi)$ is independent of ψ, the matrix element $D^j(A)_{mn}$ must also be independent of ψ. Because of the factor $e^{i(n-m)\psi}$ in (11), this requires $n = m$ and the representation matrix must be diagonal. The factor $\sin^{2t+n-m}\theta$ indicates that for $\theta = 0$ and $m = n$, $t = 0$. The matrix element is easily evaluated to be

$$D^j(0, \phi, \psi)_{mn} = e^{-2im\phi}\,\delta_{mn}. \tag{8.12}$$

Since no two diagonal elements are the same for $0 < \phi < \pi/2j$, the matrix M, which is assumed to commute with $D^j(0, \phi, \psi)$, must be diagonal with matrix elements $\lambda_m \delta_{mn}$.

Since M is diagonal, the commutator of M with an arbitrary $D^j(A)$ has elements $(\lambda_m - \lambda_n) D^j(A)_{mn} = 0$. We now consider the particular matrix elements $D^j(A)_{mj}$. The only allowed value of t in the sum (11) is $t = 0$ and the matrix element is found to be

$$D^j(A)_{mj} = (-i)^{j-m} \binom{2j}{j+m}^{1/2} \cos^{j+m}\theta \; \sin^{j-m}\theta \; e^{-i(j+m)\phi} e^{i(j-m)\psi}, \tag{8.13}$$

where $\binom{2j}{j+m}$ denotes the binomial coefficient $(2j)!/(j+m)!\,(j-m)!$.
This is in general nonzero, implying that $(\lambda_m - \lambda_j) = 0$ for all m. This in turn implies $M = \lambda_j I$. We can conclude that $MD^j(A) = D^j(A)M$ implies $M = \lambda I$, which in turn implies that $D^j(A)$ is irreducible.

The fact that the $D^j(A)$ constitute all the inequivalent irreducible representations can be proved by showing that arbitrary direct products of the faithful representation $D^{1/2}(A)$ with itself are direct sums of the $D^j(A)$.

It is first observed that any $A \in SU(2)$ can be transformed by a unitary matrix with unit determinant to the form

$$\begin{pmatrix} e^{i\rho} & 0 \\ 0 & e^{-i\rho} \end{pmatrix}$$

where $0 \le \rho \le \pi$.

Each class of A, therefore, includes exactly one such matrix and can be labeled by the variable ρ on the interval $[0, \pi]$. The class of a matrix A can be uniquely specified by the phase of its eigenvalue in the upper half-plane.

The representation $D^{1/2}(A)$ is a faithful representation of the group with character

$$\chi^{1/2}(\rho) = \omega + \omega^{-1} \tag{8.14}$$

where $\omega = e^{i\rho}$. The character of $D^j(A)$ is, from (12),

$$\chi^j(\rho) = \omega^{2j} + \omega^{2j-2} + \ldots + \omega^{-2j+2} + \omega^{-2j}. \tag{8.15}$$

It is easy to see from (14) and (15), and will be shown explicitly in the next section, that, for $j > 0$,

$$\chi^{1/2}(\rho)\chi^j(\rho) = \chi^{j-1/2}(\rho) + \chi^{j+1/2}(\rho). \tag{8.16}$$

From this it can be easily proved by induction that

$$[\chi^{1/2}(\rho)]^n = \sum c_j{}^n \chi^j(\rho) \tag{8.17}$$

where the $c_j{}^n$ are integers. This shows that the direct product of n factors of $D^{1/2}(A)$ reduces to a direct sum of $D^j(A)$. Since all the irreducible representations are obtained by reducing these direct products, the $D^j(A)$ exhaust the irreducible representations. This result could also have been established by showing that the functions $\cos n\rho = [\chi^{n/2}(\rho) - \chi^{(n-2)/2}(\rho)]/2$ are complete on $[0, \pi]$; this follows readily from the fact that the functions $e^{in\rho}$ are complete on $[0, 2\pi]$.

In some later applications the complex conjugate and transpose of the matrix $D^j(A)$ will be required. It is easy to see from (11) that

$$D^j(A)^*_{mn} = (-1)^{n-m} D^j(A)_{-m-n}. \tag{8.18}$$

The transpose of $D^j(A)$ is given by

$$D^j(A)_{nm} = D^j(A^{-1})^*_{mn} = (-1)^{m-n} D^j(A^{-1})_{-m-n} \tag{8.19}$$

where the parameters of A^{-1} are θ, $2\pi - \phi$, and $\psi + \pi$.

The particular matrix element $D^j(A)_{mj}$ is written explicitly in equation (13). The matrix element $D^j(A)_{m-j}$ will also be required. It is found that the sum (11) reduces in this case to a single term with $t = j + m$ and that

$$D^j(A)_{m-j} = \left((-i)^{j+m} \binom{2j}{j+m}\right)^{1/2} \times \cos^{j-m}\theta \, \sin^{j+m}\theta \, e^{i(j-m)\phi} e^{-i(j+m)\psi}. \tag{8.20}$$

Similarly, it can be found that

$$D^j(A)_{jn} = \left((-i)^{j-n} \binom{2j}{j+n}\right)^{1/2} \times \cos^{j+n}\theta \, \sin^{j-n}\theta \, e^{-i(j+n)\phi} e^{-i(j-n)\psi}, \tag{8.21}$$

$$D^j(A)_{-jn} = \left((-i)^{j+n} \binom{2j}{j+n}\right)^{1/2}$$
$$\times \cos^{j-n}\theta \, \sin^{j+n}\theta \, e^{i(j-n)\phi} e^{i(j+n)\psi}. \tag{8.22}$$

The two latter results could also have been obtained from equation (19).

8-3 REDUCTION OF THE DIRECT PRODUCT OF IRREDUCIBLE REPRESENTATIONS

The direct product of two irreducible representations of SU(2) and the reduction of the direct product are of considerable importance in the quantum theory of angular momentum. The detailed analysis of this problem has been given by Wigner [1]. A review of this theory will be given in this section and it will be applied in subsequent chapters to obtain some useful results.

The direct product of representations $D^j(A)$ and $D^k(A)$ will be denoted by D(A); it will be assumed for the present that $j \geq k$. It will be shown first that D(A), when reduced, contains the representation $D^l(A)$ exactly once if $j-k \leq l \leq j+k$ and $j+k-l$ is an integer, and does not contain $D^l(A)$ otherwise. This can be demonstrated by studying the characters of the representations. We can write, with $\omega = e^{2i\rho}$,

$$\chi^l(\rho) = \sum_{n=-l}^{l} \omega^n = \omega^{-l} \sum_{n=0}^{2l} \omega^n = (1-\omega)^{-1}(\omega^{-l} - \omega^{l+1})$$

and

$$\sum_{l=j-k}^{j+k} \chi^l(\rho) = (1-\omega)^{-1} \sum_{l=j-k}^{j+k} [\omega^{-l} - \omega^{l+1}]$$
$$= (1-\omega)^{-1} \sum_{l=0}^{2K} [\omega^{-j-k}\omega^l - \omega^{j-k+1}\omega^l] = (1-\omega)^{-2}[\omega^{-j-k} - \omega^{j-k+1}]$$
$$\times [1-\omega^{2k+1}] = (1-\omega)^{-2}(\omega^{-j} - \omega^{j+1})(\omega^{-k} - \omega^{k+1}) = \chi^j(\rho)\chi^k(\rho). \tag{8.23}$$

Since $\chi^j(\rho)\chi^k(\rho)$ is the character of D(A) the result is proved. It should be emphasized that the sum on l in (23) is over l values which differ from $j+k$ by an integer.

Before discussing further the reduction of the direct product we will note a property of the invariant weight function on the group. One can immediately verify that $A(\theta, \phi, \psi)A(0, \alpha, 0) = A(\theta, \phi + \alpha, \psi - \alpha)$. The right invariance of the integral implies that

$$\int f(\theta, \phi + \alpha, \psi - \alpha)w(\theta, \phi, \psi)dg = \int f(\theta, \phi, \psi)w(\theta, \phi - \alpha, \psi + \alpha)dg$$
$$= \int f(\theta, \phi, \psi)w(\theta, \phi, \psi)dg.$$

If this result is to be valid for all f it is necessary that $w(\theta, \phi, \psi) = w(\theta, \phi - \alpha, \psi + \alpha)$, which implies that w is a function only of $\phi + \psi$. Similarly, it can be found that $A(0, \alpha, 0)A(\theta, \phi, \psi) = A(\theta, \phi + \alpha, \psi + \alpha)$, and, from the left invariance of the integral, that $w(\theta, \phi, \psi) = w(\theta, \phi - \alpha, \psi + \alpha)$ so that w is a function only of $\phi - \psi$. The two results require that w be independent of ϕ and ψ. This is the only property of w that is required for the present purpose.

The direct product can be constructed in the space of functions of two variables spanned by the functions $e^m(\mathbf{x})e^n(\mathbf{y})$, $-j \le m \le j$, $-k \le n \le k$. In reducing the direct product it is necessary to take suitable linear combinations of these functions that are contained in the various invariant subspaces. These linear combinations will be denoted by $f_{l,p}(\mathbf{x}, \mathbf{y})$, $-l \le p \le l$. We write

$$f_{l,p}(\mathbf{x}, \mathbf{y}) = \sum_{mn} [l]^{1/2} \begin{pmatrix} j & k & l \\ m & n & p \end{pmatrix} e^m(\mathbf{x})e^n(\mathbf{y}). \tag{8.24}$$

The symbol $[l]$ is used to denote the function $2l + 1$. The coefficients in (24) are not uniquely determined since the reduced representation may appear in any of the possible equivalent forms. It is conventional to require that the reduced representations be $D^l(A)^*$, the complex conjugate of the representation (11).

It will be shown at the end of this section that the transformation (24) can be required to be unitary; that is, the coefficients may be chosen so that (24) is inverted by

$$e^m(\mathbf{x})e^n(\mathbf{y}) = \sum_{lp} [l]^{1/2} \begin{pmatrix} j & k & l \\ m & n & p \end{pmatrix}^* f_{l,p}(\mathbf{x}, \mathbf{y}). \tag{8.25}$$

If $\mathbf{x}$ and $\mathbf{y}$ are replaced by $A^{-1}\mathbf{x}$ and $A^{-1}\mathbf{y}$ in (25) and the representation property employed, (25) becomes, using also (24),

$$\sum_{m'n'} D^j(A)_{m'm} D^k(A)_{n'n} e^{m'}(\mathbf{x})e^{n'}(\mathbf{y}) = \sum_{lpp'} [l]^{1/2} \begin{pmatrix} j & k & l \\ m & n & p \end{pmatrix}^*$$
$$\times D^l(A)^*_{p'p} f_{l,p'}(\mathbf{x}, \mathbf{y}) = \sum_{lpp'} \sum_{m'n'} [l] \begin{pmatrix} j & k & l \\ m & n & p \end{pmatrix}^* \begin{pmatrix} j & k & l \\ m' & n' & p' \end{pmatrix}$$
$$\times D^l(A)^*_{p'p} e^{m'}(\mathbf{x})e^{n'}(\mathbf{y}). \tag{8.26}$$

Since the coefficients of $e^{m'}(\mathbf{x})e^{n'}(\mathbf{y})$ must be the same on each side of (26), they necessarily satisfy

$$D^j(A)_{m'm}D^k(A)_{n'n} = \sum_{lpp'} [l] \begin{pmatrix} j & k & l \\ m & n & p \end{pmatrix}^* \begin{pmatrix} j & k & l \\ m' & n' & p' \end{pmatrix} D^l(A)^*_{p'p}. \quad (8.27)$$

It is possible to solve equation (27) for the coefficients

$$\begin{pmatrix} j & k & l \\ m & n & p \end{pmatrix}$$

which are known as 3−j coefficients since j, k, l are often replaced by j_1, j_2, j_3. If (27) is multiplied by $D^\lambda(A)_{q'q}$ and integrated over the group the sum on the right-hand side is eliminated by the orthogonality relations (6.26). The result is (replacing λ, q, q' by l, p, p')

$$[l] \begin{pmatrix} j & k & l \\ m & n & p \end{pmatrix}^* \begin{pmatrix} j & k & l \\ m' & n' & p' \end{pmatrix} = \frac{[l]}{\Omega} \int D^l(A)_{p'p} D^j(A)_{m'm} D^k(A)_{n'n}\, dA. \quad (8.28)$$

The reason for including the factor $[l]^{1/2}$ in (24) is now apparent; $[l]$ can be conveniently eliminated from (28) and, as will be seen in the next section, the 3−j coefficients are rendered more symmetric.

From (11) it can be seen that the integrand contains factors $e^{-iS\phi}$ and $e^{-iT\psi}$ where $S = m+n+p+m'+n'+p'$ and $T = m'+n'+p'-m-n-p$. The group integral involves the integral over ϕ and ψ on $[0, 2\pi]$. Since the invariant weight function is independent of ϕ and ψ, the integral vanishes, according to (3), unless $S = T = 0$. For the particular case $m = m'$, $n = n'$, $p = p'$, $T = 0$ and $S = 2(m+n+p)$. The result implies that

$$\begin{pmatrix} j & k & l \\ m & n & p \end{pmatrix} = 0$$

unless $m+n+p = 0$.

The nonzero 3−j coefficients can be evaluated by setting $n = -k$, $m = j$, and $p = k-j$ in (28). This gives, using (11), (13), and (20) and the fact that the integrand is independent of ϕ and ψ,

$$\begin{pmatrix} j & k & l \\ j & -k & p \end{pmatrix}^* \begin{pmatrix} j & k & l \\ m' & n' & p' \end{pmatrix} = \frac{1}{\Omega}(-1)^{k+n'} \begin{pmatrix} 2k \\ k+n' \end{pmatrix}^{1/2} \begin{pmatrix} 2j \\ j+m' \end{pmatrix}^{1/2} \quad (8.29)$$

$$\cdot \sum_t (-1)^t \frac{[(l+p)!(l-p)!(l+p')!(l-p')!]^{1/2}}{(l+p'-t)!(t+p-p')!t!(l-p-t)!} \int \cos^{2\alpha}\theta \, \sin^{2\beta}\theta \, dA$$

where $2\alpha = 2l + p' - p - 2t + k - n' + j + m' = 2(l-t+j-n')$ and $2\beta = 2t + p - p' + k + n' + j - m' = 2(t+k+n')$. The integral over the group can be evaluated from the orthogonality property (6.26); for example,

$$\int |D^j(A)_{jm}|^2 dA = \frac{\Omega}{(2j+1)} = \binom{2j}{j+m} \int \cos^{2(j+m)}\theta \, \sin^{2(j-m)}\theta \, dA.$$

Substituting $\alpha = j+m$, $\beta = j-m$ yields the result

$$\int \cos^{2\alpha}\theta \, \sin^{2\beta}\theta \, dA = \frac{\Omega \, \alpha!\beta!}{(\alpha+\beta+1)!} \tag{8.30}$$

whence

$$\begin{pmatrix} j & k & l \\ j & -k & p \end{pmatrix}^* \begin{pmatrix} j & k & l \\ m' & n' & p' \end{pmatrix} = (-1)^{k+n'} \left[\frac{(2j)!(2k)!(l+p)!(l-p)!(l+p')!(l-p')!}{(k+n')!(k-n')!(j+m')!(j-m')!} \right]^{1/2}$$

$$\times \sum_t (-1)^t \frac{(l+j-n'-t)!(k+n'+t)!}{(j+k+l+1)!(l+p'-t)!(t+p-p')!t!(l-p-t)!} . \tag{8.31}$$

Equation (31) can be used to evaluate the general 3−j coefficient; we put $m' = j$, $n' = -k$, $p' = p$ and obtain

$$\left| \begin{pmatrix} j & k & l \\ j & -k & p \end{pmatrix} \right|^2 = \frac{(l+p)!(l-p)!}{(j+k+l+1)!} \sum_t (-1)^t \frac{(j+k+l-t)!}{(l+p-t)!t!(l-p-t)!}$$

$$= \frac{(j+k+p)!(j+k-p)!}{(j+k+l+1)!(j+k-l)!} .$$

The sum on t was performed using the identity

$$\sum_t (-1)^t \frac{(\alpha+\beta-t)!}{t!(\gamma-t)!(\beta-t)!} = \frac{\alpha!(\alpha+\beta-\gamma)!}{\beta!\gamma!(\alpha-\gamma)!} \tag{8.32}$$

with $\alpha = j+k+p$, $\beta = l-p$, and $\gamma = l+p$. The identity can be obtained, for $\alpha+1 > \gamma$, by expanding $(1+x)^\gamma$ and $(1+x)^{-\alpha-1}$ in powers of x, multiplying the series together and equating coefficients of x^β in the product with those in the expansion of $(1+x)^{\gamma-\alpha-1}$.

Since $p = k-j$, we can write

$$\left| \begin{pmatrix} j & k & l \\ j & -k & p \end{pmatrix} \right|^2 = \frac{(2k)!(2j)!}{(j+k+l+1)!(j+k-l)!} . \tag{8.33}$$

The functions $f_{l,p}$ for a fixed l can all be multiplied by a constant phase without affecting the form of the reduced representation. It is, therefore, possible to fix the phase of one 3−j coefficient arbitrarily for any j, k, l. We will choose the phase by writing

$$\begin{pmatrix} j & k & l \\ j & -k & p \end{pmatrix} = (-1)^{2k-2j}\left[\frac{(2k)!\,(2j)!}{(j+k+l+1)!(j+k-l)!}\right]^{1/2}. \tag{8.34}$$

This result, with (31), gives the final result for the nonzero 3−j coefficients. Replacing p by k − j and dropping the primes, we obtain

$$\begin{pmatrix} j & k & l \\ m & n & p \end{pmatrix} = (-1)^{2j-k+n}\left[\frac{(j+k-l)!\,(k+l-j)!\,(l+j-k)!\,(l+p)!\,(l-p)!}{(j+k+l+1)!\,(j+m)!\,(j-m)!\,(k+n)!\,(k-n)!}\right]^{1/2}$$

$$\times\sum_t (-1)^t\,\frac{(l+j-n-t)!\,(k+n+t)!}{(l+p-t)!\,(t+k-j-p)!\,t!\,(l-k+j-t)!}\ . \tag{8.35}$$

The sum on t, in this result as well as all the preceding expressions, is over values compatible with the condition that the arguments of all the factorial functions be nonnegative. It is noted that with the above choice of phase all the 3−j coefficients are real.

The unitarity condition on the transformation (24) gives rise to two identities which must be satisfied by the 3−j coefficients:

$$\sum_{mn} [l]\begin{pmatrix} j & k & l \\ m & n & p \end{pmatrix}\begin{pmatrix} j & k & l' \\ m & n & p' \end{pmatrix} = \delta_{ll'}\,\delta_{pp'}, \tag{8.36}$$

$$\sum_{lp} [l]\begin{pmatrix} j & k & l \\ m & n & p \end{pmatrix}\begin{pmatrix} j & k & l \\ m' & n' & p \end{pmatrix} = \delta_{mm'}\,\delta_{nn'}. \tag{8.37}$$

The sums occurring in these identities, although formally double sums, are essentially single sums since most of the terms are zero.

Another useful identity can be obtained by applying the unitarity condition (36) to equation (27); the result is

$$\sum_{m'n'}\begin{pmatrix} j & k & l \\ m' & n' & p' \end{pmatrix} D^j(A)_{m'm} D^k(A)_{n'n} = \sum_p \begin{pmatrix} j & k & l \\ m & n & p \end{pmatrix} D^l(A)^*_{p'p}. \tag{8.38}$$

The sum on the right-hand side contains only one nonzero term, that for p = −m −n.

The fact that the transformation (24) can be assumed to be unitary can be established as follows. Suppose D(A) is a unitary representation that can be reduced by a matrix S to a direct sum $\bar{D}(A)$ of irreducible unitary representations. Then $SD(A) = \bar{D}(A)S$ and, if the Hermitian conjugate is taken, $D(A^{-1})S^\dagger = S^\dagger \bar{D}(A^{-1})$. Multiplication with S yields $SS^\dagger \bar{D}(A^{-1}) = SD(A^{-1})S^\dagger = \bar{D}(A^{-1})SS^\dagger$. Therefore $SS^\dagger$ commutes with $\bar{D}(A)$ for all A in the group.

The matrix $SS^\dagger$ is Hermitian and positive definite and can, therefore, be diagonalized by a unitary matrix M. That is, $MSS^\dagger M^{-1}$ is diagonal with positive matrix elements $\lambda_i \delta_{ij}$. Since $SS^\dagger$ commutes with $\bar{D}(A)$ for all A, $MSS^\dagger M^{-1}$ commutes with $M\bar{D}(A)M^{-1}$ for all A and, hence, $(\lambda_i - \lambda_j)(M\bar{D}(A)M^{-1})_{ij} = 0$. From this it follows that the diagonal Hermitian matrix Q defined by $Q_{ij} = \lambda_i^{-1/2}\delta_{ij}$ also commutes with $M\bar{D}(A)M^{-1}$. The matrix $Q' = M^{-1}QM$ can, therefore, be seen to commute with $\bar{D}(A)$. Furthermore, $(Q'S)(Q'S)^\dagger = M^{-1}(QMSS^\dagger M^{-1}Q)M = M^{-1}M = I$ so that Q'S is unitary.

Now $Q'SD(A) = Q'\bar{D}(A)S = \bar{D}(A)Q'S$; Q'S is, therefore, a unitary matrix that transforms D(A) to $\bar{D}(A)$.

8-4 SYMMETRY AND OTHER PROPERTIES OF THE 3−j COEFFICIENTS

The 3−j coefficients satisfy symmetry identities under interchange of their columns, and, since these properties will be required for later work, they will be demonstrated in this section. The desired properties are a fairly simple consequence of equation (28). Consider performing a permutation simultaneously on the columns of $\begin{pmatrix} j & k & l \\ m & n & p \end{pmatrix}^*$ and $\begin{pmatrix} j & k & l \\ m' & n' & p' \end{pmatrix}$ in (28); it is immediately observed that the right-hand side is invariant under the permutation, and hence that these two factors are multiplied by complex conjugate phases. (The special case m = m', n = n', p = p' shows that these factors are of unit modulus.) In view of the reality of the 3−j coefficients these phases are ±1 and since the two 3−j coefficients are multiplied by the same phase, that phase must be independent of m, n, p.

Since the phases are independent of the indices in the second row, they can be determined for a particular set, and it is convenient to put $m = j$, $p = -l$, and $n = l - j$; these are chosen so that the sum in (35) will reduce to a single term. One finds then that

$$\begin{pmatrix} j & k & l \\ j & n & -l \end{pmatrix} = (-1)^{j-k+l}\left[\frac{(2l)!\,(2j)!}{(l+j-k)!\,(j+k+l+1)!}\right]^{1/2}, \tag{8.39a}$$

$$\begin{pmatrix} k & j & l \\ n & j & -l \end{pmatrix} = (-1)^{2k}\left[\frac{(2l)!\,(2j)!}{(l+j-k)!\,(j+k+l+1)!}\right]^{1/2}, \tag{8.39b}$$

$$\begin{pmatrix} j & l & k \\ j & -l & n \end{pmatrix} = (-1)^{2l-2j}\left[\frac{(2l)!\,(2j)!}{(l+j-k)!\,(j+k+l+1)!}\right]^{1/2}. \tag{8.39c}$$

The last equation is the same as (34). Inspection of (39a) and (39b) shows that under interchange of the first two columns the 3−j coefficients change by a factor $(-1)^{j-3k+l} = (-1)^{j+k+l}$ (since 4k is even). Similarly, (39a) and (39c) show that under interchange of the last two columns, the phase change is $(-1)^{l+k-3j} = (-1)^{l+k+j}$.

All the permutations can be generated by multiplying together these two odd permutations. It follows that the phase change is $(-1)^{j+k+l}$ for an odd permutation of the columns and that there is no phase change for an even permutation.

The 3−j coefficients also satisfy a symmetry condition under the simultaneous change of sign of m, n, and p. This can be established by taking the complex conjugate of (28) and using (18). Since m+n+p = m'+n'+p' = 0, one obtains, since the 3−j coefficients are real,

$$\begin{pmatrix} j & k & l \\ m & n & p \end{pmatrix}\begin{pmatrix} j & k & l \\ m' & n' & p' \end{pmatrix} = \begin{pmatrix} j & k & l \\ -m & -n & -p \end{pmatrix}\begin{pmatrix} j & k & l \\ -m' & -n' & -p' \end{pmatrix}.$$

It can be argued as before that the 3−j coefficient changes by a factor ±1 under the change of sign of m, n, p and that this factor depends only on j, k, and l. Again the explicit phase can be determined by setting m = j, p = −l, n = l−j. We find, using (39a), that

$$\begin{pmatrix} j & k & l \\ -j & -n & l \end{pmatrix} = (-1)^{j+k+l}\begin{pmatrix} l & k & j \\ l & -n & -j \end{pmatrix}$$

$$= (-1)^{2j+2l}\left[\frac{(2j)!\,(2l)!}{(j+l-k)!\,(j+k+l+1)!}\right]^{1/2} = (-1)^{j+k+l}\begin{pmatrix} j & k & l \\ j & n & -l \end{pmatrix}.$$

It can be concluded that under a change of sign of m, n, p, the 3−j coefficient changes by a factor $(-1)^{j+k+l}$.

The 3−j coefficient is undefined unless $|j-k| \le l \le j+k$ and $j+k-l$ is an integer. The inequalities imply that j, k, and l form the sides of a triangle, and this inequality is often referred to as the triangle inequality. It is conventional to define the 3−j coefficient to be zero if these conditions are not satisfied. With this convention the limits on sums involving 3−j coefficients do not need to be tediously repeated.

An alternate expression to (35) for the 3−j coefficient can be obtained. It is

$$\begin{pmatrix} j & k & l \\ m & n & p \end{pmatrix} = (-1)^{j-k-p}\,\frac{(j+k-l)!\,(j-k+l)!\,(-j+k+l)!}{(j+k+l+1)!}^{1/2} \tag{8.40}$$

$$\times \sum_s \frac{(-1)^s[(j+m)!\,(j-m)!\,(k+n)!\,(k-n)!\,(l+p)!\,(l-p)!]^{1/2}}{s!\,(k+n-s)!\,(j-m-s)!\,(l-k+m+s)!\,(l-j-n+s)!\,(j+k-l-s)!}.$$

This expression can be obtained from (35) by an application of identities like (32) involving binomial coefficients. It is possible to derive the symmetry properties of the 3−j coefficients directly from (40) fairly easily.

8-5 SPECIAL 3−j COEFFICIENTS

In order to obtain some later results, the 3−j coefficients in which one of the j, k, l is 1 will be required. It is sufficient to calculate them for $l = 1$, since the remaining ones can be obtained by using the symmetry properties. In this section we will give these coefficients, and also, for completeness, those for which $l = 0$ and $l = 1/2$. These can all be calculated from (35) or (40) and are as follows.

$$\begin{pmatrix} j & j & 0 \\ m & -m & 0 \end{pmatrix} = (-1)^{j-m}\left[\frac{1}{2j+1}\right]^{1/2}. \tag{8.41}$$

$$\begin{pmatrix} j & j-\frac{1}{2} & \frac{1}{2} \\ m & -m-\frac{1}{2} & \frac{1}{2} \end{pmatrix} = -(-1)^{j-m}\left[\frac{j-m}{2j(2j+1)}\right]^{1/2}. \tag{8.42a}$$

$$\begin{pmatrix} j & j-\frac{1}{2} & \frac{1}{2} \\ m & -m+\frac{1}{2} & -\frac{1}{2} \end{pmatrix} = -(-1)^{j-m}\left[\frac{j+m}{2j(2j+1)}\right]^{1/2}. \tag{8.42b}$$

$$\begin{pmatrix} j & j+\frac{1}{2} & \frac{1}{2} \\ m & -m-\frac{1}{2} & \frac{1}{2} \end{pmatrix} = -(-1)^{j-m}\left[\frac{j+m+1}{(2j+1)(2j+2)}\right]^{1/2}. \tag{8.42c}$$

$$\begin{pmatrix} j & j+\frac{1}{2} & \frac{1}{2} \\ m & -m+\frac{1}{2} & -\frac{1}{2} \end{pmatrix} = (-1)^{j-m}\left[\frac{j-m+1}{(2j+1)(2j+2)}\right]^{1/2}. \tag{8.42d}$$

$$\begin{pmatrix} j & j-1 & 1 \\ m & -m-1 & 1 \end{pmatrix} = (-1)^{j-m}\left[\frac{(j-m-1)(j-m)}{(2j-1)(2j)(2j+1)}\right]^{1/2}. \tag{8.43a}$$

$$\begin{pmatrix} j & j-1 & 1 \\ m & -m & 0 \end{pmatrix} = (-1)^{j-m}\left[\frac{2(j-m)(j+m)}{(2j-1)(2j)(2j+1)}\right]^{1/2}. \tag{8.43b}$$

$$\begin{pmatrix} j & j-1 & 1 \\ m & -m+1 & -1 \end{pmatrix} = (-1)^{j-m}\left[\frac{(j+m-1)(j+m)}{(2j-1)(2j)(2j+1)}\right]^{1/2}. \tag{8.43c}$$

$$\begin{pmatrix} j & j & 1 \\ m & -m-1 & 1 \end{pmatrix} = (-1)^{j-m}\left[\frac{2(j-m)(j+m+1)}{(2j)(2j+1)(2j+2)}\right]^{1/2}. \tag{8.43d}$$

$$\begin{pmatrix} j & j & 1 \\ m & -m & 0 \end{pmatrix} = (-1)^{j-m} \frac{2m}{[(2j)(2j+1)(2j+2)]^{1/2}} \cdot \qquad (8.43e)$$

$$\begin{pmatrix} j & j & 1 \\ m & -m+1 & -1 \end{pmatrix} = -(-1)^{j-m} \left[\frac{2(j+m)(j-m+1)}{(2j)(2j+1)(2j+2)}\right]^{1/2} \cdot \qquad (8.43f)$$

$$\begin{pmatrix} j & j+1 & 1 \\ m & -m-1 & 1 \end{pmatrix} = (-1)^{j-m} \left[\frac{(j+m+1)(j+m+2)}{(2j+1)(2j+2)(2j+3)}\right]^{1/2} \cdot \qquad (8.43g)$$

$$\begin{pmatrix} j & j+1 & 1 \\ m & -m & 0 \end{pmatrix} = -(-1)^{j-m} \left[\frac{2(j-m+1)(j+m+1)}{(2j+1)(2j+2)(2j+3)}\right]^{1/2} \cdot \qquad (8.43h)$$

$$\begin{pmatrix} j & j+1 & 1 \\ m & -m+1 & -1 \end{pmatrix} = (-1)^{j-m} \left[\frac{(j-m+1)(j-m+2)}{(2j+1)(2j+2)(2j+3)}\right]^{1/2} \cdot \qquad (8.43i)$$

Some of these equations are redundant; for example, all of equations (42) can be easily obtained for (42a).

8-6 REDUCTION OF A THREEFOLD PRODUCT

In this section the question of reducing the direct product of three irreducible representations will be considered, and the important 6−j coefficients that arise in this connection will be defined. Before this is done, however, it is desirable to discuss the reduction of the direct product to the form $D^l(A)$ (rather than $D^l(A)^*$).

The functions $f_{l,p}$ defined by equation (24) have the slight disadvantage in that they are transformed by the complex conjugate representation; that is, they satisfy

$$f_{l,p}(A^{-1}\mathbf{x}, A^{-1}\mathbf{y}) = \sum_{p'} D^l(A)^*_{p'p} f_{l,p'}(\mathbf{x}, \mathbf{y}).$$

This disadvantage is more than compensated for, however, by the symmetries of the 3−j coefficients that result from the reduction to the complex conjugate representation.

It is easy to find new functions that transform by $D^l(A)$; in fact, from (18), it can be seen that functions $\tilde{f}_{l,p}$ defined by $\tilde{f}_{l,p} = (-1)^{l-p} \times f_{l,-p}$ have this property. It is convenient for the discussion to regard the $\tilde{f}_{l,p}$ as the contravariant components of a vector whose covariant components are $f_{l,p}$. The contravariant and covariant components are, therefore, connected by a metric tensor whose elements are given by $g_l^{mm'} = (-1)^{l-m}\delta_{m-m'}$.

A rather peculiar aspect of this metric tensor is that it is not symmetric if $l = \frac{1}{2}, \frac{3}{2}, \ldots$. For this reason it is necessary to use caution in raising and lowering indices, and, for example, $f_m g^m \neq f^m g_m$. Rather, it is easy to determine

$$f_m g^m = (-1)^{2l} f^m g_m. \tag{8.44}$$

The 3−j coefficients can be viewed as the (covariant) elements of a rank three tensor. The indices of this tensor can be raised and lowered, and we can write, for example,

$$\begin{pmatrix} j & k & p \\ m & n & l \end{pmatrix} = (-1)^{l-p} \begin{pmatrix} j & k & l \\ m & n & -p \end{pmatrix}. \tag{8.45}$$

In this notation the contravariant components of the functions f, that transform by $D^l(A)$, are given by

$$f_l^p(\mathbf{x}, \mathbf{y}) = \sum_{mn} [l]^{1/2} \begin{pmatrix} j & k & p \\ m & n & l \end{pmatrix} e^m(\mathbf{x}) e^n(\mathbf{y}). \tag{8.46}$$

The completely contravariant 3−j coefficient is

$$\begin{pmatrix} m & n & p \\ j & k & l \end{pmatrix} = (-1)^{j+k+l-m-n-p} \begin{pmatrix} j & k & l \\ -m & -n & -p \end{pmatrix}$$

$$= (-1)^{2(j+k+l)} \begin{pmatrix} j & k & l \\ m & n & p \end{pmatrix} = \begin{pmatrix} j & k & l \\ m & n & p \end{pmatrix}$$

since $m + n + p = 0$ and $2(j + k + l)$ is an even integer. The orthogonality relations (36) and (37) can be rewritten in the invariant forms

$$\sum_{mn} \begin{pmatrix} j & k & l \\ m & n & p \end{pmatrix} \begin{pmatrix} m & n & p' \\ j & k & l' \end{pmatrix} = \frac{\delta_{ll'} \delta_{pp'}}{[l]} \tag{8.47}$$

$$\sum_{lp} [l] \begin{pmatrix} j & k & l \\ m & n & p \end{pmatrix} \begin{pmatrix} m' & n' & p \\ j & k & l \end{pmatrix} = \delta_{mm'} \delta_{nn'}. \tag{8.48}$$

We wish now to investigate the direct product of three representations which will be denoted, to simplify the later results, $D^{l_1}(A)$, $D^{j_2}(A)$, $D^{l_2}(A)$. The direct product can be defined in the space of functions of three variables spanned by products $e^{n_1}(\mathbf{x}) e^{m_2}(\mathbf{y}) e^{n_2}(\mathbf{z})$, $-l_1 \leq n_1 \leq l_1$, and so on. The reduction of the direct product is in this case complicated by the fact that it is not unique; that is, there are various invariant subspaces and the ones that are constructed will depend on how the reduction is carried out.

One way to reduce the direct product is to reduce first the product of $D^{l_1}(A)$ and $D^{j_2}(A)$; the contravariant components of the functions that do this are

$$f_{l_3}{}^{n_3}(\mathbf{x},\mathbf{y}) = \sum [l_3]^{1/2} \begin{pmatrix} l_1 & j_2 & n_3 \\ n_1 & m_2 & l_3 \end{pmatrix} e^{n_1}(\mathbf{x}) e^{m_2}(\mathbf{y}).$$

The direct product of this result with $D^{l_2}(A)$ can be taken and the result again reduced. The functions that carry the final representation are given by

$$g_{j_1 l_3}{}^{m_1} = \sum [j_1]^{1/2} \begin{pmatrix} l_2 & l_3 & m_1 \\ n_2 & n_3 & j_1 \end{pmatrix} f_{l_3}{}^{n_3}(\mathbf{x},\mathbf{y}) e^{n_2}(\mathbf{z})$$

$$= \sum ([l_3][j_1])^{1/2} \begin{pmatrix} m_1 & l_2 & l_3 \\ j_1 & n_2 & n_3 \end{pmatrix} \begin{pmatrix} l_1 & j_2 & n_3 \\ n_1 & m_2 & l_3 \end{pmatrix} e^{n_1}(\mathbf{x}) e^{m_2}(\mathbf{y}) e^{n_2}(\mathbf{z}) \tag{8.49}$$

the sum being on n_1, m_2, n_2, and n_3. The functions $g_{j_1 l_3}{}^{m_1}$ transform according to $D^{j_1}(A)$; that is,

$$g_{j_1 l_3}{}^{m_1}(A^{-1}\mathbf{x}, A^{-1}\mathbf{y}, A^{-1}\mathbf{z}) = \sum D^{j_1}(A)_{\mu_1 m_1} g_{j_1 l_3}{}^{\mu_1}(\mathbf{x},\mathbf{y},\mathbf{z}).$$

The direct product could also be reduced by reducing first the product of $D^{l_1}(A)$ and $D^{l_2}(A)$, multiplying by $D^{j_2}(A)$, and reducing the result. The functions corresponding to this reduction are

$$h_{j_1' j_3}{}^{m_1'} = \sum ([j_1'][j_3])^{1/2} \begin{pmatrix} m_1' & j_2 & j_3 \\ j_1' & m_2 & m_3 \end{pmatrix} \begin{pmatrix} m_3 & l_1 & l_2 \\ j_3 & n_1 & n_2 \end{pmatrix}$$

$$\times\, e^{n_1}(\mathbf{x}) e^{m_2}(\mathbf{y}) e^{n_2}(\mathbf{z}), \tag{8.50}$$

where the sum is on n_1, m_2, n_2, and m_3. These functions are transformed by $D^{j_1'}(A)$. The index j_3 indicates how the functions h transform in the variables $\mathbf{x}$ and $\mathbf{z}$ with $\mathbf{y}$ fixed.

The functions $g_{j_1 l_3}{}^{m_1}$ and $h_{j_1' j_3}{}^{m_1'}$ are each complete in the representation space of the direct product and it is, therefore, possible to expand one set of functions in terms of the other. It is, therefore, possible to write

$$g_{j_1 l_3}{}^{m_1}(\mathbf{x},\mathbf{y},\mathbf{z}) = \sum C(j_1 l_3 m_1, j_1' j_3 m_1') h_{j_1' j_3}{}^{m_1'}(\mathbf{x},\mathbf{y},\mathbf{z}),$$

where the sum is on j_1', j_3, m_1'.

It will now be shown that the only terms in the sum are those for which $j_1 = j_1'$, $m_1 = m_1'$. The method is to replace **x**, **y**, **z** by $A^{-1}\mathbf{x}$, $A^{-1}\mathbf{y}$, $A^{-1}\mathbf{z}$ and use the representation property to obtain

$$\sum_{\mu_1} D^{j_1}(A)_{\mu_1 m_1} g_{j_1 l_3}{}^{\mu_1}(\mathbf{x},\mathbf{y},\mathbf{z})$$
$$= \sum_{\mu_1'} C(j_1 l_3 m_1, j_1' j_3 m_1') D^{j_1'}(A)_{\mu_1' m_1'} h_{j_1' j_3}{}^{\mu_1'}(\mathbf{x},\mathbf{y},\mathbf{z}).$$

This is then multiplied by $D^{j_1}(A)^*_{mm_1}$ and integrated over the group; the result is, by the orthogonality properties,

$$g_{j_1 l_3}{}^{m}(\mathbf{x},\mathbf{y},\mathbf{z}) = \sum_{j_3} C(j_1 l_3 m_1, j_1 j_3 m_1) h_{j_1 j_3}{}^{m}(\mathbf{x},\mathbf{y},\mathbf{z}). \tag{8.51}$$

This result shows, moreover, that the expansion coefficient is independent of the argument m_1 and can be evaluated for any convenient choice of this index.

The important <u>6−j coefficients</u> are defined by

$$C(j_1 l_3 m_1, j_1 j_3 m_1) = (-1)^{2l_1} ([l_3][j_3])^{1/2} \begin{Bmatrix} j_1 & j_2 & j_3 \\ l_1 & l_2 & l_3 \end{Bmatrix}. \tag{8.52}$$

An identity relating the 3−j and 6−j coefficients can be obtained from (51) by using (49) and (50) and equating coefficients of $e^{n_1}(\mathbf{x}) \times e^{m_2}(\mathbf{y}) e^{n_2}(\mathbf{z})$ on each side:

$$\begin{pmatrix} m & l_2 & l_3 \\ j_1 & n_2 & n_3 \end{pmatrix}\begin{pmatrix} l_1 & j_2 & n_3 \\ n_1 & m_2 & l_3 \end{pmatrix} = \sum_{j_3} (-1)^{2l_1} [j_3]$$
$$\times \begin{Bmatrix} j_1 & j_2 & j_3 \\ l_1 & l_2 & l_3 \end{Bmatrix}\begin{pmatrix} m & j_2 & j_3 \\ j_1 & m_2 & m_3 \end{pmatrix}\begin{pmatrix} l_1 & l_2 & m_3 \\ n_1 & n_2 & j_3 \end{pmatrix}. \tag{8.53}$$

This can be expressed in a more symmetric form by lowering the index m and replacing it by m_1, raising the index n_2 and using the orthogonality property (47) together with (44) to transfer the last 3−j coefficient to the left-hand side.

$$\sum \begin{pmatrix} n_1 & l_2 & j_3 \\ l_1 & n_2 & m_3 \end{pmatrix}\begin{pmatrix} j_1 & n_2 & l_3 \\ m_1 & l_2 & n_3 \end{pmatrix}\begin{pmatrix} l_1 & j_2 & n_3 \\ n_1 & m_2 & l_3 \end{pmatrix} = \begin{Bmatrix} j_1 & j_2 & j_3 \\ l_1 & l_2 & l_3 \end{Bmatrix}\begin{pmatrix} j_1 & j_2 & j_3 \\ m_1 & m_2 & m_3 \end{pmatrix} \tag{8.54}$$

where the left-hand side is summed on n_1, n_2, n_3. (The sum is effectively over only one index, however.)

The numbers $C(j_1 l_3 m_1, j_1 j_3 m_1)$ are the elements of an orthogonal matrix; this implies an orthogonality condition on the 6−j coefficients, namely,

$$\sum_{j_3} [j_3] \begin{Bmatrix} j_1 & j_2 & j_3 \\ l_1 & l_2 & l_3 \end{Bmatrix} \begin{Bmatrix} j_1 & j_2 & j_3 \\ l_1 & l_2 & l_3' \end{Bmatrix} = \frac{\delta_{l_3 l_3'}}{[l_3]} . \tag{8.55}$$

The 6−j coefficients are meaningful only if certain triangular inequalities are satisfied since, given l_1, j_2, and l_2, the indices l_3, j_3, and j_1 can only assume certain values. A review of the definition shows that the four trios of numbers (l_1, j_2, l_3), (j_1, l_2, l_3), (l_1, l_2, j_3), (j_1, j_2, j_3) must each satisfy the triangle inequalities. The 6−j coefficient is, therefore, defined to be zero unless all these inequalities are satisfied. This is necessary in order that equations (53) and (54) be consistent with the definition of the 3−j coefficients.

It can be seen immediately from (54) that the 6−j coefficient is invariant under any permutation of its columns. The coefficient is also invariant under the interchange of two indices from one row with the corresponding indices of the other row; for example,

$$\begin{Bmatrix} j_1 & j_2 & j_3 \\ l_1 & l_2 & l_3 \end{Bmatrix} = \begin{Bmatrix} l_1 & j_2 & l_3 \\ j_1 & l_2 & j_3 \end{Bmatrix} .$$

This is an almost trivial consequence of (54); it is necessary, however, to use the orthogonality property of the 3−j coefficients to establish the result.

An explicit expression for the 6−j coefficient as a sum has been obtained by Racah [2]. The result can be obtained by a complicated algebraic manipulation of (54) with $m_1 = j_1$ and $m_2 = -j_2$ using the explicit expression for the 3−j coefficients. The result is

$$\begin{Bmatrix} j_1 & j_2 & j_3 \\ l_1 & l_2 & l_3 \end{Bmatrix} = (-1)^{j_1+j_2+l_1+l_2} \Delta(j_1 j_2 j_3) \Delta(j_1 l_2 l_3) \Delta(l_1 j_2 l_3) \Delta(l_1 l_2 j_3) \, S \tag{8.56a}$$

where

$$\Delta(j_1 j_2 j_3) = \left[\frac{(j_1 + j_2 - j_3)!\,(j_2 + j_3 - j_1)!\,(j_3 + j_1 - j_2)!}{(j_1 + j_2 + j_3 + 1)!} \right]^{1/2} \tag{8.56b}$$

$$S = \sum_t (-1)^t \frac{(j_1 + j_2 + l_1 + l_2 + 1 - t)!}{[t!\,(j_1 + j_2 - j_3 - t)!\,(l_1 + l_2 - j_3 - t)!\,(j_1 + l_2 - l_3 - t)!\,(l_1 + j_2 - l_3 - t)!}$$

$$\times\, (j_3 + l_3 - j_1 - l_1 + t)!\,(j_3 + l_3 - j_2 - l_2 + t)!] . \tag{8.56c}$$

In Chapter 10 the value of the right-hand side of (54) for $j_2 = 0$ will be required. The result is nonzero only if $m_2 = 0$, $j_1 = j_3$, $l_1 = l_3$, and $m_1 = -m_3$. It can be determined from (41) and (45) that

$$\begin{pmatrix} l_1 & 0 & n_1 \\ n_1 & 0 & l_1 \end{pmatrix} = (-1)^{2l_1} [l_1]^{-1/2} .$$

Then (54) becomes, from (36), (45) and the symmetry properties

$$\begin{Bmatrix} j_1 & 0 & j_1 \\ l_1 & l_2 & l_1 \end{Bmatrix} \begin{pmatrix} j_1 & 0 & j_1 \\ m_1 & 0 & -m_1 \end{pmatrix} = (-1)^{l_1+l_2-m_1} [l_1]^{-1/2} [j_1]^{-1} . \tag{8.57}$$

Chapter 9

ROTATIONS IN SPACE

The group O(3) of rotations in a three-dimensional space is of great importance in mathematical physics. In this chapter, this group will be studied in general and the irreducible representations will be discussed. This leads to a development of certain properties of some of the special functions of mathematical physics; these are the Jacobi polynomials with their special cases of Legendre polynomials and associated Legendre functions.

The representations of the rotation group can be obtained easily by establishing a homomorphic mapping of SU(2) onto O(3); it can then be shown that certain representations of SU(2) are also representations of O(3).

The representations of O(3) can also be constructed in invariant subspaces of the space of functions defined in three-dimensional space. It will be shown that the suitable invariant subspaces are composed of harmonic, homogeneous polynomials in three variables. In this way the connection between the group representations and Laplace's equation can be established. We will also consider and solve the partial differential equations that the representations are required to satisfy because of the group structure.

9-1 GENERAL PROPERTIES OF THE ROTATION GROUP

In this discussion we will denote by R any element of O(3). The matrix R is a real 3×3 matrix that satisfies

$$R^T R = I. \tag{9.1}$$

A consequence of (1) is that det $R = \pm 1$. The matrices with determinant -1 describe a rotation with a reflection; for the most part we will be concerned with the proper rotations, the subgroup of matrices of unit determinant. This group is denoted by $O(3)^+$.

An arbitrary group element R has in general three eigenvalues which, since R is orthogonal, are of unit modulus. If R is a proper rotation the three eigenvalues of R must satisfy $\lambda_1\lambda_2\lambda_3 = 1$. Since the secular equation $|R - \lambda I| = 0$ is of degree three and has real coefficients, R has one real eigenvalue, which must be ± 1, and a pair of complex eigenvalues λ and λ^*. If the rotation is proper, the real eigenvalue must be +1. For a particular R it may happen that $\lambda = \lambda^* = +1$ or $\lambda = \lambda^* = -1$. The first case is clearly R = I; it will be seen that the second case corresponds to a rotation about some axis by π.

If R is a proper rotation there is a vector **v** with the property $R\mathbf{v} = \mathbf{v}$ corresponding to the eigenvalue 1. A line through the origin in the direction of **v** is invariant under the rotation R and can be interpreted as the axis of rotation. If $\lambda = e^{-i\phi}$, ϕ real, is another eigenvalue there is associated with it a complex vector $\mathbf{u} + i\,\mathbf{w}$ satisfying

$$R(\mathbf{u} + i\mathbf{w}) = e^{-i\phi}(\mathbf{u} + i\mathbf{w}). \tag{9.2}$$

The vectors **u** and **w** are each perpendicular to **v** since **v** and $\mathbf{u} + i\mathbf{w}$ are eigenvectors corresponding to different eigenvalues implying $(\mathbf{u} + i\mathbf{w}) \cdot \mathbf{v} = 0$.

It is possible to show also that $\mathbf{u} \cdot \mathbf{w} = 0$. If the complex conjugate of (2) is taken, it is seen that, since R is real, $\mathbf{u} - i\mathbf{w}$ is also an eigenvector of R corresponding to the eigenvalue $e^{i\phi}$. The orthogonality of these two vectors (in the usual complex vector inner product) implies that $(\mathbf{u} + i\mathbf{w}) \cdot (\mathbf{u} + i\mathbf{w}) = |\mathbf{u}|^2 - |\mathbf{w}|^2 + 2i\mathbf{u} \cdot \mathbf{w} = 0$. This result shows that $|\mathbf{u}| = |\mathbf{w}|$ and $\mathbf{u} \cdot \mathbf{w} = 0$. The vectors **u** and **w** can be visualized as mutually perpendicular vectors lying in a plane perpendicular to **v**.

Taking real and imaginary parts of (2) shows that

$$R\mathbf{u} = \cos\phi\,\mathbf{u} + \sin\phi\,\mathbf{w}, \tag{9.3a}$$

$$R\mathbf{w} = -\sin\phi\,\mathbf{u} + \cos\phi\,\mathbf{w}. \tag{9.3b}$$

This result indicates that vectors in the plane perpendicular to **v**, which can be expressed as a linear combination of **u** and **w**, are rotated within the plane by an angle ϕ. An arbitrary vector **r** can be expressed in the form $\alpha\mathbf{v} + \beta\mathbf{p}$ where **p** is in the plane perpendicular to **v**. We can write $R\mathbf{r} = \alpha\mathbf{v} + \beta R\mathbf{p}$, indicating that **r** has been rotated about **v** by an angle ϕ. In Fig. 9-1 we show the vector **v**, the plane spanned by **u** and **w**, and an arbitrary vector **r** together with $R\mathbf{r}$.

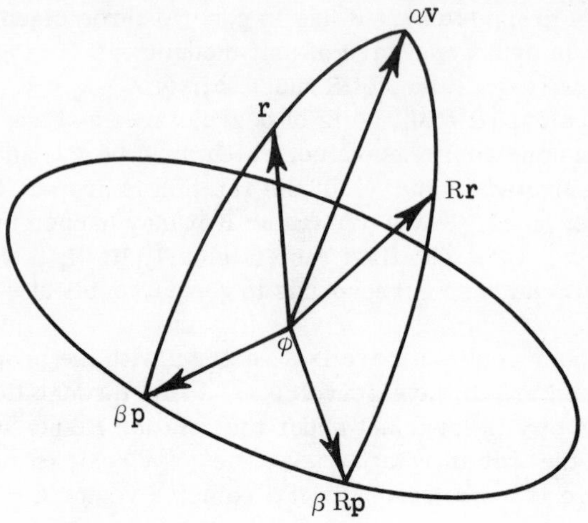

Fig. 9-1

The effect on an arbitrary vector **r** of a rotation about the **v** axis by an angle ϕ.

If the vectors **u**, **w**, **v**, are assumed to be normalized to unit length the matrix Q whose columns are **u**, **w**, **v**, in that order, is orthogonal. It can be verified that, since $Q^T = Q^{-1}$,

$$Q^{-1}RQ = R' = \begin{pmatrix} \cos\phi & -\sin\phi & 0 \\ \sin\phi & \cos\phi & 0 \\ 0 & 0 & 1 \end{pmatrix}. \tag{9.4}$$

The matrix R' defines a right-hand rotation about the z axis by ϕ. Since $Q \varepsilon O(3)$, R and R' are in the same class and we can conclude that a rotation about any axis by an angle ϕ is in the same class as a rotation about the z axis by ϕ. This implies that if two rotations are by the same angle they are in the same class. On the other hand, rotations by different angles are in different classes since their diagonal forms are different. It can be noted that since the trace is invariant under the transformation (4) the angle of rotation can be determined from

$$\text{Tr } R = 1 + 2 \cos\phi. \tag{9.5}$$

The group can be parametrized by specifying the polar coordinates of **v**, the axis of rotation, and ϕ, the angle of rotation, where $0 \leq \phi \leq \pi$. A more common parametrization, however, is by the Euler angles

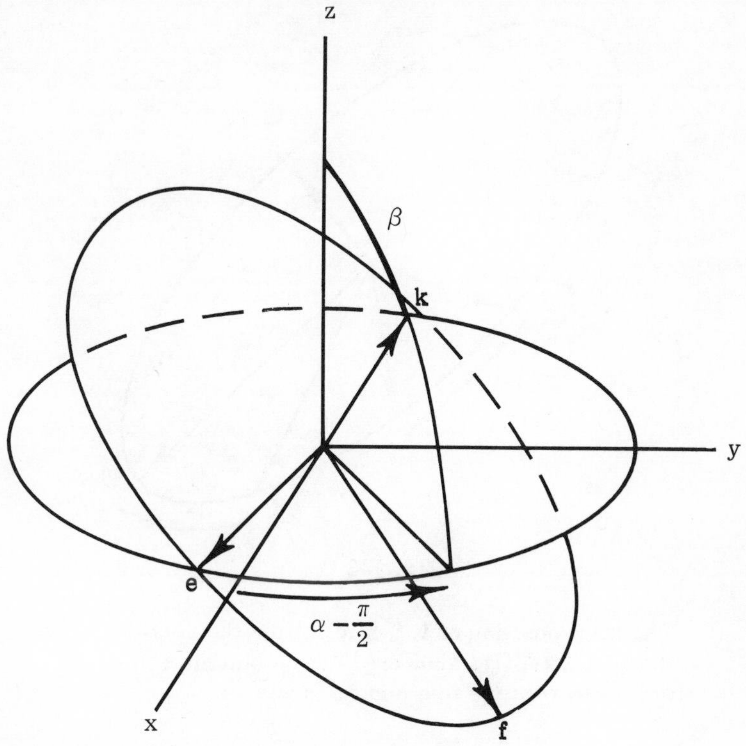

Fig. 9-2

The vectors **e**, **f**, **k** show the position of **i**, **j**, **k** following the rotation $Z(\alpha)X(\beta)$. Note that **e** is in the x-y plane perpendicular to **k** and that $\mathbf{f} = \mathbf{k} \times \mathbf{e}$. The angles β and $\alpha - \pi/2$ are the spherical polar coordinates of **k**.

which will now be defined. A rotation is uniquely specified by the final position of three unit vectors, **i**, **j**, **k** which were originally parallel to the x, y, and z axes respectively. The final components of **k** can be written $(\sin\beta \sin\alpha, -\sin\beta \cos\alpha, \cos\beta)$ where β is the colatitude of **k** and $\alpha = \varphi + \pi/2$, where φ is the azimuthal angle of **k**. In Fig. 9-2 we show the final position of **k** and the angles β and α.

The vectors **i** and **j** lie in the plane perpendicular to **k**; the rotation can be completely determined by specifying the orientation of **i** and **j** in this plane. If two unit vectors in this plane are known, **i** and **j** can be expressed as a linear combination of them. One such vector is the vector **e** lying in the x-y plane with components $(\cos\alpha, \sin\alpha, 0)$ and another, perpendicular to both **k** and **e** is $\mathbf{f} = \mathbf{k} \times \mathbf{e}$

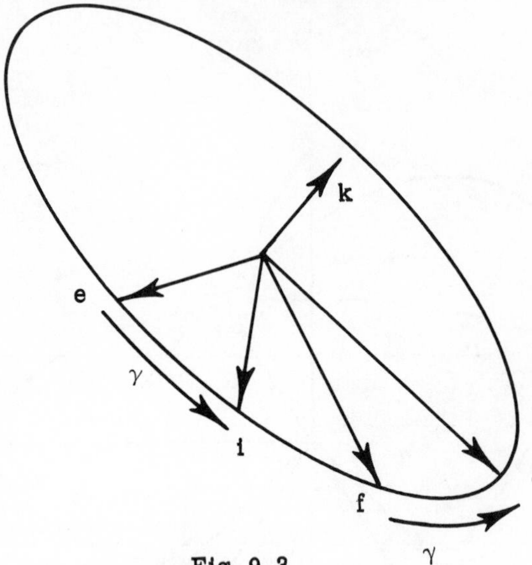

Fig. 9-3

The final position of **i**, **j**, **k** following the rotation $Z(\alpha)X(\beta)Z(\gamma)$ showing **i** and **j** rotated in the **e**-**f** plane relative to **e** and **f** and γ.

with components $(-\sin\alpha\cos\beta, \cos\alpha\cos\beta, \sin\beta)$. The vectors **i** and **j** can be expressed uniquely in the form $\mathbf{i} = \cos\gamma\,\mathbf{e} + \sin\gamma\,\mathbf{f}$, $\mathbf{j} = -\sin\gamma\,\mathbf{e} + \cos\gamma\,\mathbf{f}$. The angles α, β, γ defined in this way are the Euler angles; it is observed that these angles characterize the rotation completely. The domain of the angles is $0 \le \alpha < 2\pi$, $0 \le \beta \le \pi$, $0 < \gamma < 2\pi$. The vectors **e** and **f** are also shown in Fig. 9-2 and in Fig. 9-3 the vectors **i** and **j** are shown in the final position.

The vectors **i** and **j** have components $(\cos\alpha\cos\gamma - \sin\alpha\cos\beta\sin\gamma,\ \sin\alpha\cos\gamma + \cos\alpha\cos\beta\sin\gamma,\ \sin\beta\sin\gamma)$ and $(-\cos\alpha\sin\gamma, -\sin\alpha\cos\beta\cos\gamma, -\sin\alpha\sin\gamma + \cos\alpha\cos\beta\cos\gamma, \sin\beta\cos\gamma)$ respectively. The matrix that transforms the initial components of **i**, **j**, and **k** to the final components has for its columns the components of **i**, **j**, and **k** in their final position. The matrix R with Euler angles α, β, γ is, therefore,

$$R(\alpha,\beta,\gamma) = \begin{pmatrix} \cos\alpha\cos\gamma & -\cos\alpha\sin\gamma & \sin\beta\sin\alpha \\ -\sin\alpha\cos\beta\sin\gamma, & -\sin\alpha\cos\beta\cos\gamma, & \\ \sin\alpha\cos\gamma & -\sin\alpha\sin\gamma & -\sin\beta\cos\alpha \\ +\cos\alpha\cos\beta\sin\gamma, & +\cos\alpha\cos\beta\cos\gamma, & \\ \sin\beta\sin\gamma, & \sin\beta\cos\gamma & \cos\beta \end{pmatrix} \tag{9.6}$$

It can be verified by a direct calculation that the matrix $R(\alpha, \beta, \gamma)$ is equal to the matrix $Z(\alpha)X(\beta)Z(\gamma)$ where

$$Z(\alpha) = \begin{pmatrix} \cos\alpha & -\sin\alpha & 0 \\ \sin\alpha & \cos\alpha & 0 \\ 0 & 0 & 1 \end{pmatrix}, \quad X(\beta) = \begin{pmatrix} 1 & 0 & 0 \\ 0 & \cos\beta & -\sin\beta \\ 0 & \sin\beta & \cos\beta \end{pmatrix}. \tag{9.7}$$

The matrix $Z(\alpha)$ is a rotation about the z axis by α and the matrix $X(\beta)$ is a rotation about the x axis by β. The reason for this result can be explained as follows. Consider first the rotation $Z(\alpha)X(\beta)$. The rotation $X(\beta)$ rotates **k** within the y-z plane to have colatitude β (and azimuthal angle $-\pi/2$) and leaves **i** unchanged. The rotation $Z(\alpha)$ then rotates **k** about the z axis leaving the colatitude unchanged but increasing the azimuthal angle to $\alpha - \pi/2$; $Z(\alpha)X(\beta)$ therefore, rotates **k** to its final position. The rotation $Z(\alpha)$ rotates **i** in the x-y plane; since it remains perpendicular to **k** it is rotated into the vector that was called **e**. It follows that $\mathbf{j} = \mathbf{k} \times \mathbf{i}$ is rotated by $Z(\alpha)X(\beta)$ into the position of the vector **f**. It can now be seen that if $Z(\alpha)X(\beta)$ is preceded by $Z(\gamma)$ the result is $R(\alpha, \beta, \gamma)$ since $Z(\gamma)$ leaves **k** unchanged but rotates the x-y plane by γ; this means that **i** and **j** are rotated in the x-y plane relative to **e** and **f** by an angle γ and, following $Z(\alpha)X(\beta)$, are in their final position.

The preceding argument shows that each rotation can be expressed by some choice of the Euler angles. The parametrization is, however, not unique for rotations about the z axis for which $\beta = 0$, since any rotation $Z(\phi)$ can be expressed in the form $R(\alpha, 0, \phi - \alpha)$ for arbitrary α. This indicates that the parametrization is singular at $\beta = 0$ and in particular at the identity. This fact complicates somewhat the problem of finding the invariant weight function on the group.

To conclude the discussion of the Euler angles we indicate how they may be determined for an arbitrary orthogonal matrix R with elements a_{ij}. It can be seen by inspection of (6) that

$$\tan\alpha = -\frac{a_{13}}{a_{23}} \tag{9.8a}$$

$$\cos\beta = a_{33} \tag{9.8b}$$

$$\tan\gamma = \frac{a_{31}}{a_{32}}. \tag{9.8c}$$

Equations (8) leave the quadrants of α and γ undetermined but these can be fixed from the signs of a_{13} and a_{31}.

In later applications the Euler angles A, B, Γ of the product $X(\beta)Z(\alpha)X(\beta')$ will be required. It can be verified by multiplying the

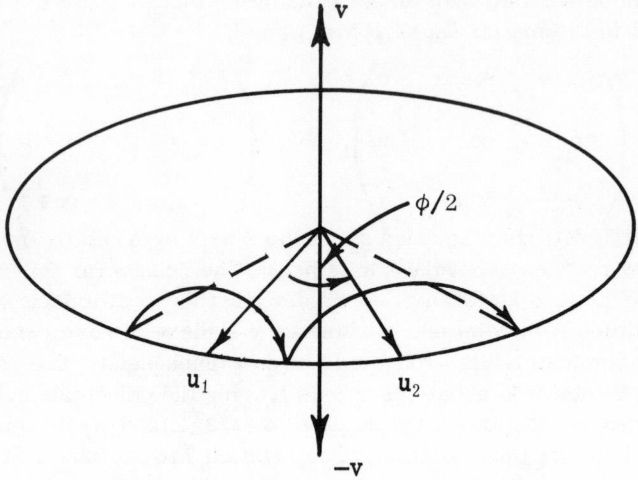

Fig. 9-4

A rotation about **v** by ϕ constructed as successive rotations about $\mathbf{u}_1$ and $\mathbf{u}_2$ by π.

matrices and comparing the result with (6) that they are given (implicitly) by

$$\sin \mathrm{A} = \frac{\sin \alpha \sin \beta'}{\sin \mathrm{B}} \tag{9.9a}$$

$$\cos \mathrm{A} = \frac{\cos \beta \cos \alpha \sin \beta' + \sin \beta \cos \beta'}{\sin \mathrm{B}} \tag{9.9b}$$

$$\cos \mathrm{B} = \cos \beta \cos \beta' - \sin \beta \sin \beta' \cos \alpha \tag{9.9c}$$

$$\sin \Gamma = \frac{\sin \alpha \sin \beta}{\sin \mathrm{B}} \tag{9.9d}$$

$$\cos \Gamma = \frac{\sin \beta \cos \alpha \cos \beta' + \cos \beta \sin \beta'}{\sin \mathrm{B}} . \tag{9.9e}$$

It is of interest to remark that any rotation can be expressed as the product of two rotations, each by π. To show this we suppose that a rotation is about an axis **v** by an angle ϕ. Let $\mathbf{u}_1$ and $\mathbf{u}_2$ be two vectors in the plane P perpendicular to **v** with an angle $\phi/2$ between them. A rotation by π about either $\mathbf{u}_1$ or $\mathbf{u}_2$ rotates P into itself and $\mathbf{v}$ into $-\mathbf{v}$. We consider a rotation about $\mathbf{u}_1$ by π followed by a rotation about $\mathbf{u}_2$ by π. The product of the two rotations is seen to leave $\mathbf{v}$ invariant and rotate P into itself. Furthermore, the first rotation leaves $\mathbf{u}_1$ invariant and the second rotation leaves $\mathbf{u}_1$ an angle $\phi/2$ on the other side of $\mathbf{u}_2$. The product of the rotations, therefore, rotates $\mathbf{u}_1$ (and all other vectors perpendicular to $\mathbf{v}$) through an angle ϕ. In Fig. 9-4 we show the axes $\mathbf{u}_1$ and $\mathbf{u}_2$ and a point that is rotated by ϕ in the plane perpendicular to $\mathbf{v}$.

The product of two rotations can be calculated from this fact. Consider rotations R_1 and R_2 by angles ϕ_1 and ϕ_2 about axes $\mathbf{v}_1$ and $\mathbf{v}_2$ respectively. We consider a vector $\mathbf{u}$ in the intersection of the planes P_1 and P_2 perpendicular to $\mathbf{v}_1$ and $\mathbf{v}_2$. Let $\mathbf{u}_1$ be a vector in P_1 such that the angle between $\mathbf{u}_1$ and $\mathbf{u}$ is $\phi_1/2$, and $\mathbf{u}_2$ be a vector in P_2 such that the angle between $\mathbf{u}$ and $\mathbf{u}_2$ is $\phi_2/2$. Then R_1 can be constructed as a rotation about $\mathbf{u}_1$ by π followed by a rotation about $\mathbf{u}$ by π. Similarly, R_2 is a rotation about $\mathbf{u}$ by π followed by a rotation about $\mathbf{u}_2$ by π. The product R_2R_1 (R_1 is performed first) is then a product of four rotations by π; the second and third are both about $\mathbf{u}$ by π and, therefore, multiply to give $\mathbf{I}$. The product R_2R_1 is, therefore, a rotation about $\mathbf{u}_1$ by π followed by a rotation about $\mathbf{u}_2$ by π.

9-2 THE FUNCTIONS $v^{\alpha}{}_{\beta}$ AND INVARIANT INTEGRATION

In this section the functions $v^{\alpha}{}_{\beta}$ defined in equation (3.8) will be calculated for $O(3)^+$. It is then possible to calculate the weight function for invariant integration immediately. It is unfortunately not useful to calculate the functions directly from (3.8) since the parametrization in the Euler angles is singular at e. It is necessary instead to introduce a new coordinate system into the neighborhood of e. To terms in first-order, an element in the neighborhood of e can be written in the form

$$B(h_1, h_2, h_3) = \begin{pmatrix} 1 & -h_3 & h_2 \\ h_3 & 1 & -h_1 \\ -h_2 & h_1 & 1 \end{pmatrix} \tag{9.10}$$

since, as we have seen, this is orthogonal in first-order in h.

For convenience we will replace α by α_1, β by α_2 and γ by α_3 and denote by $\mathbf{h}$ and $\boldsymbol{\alpha}$ vectors with components (h_1, h_2, h_3) and $(\alpha_1, \alpha_2, \alpha_3)$ respectively. We consider the product functions $\mathbf{f}(\boldsymbol{\alpha}, \mathbf{h})$ that are defined to be the Euler angles of the product rotation $R(\boldsymbol{\alpha})B(\mathbf{h})$; that is,

$$R(\mathbf{f}(\boldsymbol{\alpha}, \mathbf{h})) = R(\boldsymbol{\alpha})B(\mathbf{h}). \tag{9.11}$$

The functions v for the group O(3) will be defined by

$$v^i{}_j(\boldsymbol{\alpha}) = \frac{\partial f^i}{\partial h^j}(\boldsymbol{\alpha}, 0). \tag{9.12}$$

The calculation of $v^i{}_j$ is apparently very tedious, since it is necessary to multiply the matrices R and B together, determine the Euler angles of the product, and differentiate with respect to h_j. It is possible, however, by various tricks to simplify the procedure considerably. To illustrate the procedure, we will calculate the functions $v^i{}_1(\boldsymbol{\alpha})$. This requires partial derivatives with respect to h_1 evaluated at $h = 0$; it is, therefore, possible to set $h_2 = h_3 = 0$ initially. We write R in the form

$$R = \begin{pmatrix} a_{11} & a_{12} & a_{13} \\ a_{21} & a_{22} & a_{23} \\ a_{31} & a_{32} & a_{33} \end{pmatrix}.$$

Matrix multiplication of RB gives the result

$$RB = \begin{pmatrix} a_{11} & a_{12} + ha_{13} & a_{13} - ha_{12} \\ a_{21} & a_{22} + ha_{23} & a_{23} - ha_{22} \\ a_{31} & a_{32} + ha_{33} & a_{33} - ha_{32} \end{pmatrix}$$

where h_1 has been replaced by h. Comparison of this result with equations (8) shows that

$$\tan f^1 = -\frac{a_{13} - ha_{12}}{a_{23} - ha_{22}}$$

$$\cos f^2 = a_{33} - ha_{32}$$

$$\tan f^3 = \frac{a_{31}}{a_{32} + ha_{33}}.$$

The functions $v^i{}_1(\boldsymbol{\alpha})$ can now be found by differentiating implicitly with respect to h, setting $h = 0$, and using the fact that $\mathbf{f}(\boldsymbol{\alpha}, 0) = \boldsymbol{\alpha}$.

This gives for $v^1{}_1$

$$\sec^2 \alpha_1 \, v^1{}_1(\alpha) = \frac{a_{12}a_{23} - a_{13}a_{22}}{a_{23}^2} = \frac{a_{31}}{a_{23}^2}$$

or, from (6), $v^1{}_1(\alpha) = \sin\gamma/\sin\beta$. We were able to write $a_{12}a_{23} - a_{22}a_{13} = a_{31}$ since, if the columns of R are denoted by **i**, **j**, and **k**, we know that $\mathbf{i} \times \mathbf{j} = \mathbf{k}$, $\mathbf{j} \times \mathbf{k} = \mathbf{i}$, and $\mathbf{k} \times \mathbf{i} = \mathbf{j}$. In particular, $a_{12}a_{23} - a_{22}a_{13} = (\mathbf{j} \times \mathbf{k})_Z = \mathbf{i}_Z = a_{31}$. Differentiating $\cos f^2$ and $\tan f^3$ in a similar way we find

$$-\sin \alpha_2 \, v^2{}_1 = -a_{32},$$

or,

$$v^2{}_1 = \cos\gamma$$

and

$$\sec^2\alpha_3 \, v^3{}_1 = \frac{-a_{31}a_{33}}{a_{32}^2}$$

or

$$v^3{}_1 = -\sin\gamma\cot\beta.$$

A similar calculation with $h_1 = h_3 = 0$ yields the results:

$$v^1{}_2 = \frac{\cos\gamma}{\sin\beta},$$

$$v^2{}_2 = -\sin\gamma,$$

$$v^3{}_2 = -\cos\gamma\cot\beta.$$

In the case that $h_1 = h_2 = 0$ the results are

$$v^1{}_3 = v^2{}_3 = 0$$

$$v^3{}_3 = 1.$$

The last results can be obtained by observing that $B(0, 0, h_3)$ describes, in first-order, a rotation about the z axis by h and that the product RB is, therefore, $Z(\alpha_1)X(\alpha_2)Z(\alpha_3)Z(h) = Z(\alpha_1)X(\alpha_2)Z(\alpha_3 + h)$. The Euler angles of the product are, therefore, α_1, α_2, $\alpha_3 + h$ and the results for $v^i{}_3$ follow immediately. We can summarize the results by writing

$$v^i{}_j(\alpha) = \begin{pmatrix} \sin\gamma\csc\beta & \cos\gamma\csc\beta & 0 \\ \cos\gamma & -\sin\gamma & 0 \\ -\sin\gamma\cot\beta & -\cos\gamma\cot\beta & 1 \end{pmatrix} \tag{9.13}$$

where $v^i{}_j(\alpha)$ is the element in row i and column j.

The determinant of the matrix in (13) is observed to be $-\csc\beta$. The weight function for invariant group integration has been found to be the reciprocal of this determinant and is, therefore, $-\sin\beta$. The fact that the weight function is negative is rather disconcerting. This difficulty arises because the parametrization in the Euler angles is singular at e and there is no unique prescription for carrying the coordinates **h** into the coordinates α. Another manifestation of this difficulty is that $w(e) = 0$. This shows that an attempt to evaluate w by (5.9) would necessarily fail since it was assumed in the derivation of (5.9) that $w(e) = 1$. Since it is desirable that the weight function be positive we arbitrarily change the sign and write

$$w(\alpha, \beta, \gamma) = \sin\beta. \tag{9.14}$$

This sign change can be justified by permuting the rows of (1.3) since there is no a priori ordering of the Euler angles.

9-3 THE HOMOMORPHISM OF SU(2) ONTO O(3)$^+$

The Lie algebra of O(3) is known to be composed of all skew-symmetric 3×3 matrices with real elements. A matrix of this form can be expressed as a linear combination of the matrices **i**, **j**, **k** of equation (4.50). Since these matrices satisfy the same commutation relations (up to a factor) as the matrices I_x, I_y, I_z of (8.7) the groups O(3) and SU(2) must be locally isomorphic. It will now be shown that there is a homomorphic mapping of SU(2) onto the group O(3)$^+$.

We consider for each point in space with coordinates (x, y, z) the matrix

$$P(x, y, z) = \begin{pmatrix} ix & ix - y \\ ix + y & -iz \end{pmatrix}. \tag{9.15}$$

The matrix P(x, y, z) can be expressed in the form $xI_x + yI_y + zI_z$ where I_x, I_y, and I_z are the matrices defined in equation (8.7). It is observed that P is a skew-Hermitian matrix and has determinant

$x^2 + y^2 + z^2$. It is also true that any 2×2 skew-Hermitian matrix with zero trace can be expressed in the form (15) for a suitable choice of x, y, z.

We consider now, for an arbitrary matrix $A \varepsilon SU(2)$ the matrix P' defined by

$$P' = APA^{-1} = APA^{\dagger}. \tag{9.16}$$

It if observed that $P'^{\dagger} = AP^{\dagger}A^{\dagger} = -APA^{\dagger} = -P^{\dagger}$ so that P' is skew-Hermitian. Furthermore, $Tr(P') = Tr(P) = 0$ by the trace invariance property. It is, therefore, possible to write

$$P' = \begin{pmatrix} iz' & ix' - y' \\ ix' + y' & -iz' \end{pmatrix}.$$

It follows from the form of (16) that the numbers x', y', z' are linear functions of x, y, z. It can, furthermore, be seen that the determinant of P' is equal to the determinant of P, since $|APA^{-1}| = |A||P||A^{-1}| = |P|$. This result implies that

$$x'^2 + y'^2 + z'^2 = x^2 + y^2 + z^2$$

and that the linear transformation on x, y, z generated by (16) is in fact a rotation. We conclude that for each $A \varepsilon SU(2)$ there is a corresponding rotation $f(A) \varepsilon O(3)^+$.

The mapping f is a homomorphism since, if A_1 and A_2 are any two elements of SU(2), $f(A_1A_2)$ is the rotation generated by transforming P to $A_1A_2P(A_1A_2)^{-1} = A_1(A_2PA_2^{-1})A_1^{-1}$. This is, however, the transformation generated by transforming P first by A_2 and then by A_1; the resulting rotation is that obtained by rotating first by $f(A_2)$ and then by $f(A_1)$ or $f(A_1A_2) = f(A_1)f(A_2)$.

It will now be shown that each proper rotation is the image under f of the same element in SU(2). This is proved by exhibiting explicitly elements of SU(2) that generate rotations by an arbitrary angle about the x and z axes. We will require the following multiplication laws of the matrices I_x, I_y, I_z.

$$I_xI_y = -I_yI_x = I_z$$

$$I_yI_z = -I_zI_y = I_x$$

$$I_zI_x = -I_xI_z = I_y.$$

We consider now the matrix

$$A(0,\ \phi,\ 0) = \begin{pmatrix} e^{i\phi} & 0 \\ 0 & e^{-i\phi} \end{pmatrix} = \cos\ \phi + \sin\ \phi\, I_z.$$

It is apparent that this matrix commutes with I_z so that

$$A(0,\ \phi,\ 0)PA(0,\ \phi,\ 0)^\dagger = x'I_x + y'I_y + zI_z.$$

Since z is unchanged, $A(0, \phi, 0)$ evidently generates a rotation about the z axis. We can calculate explicitly

$$(\cos\ \phi + \sin\ \phi\ I_z)(xI_x + yI_y + zI_z)(\cos\ \phi - \sin\ \phi\, I_z)$$

$$= zI_z + [(\cos^2\phi - \sin^2\phi)\ x - 2\sin\ \phi\cos\ \phi\, y]I_x$$

$$+ [2\sin\ \phi\cos\ \phi\, x + (\cos^2\phi - \sin^2\phi) y]I_y$$

$$= (\cos\ 2\phi\ x - \sin\ 2\phi\ y)I_x + (\sin\ 2\phi\ x + \cos\ 2\phi\ y)I_y + zI_z.$$

This result indicates that

$$x' = \cos\ 2\phi\, x - \sin\ 2\phi\, y,$$

$$y' = \sin\ 2\phi\, x + \cos\ 2\phi\ y,$$

$$z' = z,$$

and that $A(0, \phi, 0)$ generates a rotation about the z axis by 2ϕ. It can be shown in the same way that the matrix

$$A(\theta,\ 0,\ 0) = \begin{pmatrix} \cos\ \theta & i\sin\ \theta \\ i\sin\ \theta & \cos\ \theta \end{pmatrix} = \cos\ \theta\ I + \sin\ \theta\ I_x$$

generates a rotation by 2θ about the x axis.

Since an arbitrary proper rotation $R(\alpha, \beta, \gamma)$ can be expressed in the form $Z(\alpha)\ X(\beta)\ Z(\gamma)$, it can be generated by the element $A(0, \alpha/2, 0)\ A(\beta/2, 0, 0)\ A(0, \gamma/2, 0)$ in SU(2). This element can be written

$$\begin{pmatrix} e^{i\alpha/2} & 0 \\ 0 & e^{-i\alpha/2} \end{pmatrix}\begin{pmatrix} \cos\frac{\beta}{2} & i\sin\frac{\beta}{2} \\ i\sin\frac{\beta}{2} & \cos\frac{\beta}{2} \end{pmatrix}\begin{pmatrix} e^{i\gamma/2} & 0 \\ 0 & e^{-i\gamma/2} \end{pmatrix}$$

$$= \begin{pmatrix} e^{i(\alpha+\gamma)/2}\cos\frac{\beta}{2} & i\,e^{i(\alpha-\gamma)/2}\sin\frac{\beta}{2} \\ i\,e^{-i(\alpha-\gamma)/2}\sin\frac{\beta}{2} & i^{-i(\alpha+\gamma)/2}\cos\frac{\beta}{2} \end{pmatrix}$$

$$= A\left(\frac{\beta}{2}, \frac{\alpha+\gamma}{2}, \frac{\alpha-\gamma}{2}\right). \qquad (9.17)$$

It is important to observe that the mapping f of SU(2) onto $O(3)^+$ is not an isomorphism; since $APA^{-1} = (-A)P(-A)^{-1}$ it is immediately apparent that f(A) = f(-A) and that the mapping f cannot be isomorphic. It is important to calculate the kernel of f, that is, the set of elements $A \in SU(2)$ that satisfy f(A) = I. In order that f(A) = I, it is necessary that A satisfy $APA^{-1} = P$ or AP = PA for all matrices P of the form (15). In particular, the matrices I_x and I_z must commute with A. It can be observed from (8.6) and (8.7) that an arbitrary matrix A can be written $\cos\theta\cos\phi + \cos\theta\sin\phi\, I_z + \sin\theta\cos\psi\, I_x + \sin\theta \sin\psi\, I_y$. In order that this commute with I_z it is necessary that

$$-\sin\theta\cos\psi\, I_y + \sin\theta\sin\psi\, I_x = 0$$

which implies $\sin\theta = 0$ and $\cos\theta = 1$. The requirement that $\cos\phi + \sin\phi\, I_z$ commute with I_x implies that $\sin\phi = 0$ and $\cos\phi = \pm 1$. We can conclude that the kernel of the homomorphism consists of the matrices I and -I. This subgroup is denoted by Z_2.

To conclude this discussion, we can state that the group $O(3)^+$ is isomorphic to the factor group $SU(2)/Z_2$. The elements of this group are the cosets of Z_2 consisting of pairs of elements of SU(2) which differ only in sign.

9-4 REPRESENTATIONS OF THE ROTATION GROUP

Certain of the representations $D^j(A)_{mn}$ of SU(2) given by equation (8.11) also provide representations of the group $O(3)^+$. In order that this occur it is sufficient that $D^j(A) = D(-A)$; in this case each element of a coset of Z_2 is represented by the same matrix. The $D^j(A)$, therefore, provide a representation of $SU(2)/Z_2$, and hence, also of $O(3)^+$. If the parameters of A are θ, ϕ, ψ the parameters of -A are θ, $\phi \pm \pi$, $\psi \pm \pi$. Inspection of (8.11) shows that $D^j(A) = D^j(-A)$ if

$$e^{\pm i(m+n)\pi}\, e^{\pm i(n-m)\pi} = 1. \qquad (9.18)$$

The left-hand side of (18) is one of $e^{\pm 2in\pi}$, $e^{\pm 2im\pi}$. If j is an integer m and n are each integers and (18) is satisfied; if j = 1/2, 3/2, ...,

2m and 2n are each odd and $D^j(-A) = -D^j(A)$. It can be concluded that the matrices $D^j(A)$ can be used to construct representations of $O(3)^+$ provided j is an integer.

The representations can be obtained immediately by substituting $\theta = \beta/2$, $\phi = (\alpha + \gamma)/2$, $\psi = (\alpha - \gamma)/2$ into (8.11). The result is

$$D^l(\alpha, \beta, \gamma)_{mn} = i^{m-n} e^{-im\alpha} e^{-in\gamma}$$

$$\times \sum_t (-1)^t \frac{[(l + m)!(l - m)!(l + n)!(l - n)!]^{1/2}}{(l + m - t)!(t + n - m)!t!(l - n - t)!}$$

$$\times \cos^{2l+m-n-2t} \frac{\beta}{2} \sin^{2t+n-m} \frac{\beta}{2}$$

$$= i^{m-n} e^{-im\alpha} d^l_{mn}(\beta) e^{-in\gamma} \tag{9.19}$$

where

$$d^l_{mn}(\beta) = \sum_t (-1)^t \frac{[(l + m)!(l - m)!(l + n)!(l - n)!]^{1/2}}{(l + m - t)!(t + n - m)!t!(l - n - t)!}$$

$$\times \cos^{2l+m-n-2t} \frac{\beta}{2} \sin^{2t+n-m} \frac{\beta}{2}. \tag{9.20}$$

It should be pointed out that we have used the symbol D to denote two different functions defined by (19) and (8.11). This should, however, give rise to no confusion.

The representations $D^l(R)$ are unitary and irreducible since they are unitary and irreducible as representations of SU(2). They also exhaust the irreducible representations of $O(3)^+$, since any other irreducible representation would give rise to an irreducible representation of SU(2) with the property that D(A) = D(-A). It is known, however, that the only irreducible representations with this property are the $D^j(A)$, j an integer.

It can be seen from (8.13) and $(8.20)\frac{1}{w}(8.22)$ that, in the special cases $m = \pm l$, or $n = \pm l$, the functions $d^l_{mn}(\beta)$ are given by

$$d^l_{-ln}(\beta) = \left(\frac{2l}{l+n}\right)^{1/2} \cos^{l-n}\frac{\beta}{2} \sin^{l+n}\frac{\beta}{2},$$

$$d^l_{ln}(\beta) = (-1)^{l-n}\left(\frac{2l}{l+n}\right)^{1/2} \cos^{l+n}\frac{\beta}{2} \sin^{l-n}\frac{\beta}{2},$$

$$d^l_{m-l}(\beta) = (-1)^{l+m}\left(\frac{2l}{l+m}\right)^{1/2} \cos^{l-m}\frac{\beta}{2} \sin^{l+m}\frac{\beta}{2}, \tag{9.21}$$

$$d^l_{ml}(\beta) = \left(\frac{2l}{l+m}\right)^{1/2} \cos^{l+m}\frac{\beta}{2} \sin^{l-m}\frac{\beta}{2}.$$

The representation $D^1(\alpha, \beta, \gamma)$ can be calculated to be

$$\begin{pmatrix} e^{i(\alpha+\gamma)}\dfrac{1+\cos\beta}{2} & -ie^{i\alpha}\dfrac{\sin\beta}{\sqrt{2}} & -e^{i(\alpha-\gamma)}\dfrac{1-\cos\beta}{2} \\ -ie^{i\gamma}\dfrac{\sin\beta}{\sqrt{2}} & \cos\beta & -ie^{-i\gamma}\dfrac{\sin\beta}{\sqrt{2}} \\ -e^{i(\gamma-\alpha)}\dfrac{1-\cos\beta}{2} & -ie^{-i\alpha}\dfrac{\sin\beta}{\sqrt{2}} & e^{-i(\alpha+\gamma)}\dfrac{1+\cos\beta}{2} \end{pmatrix}. \tag{9.22}$$

It can be observed from (22) that rotations about the z axis are represented by diagonal matrices. This is in general the case; it follows immediately from (8.12) that

$$D^{l}(\alpha, 0, \gamma)_{mn} = e^{-i(\alpha+\gamma)m}\,\delta_{mn}. \tag{9.23a}$$

The group element $R(\alpha, 0, \gamma)$ is, of course, a rotation about the z axis by $\alpha + \gamma$. Rotations about the x axis are represented by

$$D^{l}(0, \beta, 0)_{mn} = i^{m-n} d^{l}{}_{mn}(\beta). \tag{9.23b}$$

It is not difficult to see that a rotation about the y axis by an angle β can be generated by rotating first about the z axis by $-\pi/2$, rotating about the x axis by β and then rotating about the z axis by $\pi/2$. The rotation is, therefore, represented by

$$D^{l}\left(\frac{\pi}{2}, \beta, -\frac{\pi}{2}\right)_{mn} = d^{l}{}_{mn}(\beta). \tag{9.23c}$$

The representation (19) differs from that frequently given in that it includes an additional factor of i^{m-n}. This has been included to compensate for the fact that the Euler angles have been defined in the classical way so that the second rotation is about the x axis rather than about the y axis as is the case in most quantum-mechanical applications. The present results relations can be transcribed to the usual quantum-mechanical phase conventions by deleting the factor i^{m-n}, and regarding a rotation about the x axis as being about the y axis and a rotation about the y axis as a negative rotation about the x axis. The phases of the spherical harmonics, to be discussed in the next section, conform to the usual convention because of the inclusion of the extra factor i^{m-n}.

9-5 HARMONIC POLYNOMIALS AND REPRESENTATIONS OF O(3)+

Another possible method of constructing representations of the rotation group is to consider homogeneous polynomials of fixed degree in the variables x, y, and z. The methods described in Section 6–9 can be applied to construct representations in the invariant subspaces of such functions. This method, which was used successfully in Section 8–2, is less satisfactory for the present problem since it does not generate irreducible representations. This method will, however, be discussed in this section to demonstrate the relation between the group representations obtained in the previous section and the important functions, the spherical harmonics.

We consider the space S_l of homogeneous polynomials of degree l in the variables x, y, z. This space is spanned by the monomials of the form $x^m y^n z^{l-m-n}$. There are

$$\sum_{m=0}^{l} \sum_{n=0}^{l-m} 1 = \sum_{m=0}^{l} (l - m + 1) = \frac{(l+2)(l+1)}{2}$$

such monomials, which are clearly linearly independent, so that S_l is of dimension $(l+2)(l+1)/2$. The representations defined by S_l must be reducible since S_l contains an invariant subspace, the space S_{l-2} of all polynomials of the form $(x^2 + y^2 + z^2)P_{l-2}$ where P_{l-2} is a polynomial of degree $l-2$. Since the group is orthogonal, the function $x^2 + y^2 + z^2$ is invariant under the group transformations and S_{l-2} is an invariant subspace (of dimension $l(l-1)/2$). The representation defined by S_l can be assumed to be unitary, in which case the subspace $S_{l-2}^{\perp}$ orthogonal to S_{l-2} is also invariant. This subspace is of dimension $(l+2)(l+1)/2 - l(l-1)/2 = 2l + 1$. This invariant subspace is rather nebulous since no inner product has been defined on S_l. It is possible, however, to construct a $(2l+1)$-dimensional invariant subspace of S_l in another way. We consider the mapping of S_l onto S_{l-2} defined by

$$P_l(\mathbf{x}) \rightarrow P_{l-2}(\mathbf{x}) = \nabla^2 P_l(\mathbf{x})$$

where the image of P_l is obviously in S_{l-2}. It is convenient to denote the points whose coordinates are (x, y, z) by **x**. It will now be shown that, for any rotation R,

$$\nabla^2[P_l(R^{-1}\mathbf{x})] = P_{l-2}(R^{-1}\mathbf{x}) \tag{9.24}$$

where $P_{l-2}(\mathbf{x}) = \nabla^2 P_l(\mathbf{x})$. We will denote $R^{-1}\mathbf{x}$ by $\mathbf{x}'$. If the elements of R are a_{ij}, the component j of $\mathbf{x}'$ is given by $\Sigma_i a_{ij} x_i$. We can now write

$$\begin{aligned}\sum_i \frac{\partial^2}{\partial x_i^2} P_l(R^{-1}\mathbf{x}) &= \sum_{ijk} \frac{\partial^2 P_l}{\partial x_j' \, \partial x_k'}(\mathbf{x}') \frac{\partial x_j'}{\partial x_i} \frac{\partial x_k'}{\partial x_i} \\ &= \sum_{ijk} a_{ij} a_{ik} \frac{\partial^2 P_l}{\partial x_j' \, \partial x_k'}(\mathbf{x}') \\ &= \sum_j \frac{\partial^2 P_l}{\partial x_j'^2}(\mathbf{x}') \\ &= P_{l-2}(R^{-1}\mathbf{x}).\end{aligned}$$

The implication of this result is that the mapping ∇^2 from S_l onto S_{l-2} satisfies

$$\nabla^2 D^l(R) = D^{l-2}(R)\nabla^2 \tag{9.25}$$

where the $D^l(R)$ are defined by equation (6.42).

We consider now the subspace H_l of S_l composed of polynomials P_l satisfying

$$\nabla^2 P_l = 0. \tag{9.26}$$

A function satisfying this equation, which is Laplace's equation, is said to be harmonic. It follows immediately from (25) that H_l is invariant; if $\nabla^2 P_l = 0$, $\nabla^2 D^l(R) P_l = D^{l-2}(R)\nabla^2 P_l = 0$ and $D^l(R)P_l$ is also harmonic. It will now be shown that the representation of the rotation group generated by H_l, the set of harmonic polynomials of degree l, is equivalent to the representation $D^l(R)$ defined by (19).

It is possible to obtain $2l + 1$ linearly independent solutions of (26) explicitly. For this purpose it is convenient to introduce new variables $u = (x + iy)/2$, $v = (x - iy)/2$ in terms of which (26) becomes

$$\frac{\partial^2 P_l}{\partial u \, \partial v} + \frac{\partial^2 P_l}{\partial z^2} = 0. \tag{9.27}$$

If P_l is a homogeneous polynomial of degree l in u, v, and z it is also a homogeneous polynomial of degree l in x, y, and z. It is possible to write down four solutions of (27), u^l, v^l, $u^{l-1}z$, $v^{l-1}z$ immediately. More generally, we look for a solution that contains a term of the form $u^{l-m}v^m$, $m = 0, 1, \ldots, l$. This is not a solution since

$$\nabla^2 u^{l-m} v^m = (l-m)m\, u^{l-m-1} v^{m-1}.$$

It is possible to eliminate the right-hand side by adding to $u^{l-m}v^m$ a term $(-1)(l-m)mu^{l-m-1}v^{m-1}z^2/2$. One then obtains

$$\nabla^2\left[u^{l-m}v^m - \frac{(l-m)m\, u^{l-m-1}v^{m-1}z^2}{2}\right] = -\frac{(l-m)(l-m-1)m(m-1)u^{l-m-2}v^{m-2}z^2}{2}.$$

It is now possible to add a third term, $(l-m)(l-m-1)m(m-1)$ $u^{l-m-2}v^{m-2}z^4/4!$ to eliminate the new term on the right-hand side. Proceeding in this way one eventually obtains a harmonic polynomial of degree l which can be written

$$f_{lm}(u,v,z) = \sum_p (-1)^p \frac{(l-m)!m!}{(l-m-p)!(m-p)!(2p)!} u^{l-m-p}\, v^{m-p}\, z^{2p} \qquad (9.28)$$

The sum on p is from 0 to the smaller of m and $l-m$. It can be verified by direct substitution into (27) that f_{lm} is a harmonic polynomial. The functions f_{lm} have the further property, which will prove to be important, that the difference of the exponents of u and v, $l-2m$, is the same for each term. We note that there are $(l+1)$ functions f_{lm}.

In a similar way, it is possible to find solutions that contain a term $u^{l-m}v^{m-1}z$, where $m = 1, 2, \ldots, l$. These solutions can be written

$$g_{lm} = \sum_p (-1)^p \frac{(l-m)!(m-1)!}{(l-m-p)!(m-p-1)!(2p+1)!} \times u^{l-m-p}\, v^{m-p-1}\, z^{2p+1}. \qquad (9.29)$$

In this case the index p runs from 0 to the smaller of $m-1$ and $l-m$. There are l such solutions with the property that the difference of the exponents of u and v is $l-2m+1$ for each term in the sum.

There are altogether $(2l+1)$ functions f_{lm}, g_{lm}. These can be labeled by an index s, $s = -l, -l+1, \ldots, l-1, l$, s being the difference of the exponents of u and v in each term of a particular function. These functions will be denoted by k_{ls}. The functions k_{ls} are obviously linearly independent since no two of them can contain the same monomial. It can also be seen that the functions k_{ls} span H_l. Let $P_l(x)$ be a harmonic polynomial of degree l. Consider a term $u^p v^q z^{l-p-q}$ in P_l; it can be seen from (27) that the coefficient of every term in P_l of the form $u^{p-m} v^{q-m} z^{l-p-q+2m}$ is uniquely determined by the coefficient of $u^p v^q z^{l-p-q}$. In fact, all the terms of this form must occur as a constant multiple of $k_{l,p-q}$, and can be removed by subtracting $ck_{l,p-q}$ from P_l for some c. It is, therefore, apparent that P_l can be expressed as a linear combination of the k_{ls}.

The functions k_{ls} generate, by equation (6.44), a representation of the proper rotation group. This representation will be denoted by $\Delta^l(R)$. We will not calculate $\Delta^l(R)$ explicitly but rather show that it is equivalent to the representation $D^l(R)$ defined by (19). It will be shown first that $\Delta^l(R)$ is diagonal if R is a rotation by an angle ϕ about the z axis. Under the inverse of such a rotation, x is transformed to $\cos\phi\ x + \sin\ \ y$, y is transformed to $-\sin\phi\ x + \cos\phi\ y$, and z is unchanged. It follows that u is transformed to $(\cos\phi\ x + \sin\phi\ y) + i(-\sin\phi\ x + \cos\phi\ y) = e^{-i\phi}\ x + ie^{-i\phi}\ y = e^{-i\phi}\ u$. Similarly, $v = u^*$ is transformed to $e^{i\phi}v$. It follows that a monomial of the form $u^\alpha v^\beta z^\gamma$ is transformed to $e^{i(\beta-\alpha)\phi}\ u^\alpha v^\beta z^\gamma$, and hence that

$$k_{ls}(R^{-1}\mathbf{x}) = c^{-is\phi} k_{ls}(\mathbf{x})$$

since each term of k_{ls} is multiplied by the same factor $e^{-is\phi}$. From (6.44) we can write, for R a rotation by ϕ about the z axis,

$$\Delta^l(R)_{st} = e^{-is\phi}\,\delta_{st}. \tag{9.30}$$

Each class of the rotation group has been shown to contain a rotation about the z axis. Comparison of (23a) and (30) shows that rotations about the z axis are represented by the same matrices in D and Δ; the characters of the two representations are, therefore, the same and the representations are equivalent.

We consider now the matrix M that transforms $D^l(R)$ to $\Delta^l(R)$:

$$M^{-1}\Delta^l(R)M = D^l(R) \tag{9.31}$$

for all R. If R is, in particular, a rotation about the z axis, $\Delta^l(R) = D^l(R)$ and M satisfies $MD^l(R) = D^l(R)M$. In this case $D^l(R)$ is, however, diagonal with diagonal elements which are in general different. It has been seen previously that this implies M is diagonal; the matrix elements of M will, therefore, be denoted by $\mu_i\delta_{ij}$.

Equation (31) can now be written

$$\Delta^l(R)_{mn} = \mu_m D^l(R)_{mn}\mu_n^{-1}. \tag{9.32}$$

The functions $k_{ls}(\mathbf{x})$ and the representations $\Delta^l(R)$ are related by

$$k_{lt}(R^{-1}\mathbf{x}) = \sum_s \Delta^l(R)_{st} k_{ls}(\mathbf{x}).$$

Substituting (32) into this relation yields the result

$$\mu_t k_{lt}(R^{-1}\mathbf{x}) = \sum_s D^l(R)_{st}\mu_s k_{ls}(\mathbf{x}). \tag{9.33}$$

It can be concluded that the representation $D^l(R)_{st}$ that was obtained in equation (19) is also the representation generated by the harmonic polynomials $\mu_s k_{ls}(\mathbf{x})$. We will, henceforth, consider these functions rather than the functions f and g defined in equations (28) and (29), from which they differ by an undetermined factor.

The coordinates of the point $\mathbf{x}$ can be expressed in spherical polar coordinates as $x = r\sin\theta\cos\phi$, $y = r\sin\theta\sin\phi$, $z = r\cos\theta$. If the functions $\mu_m k_{lm}(\mathbf{x})$ are written in terms of these coordinates it is evident that they have the form $r^l Y_{lm}(\theta, \phi)$ where $Y_{lm}(\theta, \phi)$ is a polynomial in $\sin\theta$, $\cos\theta$, $\sin\phi$, $\cos\phi$. The functions Y_{lm} are the important <u>spherical harmonics</u>. Since $r^l Y_{lm}(\theta, \phi)$ must satisfy Laplace's equation in spherical polar coordinates, the spherical harmonics must satisfy

$$\frac{1}{\sin\theta}\frac{\partial}{\partial\theta}\sin\theta\,\frac{\partial Y_{lm}}{\partial\theta} + \frac{1}{\sin^2\theta}\frac{\partial^2 Y_{lm}}{\partial\varphi^2} + l(l+1)Y_{lm} = 0. \tag{9.34}$$

It will now be shown that for fixed l the spherical harmonics are determined up to an arbitrary constant by equation (33). We denote by (θ, ϕ) and (θ', ϕ') the angular coordinates of the points $\mathbf{x}$ and $R^{-1}\mathbf{x}$ respectively. In terms of the spherical harmonics (33) becomes

$$Y_{lm}(\theta', \phi') = \sum_n D^l(R)_{nm} Y_{ln}(\theta, \phi). \tag{9.35}$$

If R is a rotation about the z axis by α the angles (θ', ϕ') are simply $(\theta, \phi - \alpha)$. Using equation (23a), we can write (35) as

$$Y_{lm}(\theta, \varphi - \alpha) = e^{-im\alpha} Y_{lm}(\theta, \phi).$$

Putting $\phi = 0$ and changing the sign of α, we obtain

$$Y_{lm}(\theta, \alpha) = e^{im\alpha} Y_{lm}(\theta, 0), \tag{9.36}$$

indicating that the only dependence of Y_{lm} on the azimuthal angle is in the factor $e^{im\alpha}$.

In the direction of the positive z axis the spherical harmonics must be independent of the azimuthal angle, that is, $Y_{lm}(0, \alpha) = Y_{lm}(0, 0)$. If $m \neq 0$, however, this can only be the case if $Y_{lm}(0, 0) = 0$ in view of the known dependence of Y_{lm} on the azimuthal angle. On the other hand $Y_{lo}(0, 0) \neq 0$ since otherwise the spherical harmonics would vanish identically. The value of $Y_{lo}(0, 0)$ will be chosen arbitrarily to be 1 so that

$$Y_{lm}(0, \phi) = \delta_{mo}. \tag{9.37}$$

We now put $\theta = \phi = 0$ in (35) and replace R by R^{-1}; the result is, since $D^l(R^{-1})_{nm} = D^l(R)^*_{mn}$

$$Y_{lm}(\theta', \phi') = D^l(R)^*_{mo}$$

where θ', ϕ' are the polar angles of the direction into which R rotates the z axis. The rotation $Z(\alpha + \pi/2)X(\beta)$ is known from the definition of the Euler angles to rotate the vector **k** parallel to the z axis into the direction whose angular coordinates are (β, α). We can, therefore, write,

$$Y_{lm}(\beta, \alpha) = D^l\left(\alpha + \frac{\pi}{2}, \beta, 0\right)^*_{mo} \tag{9.38}$$

or

$$Y_{lm}(\theta, \phi) = e^{im\phi} d^l{}_{mo}(\theta). \tag{9.39}$$

This result will be applied to obtain various properties of the spherical harmonics.

9-6 DIFFERENTIAL EQUATIONS FOR THE GROUP REPRESENTATIONS

It was shown in Section 6-10 that the representations of a Lie group must satisfy the partial differential equations (6.52). In this section we will obtain these equations for the representations $D^l(R)$ of the rotation group. This task is again complicated by the singularity in the Euler angle coordinate system at the identity, so that the representation of the Lie algebra of the group cannot be obtained by straightforward differentiation of the group representations. It is possible to obtain the representations of the algebra in this way, but it is somewhat instructive to calculate them in part from first principles, and this course will be followed.

A group element in the neighborhood of the identity can be written in first order in the form (10). The matrix $B(h_1, 0, 0)$ represents in first order a rotation by h_1 about the x axis. We will, therefore, denote by J_x the matrix

$$J_x = \frac{\partial B}{\partial h_1}(0) = \begin{pmatrix} 0 & 0 & 0 \\ 0 & 0 & -1 \\ 0 & 1 & 0 \end{pmatrix}.$$

Similarly, we write

$$J_y = \frac{\partial B}{\partial h_2}(0) = \begin{pmatrix} 0 & 0 & 1 \\ 0 & 0 & 0 \\ -1 & 0 & 0 \end{pmatrix}$$

$$J_z = \frac{\partial B}{\partial h_3}(0) = \begin{pmatrix} 0 & -1 & 0 \\ 1 & 0 & 0 \\ 0 & 0 & 0 \end{pmatrix}.$$

It is observed that these are the matrices of equation (4.50) and, therefore, satisfy

$$[J_x, J_y] = J_z, \quad [J_y, J_z] = J_x, \quad [J_z, J_x] = J_y. \tag{9.40}$$

The matrices that represent the Lie algebra will also be denoted, at a slight risk of confusion, by J_x, J_y, J_z. Since we wish the representation to correspond to the $D^l(R)$, we look for a representation by skew-Hermitian matrices in which J_z is diagonal. In fact,

$$(J_z)_{mn} = \frac{\partial D^l}{\partial \gamma}(0)_{mn} = -im\delta_{mn}, \tag{9.41}$$

or

$$J_z = i\begin{pmatrix} l & 0. & . & . & 0 \\ 0 & l-1. & . & . & 0 \\ . & . & & & . \\ 0 & 0. & . & . & -l \end{pmatrix}. \tag{9.42}$$

It is convenient to introduce matrices $M = J_x + iJ_y$ and $N = -M^\dagger = J_x - iJ_y$. It is easy to verify from (40) that

$$[M, J_z] = iM \tag{9.43a}$$

$$[N, J_z] = -iN \tag{9.43b}$$

$$[M, N] = -2iJ_z. \tag{9.43c}$$

Equation (43a) is, in explicit component form,

$$-i(M_{mn}n - mM_{mn}) = iM_{mn}$$

or

$$(n - m + 1)M_{mn} = 0.$$

This shows that M_{mn} vanishes unless $n = m - 1$ and, therefore, that M has nonzero elements only immediately below the main diagonal. We can, therefore, write for $-l \leq n \leq l - 1$

$$M_{mn} = \lambda_n \delta_{m-1n} \cdot \tag{9.44}$$

Since $N = -M^\dagger$, N has nonzero elements only immediately above the main diagonal, and we can write

$$N_{mn} = -M^*_{nm} = -\lambda^*_m \delta_{n-1m} = -\lambda^*_{n-1} \delta_{m+1n}. \tag{9.45}$$

Equation (43c) can be used to obtain a recurrence relation for the numbers λ_n; the diagonal elements of each side of (43c) are given by, from (41), (44) and (45),

$$|\lambda_n|^2 - |\lambda_{n-1}|^2 = -2n \tag{9.46}$$

unless $n = \pm l$. In these cases, one obtains $|\lambda_{l-1}|^2 = 2l$ and $|\lambda_{-l}|^2 = 2l$. We will define arbitrarily $\lambda_{-l-1} = \lambda_l = 0$ so that these are special cases of (46).

Equation (46) has solutions of the form $|\lambda_n|^2 = c - n(n+1)$ where c is an arbitrary constant. The condition $\lambda_l = 0$ (or $\lambda_{-l-1} = 0$) determines c to be $l(l+1)$, and hence,

$$|\lambda_n|^2 = l(l+1) - n(n+1) = (l-n)(l+n+1). \tag{9.47}$$

Equation (47) determines the matrix elements λ_n up to an arbitrary phase factor; they cannot be determined further from the commutation relations, however, since it is possible to transform J_z, M, and N by an arbitrary diagonal unitary matrix. This does not affect J_z, but can change the phase of any element of M.

To proceed further it is necessary to refer back to the explicit representations given by equations (19) and (20). The element J_x is given by $(M+N)/2$. This has nonzero elements only immediately above and below the main diagonal, and it can be seen by inspection of (19) that these elements are pure imaginary, and hence, that

$$\lambda_n = \pm i\,[(l-n)(l+n+1)]^{1/2}. \tag{9.48}$$

The sign in (48) is still ambiguous and can only be determined by differentiating (19) with respect to β and evaluating the result at $\alpha = \beta = \gamma = 0$. One finds that

$$(J_x)_{mm-1} = -\frac{i}{2}[(l+m)(l-m+1)]^{1/2}$$

$$(J_x)_{mm+1} = -\frac{i}{2}[(l-m)(l+m+1)]^{1/2}$$

showing that the sign in (48) should be chosen negative. It can be concluded that the elements of the matrices M and N are given by

$$M_{mn} = -i[(l-n)(l+n+1)]^{1/2}\delta_{m-1n} \tag{9.49a}$$

$$N_{mn} = -i[(l+n)(l-n+1)]^{1/2}\delta_{m+1n}. \tag{9.49b}$$

The matrices J_x and J_y can now be expressed as $(M+N)/2$ and $(M-N)/2i$ respectively. They are explicitly

$$J_x = -\frac{i}{2}\begin{pmatrix} 0 & \sqrt{(2l)\cdot 1} & 0 & & & \\ \sqrt{(2l)\cdot 1} & 0 & \sqrt{(2l-2)\cdot 2} & 0 & & \\ 0 & \sqrt{(2l-1)\cdot 2} & 0 & \sqrt{(2l-2)\cdot 3} & & \\ & \cdot & \cdot & \cdot & & \\ & & & & 0 & \sqrt{(2l)\cdot 1} \\ & & & & \sqrt{(2l)\cdot 1} & 0 \end{pmatrix} \tag{9.50a}$$

$$J_y = \frac{1}{2}\begin{pmatrix} 0 & \sqrt{(2l)\cdot 1} & 0 & & & \\ -\sqrt{(2l)\cdot 1} & 0 & \sqrt{(2l-1)\cdot 2} & 0 & & \\ 0 & -\sqrt{(2l-1)\cdot 2} & 0 & \sqrt{(2l-2)\cdot 3} & & \\ & \cdot & \cdot & \cdot & & \\ & & & & 0 & \sqrt{(2l)\cdot 1} \\ & & & & -\sqrt{(2l)\cdot 1} & 0 \end{pmatrix} \tag{9.50b}$$

It is probably recognized that the theory that has been developed is essentially that of the quantum theory of angular momentum. The only essential difference is that we have assumed the matrix J_z to be known, as given by (42). It can be shown independently and by rather familiar arguments that if J_z is diagonal, the diagonal elements differ by integral multiples of i and run through $-il$, $-(l-1)i$, ..., il where $l = 0, 1/2, 1, \ldots$. The values 1/2, 3/2, ... for l do not pertain to representations of O(3) but rather to representations of SU(2) which we know has the same Lie algebra.

It is now possible to obtain differential equations for the group representations. Equation (11) requires that the group representations should satisfy

$$D(\mathbf{f}(\alpha, \mathbf{h})) = D(\boldsymbol{\alpha})\, D(\mathbf{h}).$$

If this equation is differentiated with respect to h_j and the result evaluated at $\mathbf{h} = 0$, a set of three differential equations corresponding to j = 1, 2, 3 is obtained. The results are, keeping in mind equations (13),

$$\sin\gamma \csc\beta \frac{\partial D}{\partial\alpha} + \cos\gamma \frac{\partial D}{\partial\beta} - \sin\gamma \cot\beta \frac{\partial D}{\partial\gamma} = DJ_x, \qquad (9.51a)$$

$$\cos\gamma \csc\beta \frac{\partial D}{\partial\alpha} - \sin\gamma \frac{\partial D}{\partial\beta} - \cos\gamma \cot\beta \frac{\partial D}{\partial\gamma} = DJ_y, \qquad (9.51b)$$

$$\frac{\partial D}{\partial\gamma} = DJ_z. \qquad (9.51c)$$

It is convenient to combine (51a) and (51b) by multiplying (51b) by ± i and adding to obtain

$$e^{-i\gamma}\left[\frac{\partial}{\partial\beta} + i \csc\beta \frac{\partial}{\partial\alpha} - i \cot\beta \frac{\partial}{\partial\gamma}\right]D = DM, \qquad (9.52)$$

$$e^{i\gamma}\left[\frac{\partial}{\partial\beta} - i \csc\beta \frac{\partial}{\partial\alpha} + i \cot\beta \frac{\partial}{\partial\gamma}\right]D = DN. \qquad (9.53)$$

The differential operators on the left-hand side of equations (51)-(53) constitute a representation of the Lie algebra by differential operators. These operators will be denoted by $\tilde{J}_x$, $\tilde{J}_y$, and so on; for example, $\tilde{J}_z = \partial/\partial\gamma$. They operate on the space of functions defined on the group. It can be shown that they are a representation since, for example, $(\tilde{M}\tilde{N} - \tilde{N}\tilde{M})D = \tilde{M}DN - \tilde{N}DM = D(MN - NM) = -2iDJ_z = -2i\tilde{J}_z D$. This is valid for all the all the irreducible representations, and since the matrix elements of these representations are complete on the group, it is seen that $\tilde{M}\tilde{N} - \tilde{N}\tilde{M} = -2i\tilde{J}_z$, provided the operators are meaningful. (Because the operators are differential, they are not defined for all the functions on the group.)

The above differential equations are complicated by the fact that the various elements of D are coupled in the equations. Moreover, the form of the equations depends on the particular representation of the algebra chosen. It is possible, however, to derive a second-order equation for the irreducible representations in which the matrix elements are uncoupled.

The construction of the second-order equation is based on the observation that the operator $J^2 = J_x^2 + J_y^2 + J_z^2 = J_z^2 + (MN + NM)/2$ commutes with J_x, J_y, J_z, and hence, that $J^2 = \lambda I$ if the representation is irreducible. The operator J^2 is known as a Casimir operator. The value of λ can be determined from equations (41) and (49) to be $-l(l+1)$.

It can now be seen by repeated application of (51c), (52), and (53) that

$$\left[\frac{\tilde{M}\tilde{N} + \tilde{N}\tilde{M}}{2} + \tilde{J}_z^2\right] D^l(R) = D^l(R)J^2 = -l(l+1)D^l(R). \qquad (9.54)$$

The operators $\tilde{M}$ and $\tilde{N}$ are given by

$$\tilde{M} = e^{-i\gamma}\left[\frac{\partial}{\partial\beta} + i \csc\beta \frac{\partial}{\partial\alpha} - i \cot\beta \frac{\partial}{\partial\gamma}\right]$$

$$\tilde{N} = e^{i\gamma}\left[\frac{\partial}{\partial\beta} - i \csc\beta \frac{\partial}{\partial\alpha} + i \cot\beta \frac{\partial}{\partial\gamma}\right].$$

Equation (54) is found after some calculation to be

$$\left\{\frac{1}{\sin\beta}\frac{\partial}{\partial\beta}\sin\beta\frac{\partial}{\partial\beta} + \frac{1}{\sin^2\beta}\left[\frac{\partial^2}{\partial\alpha^2} - 2\cos\beta\frac{\partial^2}{\partial\alpha\partial\gamma} + \frac{\partial^2}{\partial\gamma^2}\right] + l(l+1)\right\} D^l(R) = 0. \qquad (9.55)$$

Equation (55) applies to each element of $D^l(R)$ separately. It should be emphasized that (55) applies only to irreducible representations, whereas equations (51)-(53) govern any representation of the group.

9-7 PROPERTIES OF THE FUNCTIONS $d^l{}_{mn}$

In this section various properties of the functions $d^l{}_{mn}$ defined in equation (20) will be derived using the fact that they are closely related to representations of the rotation group through (19).

The functions $d^l{}_{mn}$ satisfy the symmetry identities

$$d^l{}_{mn}(\beta) = (-1)^{n-m} d^l{}_{-m-n}(\beta) \qquad (9.56)$$

$$d^l{}_{mn}(\beta) = d^l{}_{-n-m}(\beta) \qquad (9.57)$$

which follow readily from (8.18) and (8.19), and the simple relation between representations of SU(2) and O(3). The property (57) is also a simple consequence of (20). Equations (56) and (57) together imply that

$$d^l{}_{mn}(\beta) = (-1)^{m-n} d^l{}_{nm}(\beta). \qquad (9.58)$$

Equations (52) and (53) provide a pair of first-order differential equations for the $d^l_{mn}(\beta)$, relating these functions to $d^l_{mn\pm1}(\beta)$. In order to obtain the equations, the matrix elements of $D^l M$ and $D^l N$ are needed explicitly; one finds from (49) that

$$(D^l M)_{mn} = (-i)[(l - n)(l + n + 1)]^{1/2} D^l_{mn+1},$$

$$(D^l N)_{mn} = (-i)[(l + n)(l - n + 1)]^{1/2} D^l_{mn-1}.$$

Equations (52) and (53) are, therefore, keeping in mind (19),

$$\left[\frac{d}{d\beta} + m \csc \beta - n \cot \beta\right] d^l_{mn} = -[l - n)(l + n + 1)]^{1/2} d^l_{mn+1} \quad (9.59)$$

$$\left[\frac{d}{d\beta} - m \csc \beta + n \cot \beta\right] d^l_{mn} = [l + n)(l - n + 1)]^{1/2} d^l_{mn-1}. \quad (9.60)$$

These equations can be used to establish an expression for the d^l_{mn} that can be termed a generalized Rodrigues' formula. The procedure will be illustrated for equation (59). It is convenient first to eliminate the numerical factor from the right-hand side by putting

$$d^l_{mn}(\beta) = \left[\frac{(l - n)!}{(l + n)!}\right]^{1/2} f_n(\beta).$$

(The indices l and m will be ignored.) The functions f_n satisfy

$$\left[\frac{d}{d\beta} + m \csc \beta - n \cot \beta\right] f_n = -f_{n+1}.$$

This recurrence relation for f_n can be simplified by looking for functions X_n such that

$$f_{n+1} = -\frac{1}{X_n}\frac{d}{d\beta} X_n f_n = -\left[\frac{d}{d\beta} + \frac{X_n'}{X_n}\right] f_n.$$

It is seen that the function X_n should satisfy

$$\frac{X_n'}{X_n} = m \csc \beta - n \cot \beta,$$

for which the solution

$$X_n(\beta) = (1 + \cos \beta)^{-m} \sin^{m-n}\beta$$

can be found by integration. If we now put $g_n = X_n f_n$, it is found that $dg_n/d\beta = -(X_n/X_{n+1})g_{n+1}$ or $g_{n+1} = (-\sin\beta)^{-1}dg_n/d\beta = dg_n/d(\cos\beta)$. This equation has the solution

$$g_n = \frac{d^{l+n}}{d(\cos)^{l+n}} g_{-l}.$$

The functions g_{-l} can be found from (21) to be

$$\begin{aligned} g_{-l}(\beta) &= [(2l)!]^{-1/2} X_{-l}(\beta) d^l{}_{m-l}(\beta) \\ &= \frac{(-1)^{l+m}}{[(l+m)!(l-m)!]^{1/2}} \frac{\sin^{l+m}\beta}{(1+\cos\beta)^m} \cos^{l-m}\frac{\beta}{2} \sin^{l+m}\frac{\beta}{2} \\ &= \frac{(-1)^{l+m}}{2^l[(l+m)!(l-m)!]^{1/2}} (1-\cos\beta)^{l+m}(1+\cos\beta)^{l-m}. \end{aligned}$$

Assembling the various factors now gives the final result

$$d^l{}_{mn}(\beta) = \frac{\sin^{n-m}\beta(1+\cos\beta)^m}{2^l(l+m)!(l-m)!]^{1/2}} \left[\frac{(l-n)!}{(l+n)!}\right]^{1/2} \frac{d^{l+n}}{d(\cos\beta)^{l+n}} (\cos\beta-1)^{l+m}(\cos\beta+1)^{l-m}. \tag{9.61}$$

The above procedure can also be applied to equation (60) but gives nothing essentially new, but rather $(-1)^{m-n}d^l{}_{-m-n}$ (as expressed through (61)) as an expression for $d^l{}_{mn}$.

A consequence of (55) and (19) is that the $d^l{}_{mn}$ satisfy the second-order differential equation

$$\left\{\sin\beta\frac{d}{d\beta}\sin\beta\frac{d}{d\beta} - (m^2 - 2mn\cos\beta + n^2) + l(l+1)\sin^2\beta\right\} d^l{}_{mn} = 0. \tag{9.62}$$

It is apparent that equations (59) and (60) provide a factorization of this equation.

According to Theorem 6-4 the matrix elements of the irreducible unitary representations D^l are orthogonal on the group; explicitly, they satisfy

$$\int D^l(R)^*_{mn} D^{l'}(R)_{m'n'} dR = \frac{8\pi^2}{2l+1} \delta_{ll'}\delta_{mm'}\delta_{nn'}. \tag{9.63}$$

The value $8\pi^2$ for the group volume in the Euler angle parametrization corresponds to the selection of sin β as the group invariant weight function. The factors $\delta_{mm'}$ and $\delta_{nn'}$ in (63) are also a consequence of (8.3), the expression (19) for the representations, and the fact that the invariant weight function is independent of α and γ. In the case m = m' and n = n', however, (63) implies an orthogonality condition for the functions $d^l{}_{mn}$, namely that

$$\int_0^\pi d^l{}_{mn}(\beta) d^{l'}{}_{mn}(\beta) \sin\beta \, d\beta = \frac{2}{2l+1}\delta_{ll'}. \tag{9.64}$$

The functions $D^l(R)_{mn}$ are known to be complete on the group. It will now be shown that this implies that the set of functions $d^l{}_{mn}$, with m and n fixed and $l \geq \max(m, n)$, are complete on the interval $[0, \pi]$. The completeness relation on the group is

$$\sum_{l\mu\nu} |a^l{}_{\mu\nu}|^2 = \int |f(R)|^2 dR \tag{9.65a}$$

where

$$a^l{}_{\mu\nu} = \left[\frac{2l+1}{8\pi^2}\right]^{1/2} \int D^l(R)^*_{\mu\nu} f(R) dR \tag{9.65b}$$

and f is any function continuous on the group. Suppose now that f is taken to be of the form $e^{-im\alpha}g(\beta)e^{-in\gamma}$. It is readily apparent that $a^l{}_{\mu\nu} = 0$ unless $\mu = m$ and $\nu = n$. The completeness relation in this case, therefore, reduces to

$$\sum_l |b^l{}_{mn}|^2 = \int_0^\pi |g(\beta)|^2 \sin\beta \, d\beta \tag{9.66a}$$

where

$$b^l{}_{mn} = \left[\frac{2l+1}{2}\right]^{1/2} \int_0^\pi d^l{}_{mn}(\beta) g(\beta) \sin\beta \, d\beta \tag{9.66b}$$

which is the desired result.

If $m \neq n$, this argument is not completely valid since the function g is not single-valued at $\beta = 0$ and $\beta = \pi$. This reflects the fact that in this case $d^l{}_{mn}(0) = d^l{}_{mn}(\pi) = 0$ and the function f can be expanded in terms of the $d^l{}_{mn}$ only if $f(0) = f(\pi) = 0$.

The product of two of the functions $d^l{}_{mn}$ can be expanded in a finite series through equation (8.27) which gives

$$d^l{}_{mn}(\beta) d^{l'}{}_{m'n'}(\beta) = \sum_L [L] \begin{pmatrix} l & l' & L \\ m & m' & M \end{pmatrix} \begin{pmatrix} l & l' & L \\ n & n' & N \end{pmatrix} d^L{}_{MN}(\beta) \tag{9.67}$$

where $M = -m - m'$, $N = -n - n'$ and $|l - l'| \le L \le l + l'$. In the special case $l' = 1$, $m' = n' = 0$, $d^{l'}_{m'n'} = \cos\beta$. Equation (67) becomes in this case, using (8.43) and rearranging the terms,

$$(2l + 1)[l(l + 1)\cos\beta - mn]d^{l}_{mn}(\beta)$$

$$= (l + 1)[(l^2 - m^2)(l^2 - n^2)]^{1/2} d^{l-1}_{mn}(\beta)$$

$$+ l[((l + 1)^2 - m^2)((l + 1)^2 - n^2)]^{1/2} d^{l+1}_{mn}(\beta). \quad (9.68)$$

Various other identities can be obtained in a similar way by putting $l' = 1$, $m' = 1$, $n' = 0$, and so on, in (67) and using (8.43).

The group representation property implies a general addition theorem for the d^{l}_{mn}. The most general result is implied in equations (9) which require that

$$\sum_{pq} D^{l}(0, \beta, 0)_{mp} D^{l}(\alpha, 0, 0)_{pq} D^{l}(0, \beta', 0)_{qn} = D^{l}(A, B, \Gamma)_{mn}.$$

From (23) and (19) it is seen that this reduces to

$$\sum_{p=-l}^{l} e^{-ip\alpha} d^{l}_{mp}(\beta) d^{l}_{pn}(\beta') = e^{-imA} d^{l}_{mn}(B) e^{-in\Gamma} \quad (9.69)$$

where A, B, Γ are to be determined from (9). The special cases for which $\alpha = 0$ or π may be of more interest than (69); these are

$$\sum_{p} d^{l}_{mp}(\beta) d^{l}_{pn}(\beta') = d^{l}_{mn}(\beta + \beta') \quad (9.70a)$$

$$\sum_{p} (-1)^{p} d^{l}_{mp}(\beta) d^{l}_{pn}(\beta') = d^{l}_{mn}(\beta - \beta'). \quad (9.70b)$$

A note of explanation on the meaning of $d^{l}_{mn}(\beta)$ for β outside the interval $[0, \pi]$ may be necessary to interpret (69). Suppose β is negative and in the interval $[-\pi, 0]$. It is easy to see geometrically that $X(\beta)$, a rotation about the x axis by the negative angle β, is the same as $Z(\pi)X(-\beta)Z(\pi)$ and that, therefore, $X(\beta)$ is represented by $(-1)^{m+n} d^{l}_{mn}(-\beta)$. We therefore define, for β in $[-\pi, 0]$, $d^{l}_{mn}(\beta) = (-1)^{m+n} d^{l}_{mn}(-\beta)$. This definition is obviously consistent with equation (61). For other values of β, $d^{l}_{mn}(\beta)$ is defined by reducing β modulo 2π to the interval $(-\pi, \pi)$.

The functions $d^l{}_{mn}$ are expressible in terms of the hypergeometric functions defined by

$$F(a,b,c;x) = 1 + \frac{ab}{c}x + \frac{a(a+1)b(b+1)}{c(c+1)}\frac{x^2}{2!} \cdots$$

$$= \sum_r \frac{(a)_r(b)_r}{(c)_r}\frac{x^r}{r!} \qquad (9.71)$$

where

$$(a)_r = 1, \quad r = 0$$

$$= a(a+1)(a+2) \ldots (a+r-1), \qquad r > 0.$$

It is observed that if a (or b) is a negative integer, the hypergeometric function reduces to a polynomial of degree -a (or -b). The connection between $d^l{}_{mn}$ and the hypergeometric functions can be established by putting $x = \sin^2(\beta/2)$ in (61); then $\cos\beta = 1 - 2x$; $d/d(\cos\beta) = -(1/2)d/dx$; and so on. Equation (61) becomes, if $(1+\cos\beta)^m$ is replaced by $\sin^{2m}\beta(1-\cos\beta)^{-m}$,

$$d^l{}_{mn}(\beta) = \frac{(-1)^{l+n}\sin^{m+n}\beta}{2^{m+n}[(l+m)!(l-m)!]^{1/2}}\left[\frac{(l-n)!}{(l+n)!}\right]^{1/2}$$

$$x^{-m}\frac{d^{l+n}}{dx^{l+n}}x^{l+m}(x-1)^{l-m}.$$

It will be assumed for the present that $m \geq n$. We can now write

$$x^{-m}\frac{d^{l+n}}{dx^{l+n}}x^{l+m}(x-1)^{l-m}$$

$$\sum_{r=0}^{l-m}\frac{(l-m)!}{r!(l-m-r)!}(-1)^{l-m-r}x^{-m}\frac{d^{l+n}}{dx^{l+n}}x^{l+m+r}$$

$$= (-1)^{l-m}\sum_{r=0}^{l-m}(-1)^r\frac{(l-m)!(l+m+r)!}{r!(l-m-r)!(m-n+r)!}x^{r-n}$$

$$= (-1)^{l-m}x^{-n}\frac{(l+m)!}{(m-n)!}$$

$$\left\{1 + \frac{(l+m+1)(m-l)}{(m-n+1)}x + \frac{(l+m+1)(l+m+2)(m-l)(m-l+1)}{(m-n+1)(m-n+2)}\frac{x^2}{2!} + \cdots\right\}$$

$$= (-1)^{l-m}x^{-n}\frac{(l+m)!}{(m-n)!}F(l+m+1, m-l, m-n+1; x).$$

It can be concluded that

$$d^{l}_{mn}(\beta) = (-1)^{n-m} \sin^{m-n}\frac{\beta}{2} \cos^{m+n}\frac{\beta}{2} \frac{1}{(m-n)!}\left[\frac{(l+m)!(l-n)!}{(l-m)!(l+n)!}\right]^{1/2}$$

$$\times F\left(l+m+1, m-l, m-n+1; \sin^2\frac{\beta}{2}\right). \qquad (9.72)$$

In the case n > m, the sum on r does not commence at r = 0, but rather at r = n − m. It is not difficult to discover in this case that $d^{l}_{mn}(\beta)$ is given by $(-1)^{n-m} d^{l}_{nm}(\beta)$, as expressed through (72).

It can be shown in a similar way, but changing the variable to $\cos^2(\beta/2)$, that for $m + n \geq 0$

$$d^{l}_{mn}(\beta) = (-1)^{l-n} \cos^{m+n}\frac{\beta}{2} \sin^{n-m}\frac{\beta}{2} \frac{1}{(m+n)!}\left[\frac{(l+m)!(l+n)!}{(l-m)!(l-n)!}\right]^{1/2}$$

$$\times F\left(l+n+1, n-l, m+n+1; \cos^2\frac{\beta}{2}\right). \qquad (9.73)$$

If $m + n < 0$, equation (73) is valid if m and n are replaced by −n and −m respectively in the right-hand side.

It is also possible to express the sum in equation (20) in terms of a hypergeometric function of $-\tan^2 \beta/2$. If $n \geq m$, the sum can be written

$$d^{l}_{mn}(\beta) = \frac{1}{(n-m)!}\left[\frac{(l-m)!(l+n)!}{(l+m)!(l-n)!}\right]^{1/2} \cos^{2l+m-n}\frac{\beta}{2} \sin^{n-m}\frac{\beta}{2}$$

$$\times \left\{1 - \frac{(-l-m)(n-l)}{(n-m+1)} \tan^2\frac{\beta}{2} + \frac{(-l-m)(-l-m+1)(n-l)(n-l+1)}{(n-m+1)(n-m+2)2!} \tan^4\frac{\beta}{2} \cdots\right\}$$

$$= \frac{1}{(n-m)!}\left[\frac{(l-m)!(l+n)!}{(l+m)!(l-n)!}\right]^{1/2} \cos^{2l+m-n}\frac{\beta}{2} \sin^{n-m}\frac{\beta}{2}$$

$$\times \left(F -m-l, n-l, n-m+1; -\tan^2\frac{\beta}{2}\right). \qquad (9.74)$$

If m > n the sum in (20) commences at t = m − n; it is not hard to see that in this case the sum gives $(-1)^{m+n} d^{l}_{nm}(\beta)$, as expressed through (74), as an expression for $d^{l}_{mn}(\beta)$.

9-8 PROPERTIES OF SPHERICAL HARMONICS

The results of the previous sections can be applied in a straightforward way to obtain many of the important properties of the spherical harmonics and associated Legendre functions. The results are based on the relation $Y_{lm}(\theta, \phi) = d^l{}_{m0}(\theta)e^{im\phi} = (-1)^m d^l{}_{0m}(\theta) \times e^{im\phi}$. The relations that will be obtained are for unnormalized spherical harmonics; they can be transcribed for normalized spherical harmonics by including with each Y_{lm} a factor $[4\pi/(2l+1)]^{1/2}$.

It is an immediate consequence of (61) that

$$Y_{lm}(\theta,\phi) = \frac{[-\sin\theta\, e^{i\phi}]^m}{2^l l!}\left[\frac{(l-m)!}{(l+m)!}\right]^{1/2} \frac{d^{l+m}}{d(\cos\theta)^{l+m}}(\cos^2\theta - 1)^l . \tag{9.75}$$

It is conventional to define the associated Legendre functions, for $0 \le m \le l$, by

$$P_l{}^m(z) = \frac{(1-z^2)^{m/2}}{2^l l!}\frac{d^{l+m}}{dz^{l+m}}(z^2-1)^l . \tag{9.76}$$

In the special case $m = 0$, $P_l{}^m(z)$ is the Legendre polynomial $P_l(z)$ defined by

$$P_l(z) = \frac{1}{2^l l!}\frac{d^l}{dz^l}(z^2-1)^l . \tag{9.77}$$

Equation (77) is known as Rodrigues' formula. The following results, which are valid for $m \ge 0$, are quite obvious.

$$P_l{}^m(z) = (1-z^2)^{m/2}\frac{d^m}{dz^m}P_l(z). \tag{9.78}$$

$$d^l{}_{m0}(\theta) = (-1)^m\left[\frac{(l-m)!}{(l+m)!}\right]^{1/2} P_l{}^m(\cos\theta). \tag{9.79}$$

$$Y_{lm}(\theta,\phi) = (-1)^m\left[\frac{(l-m)!}{(l+m)!}\right]^{1/2} P_l{}^m(\cos\theta)\, e^{im\phi}. \tag{9.80}$$

The spherical harmonics for $m < 0$ can be calculated from (80) by the identity

$$Y_{l\,-m}(\theta,\phi) = (-1)^m\, Y_{lm}(\theta,\phi)^*, \tag{9.81}$$

which follows from (39) and (56). Equation (81) gives rise to an alternate expression for the associated Legendre function, namely

$$P_l{}^m(z) = \frac{(-1)^m (1-z^2)^{-m/2}}{2^l l!}\,\frac{(l+m)!}{(l-m)!}\,\frac{d^{l-m}}{dz^{l-m}}\,(z^2-1)^l\,. \tag{9.82}$$

A result that is important in many applications is the expansion of the product of two spherical harmonics as a linear combination of spherical harmonics. Equation (67) with n = n' = 0 shows readily that

$$Y_{lm}(\theta,\phi)\, Y_{l'm'}(\theta,\phi)$$

$$= (-1)^M \sum_L [L] \begin{pmatrix} l & l' & L \\ m & m' & -M \end{pmatrix} \begin{pmatrix} l & l & L \\ 0 & 0 & 0 \end{pmatrix} Y_{LM}(\theta,\phi), \tag{9.83}$$

where M = m + m'. In the special cases l' = 1, and m' = 0 or 1, equation (83) provides recurrence relations for the spherical harmonics. They are, using (8.43)

$$(2l+1)\cos\theta\, Y_{lm}(\theta,\phi) = [(l-m)(l+m)]^{1/2}\, Y_{l-1m}(\theta,\phi)$$
$$+ [(l+m+1)(l-m+1)]^{1/2}\, Y_{l+1m}(\theta,\phi), \tag{9.84}$$

$$(2l+1)\sin\theta\, e^{i\phi}\, Y_{lm}(\theta,\phi) = [(l-m-1)(l-m)]^{1/2}\, Y_{l-1\,m+1}(\theta,\phi)$$
$$- [(l+m+1)(l+m+2)]^{1/2}\, Y_{l+1\,m+1}(\theta,\phi). \tag{9.85}$$

The case l' = 1, m' = -1 is not essentially different from (85). In terms of associated Legendre functions these are

$$(2l+1)zP_l{}^m(z) = (l+m)P_{l-1}{}^m(z) + (l-m+1)P_{l+1}{}^m(z) \tag{9.86}$$

$$(2l+1)(1-z^2)^{1/2}P_l{}^m(z) = -P_{l-1}{}^{m+1}(z) + P_{l+1}{}^{m+1}(z) \tag{9.87}$$

$$(2l+1)(1-z^2)^{1/2}P_l{}^m(z) = (l+m-1)(l+m)P_{l-1}{}^{m-1}(z)$$
$$-(l-m+1)(l-m+2)P_{l+1}{}^{m-1}(z). \qquad (9.88)$$

Equation (88) is obtained by taking the complex conjugate of (85) and replacing m with -m.

Equations (59) and (60), with m = 0, provide two further identities that relate spherical harmonics of the same l.

$$e^{i\phi}\left[\frac{d}{d\theta} - n \cot\theta\right] Y_{ln}(\theta,\phi) = \left[(l-n)(l+n+1)\right]^{1/2} Y_{l\,n+1}(\theta,\phi). \qquad (9.89a)$$

$$e^{-i\phi}\left[\frac{d}{d\theta} + n \cot\theta\right] Y_{ln}(\theta,\phi) = -\left[(l+n)(l-n+1)\right]^{1/2} Y_{l\,n-1}(\theta,\phi). \qquad (9.90a)$$

These give the following relations for the associated Legendre functions.

$$\left[(1-z^2)\frac{d}{dz} + nz\right] P_l{}^n(z) = (1-z^2)^{1/2} P_l{}^{n+1}(z) \qquad (9.89b)$$

$$\left[(1-z^2)\frac{d}{dz} - nz\right] P_l{}^n(z) = -(l+n)(l-n+1)(1-z^2)^{1/2} P_l{}^{n-1}(z). \quad (9.90b)$$

Equations (89b) and (90b) can also be easily derived from (78) and (82).

The spherical harmonics have been seen to satisfy equation (34). This could also have been established completely independently of the discussion of Section 5 from equations (55) and (38), and the fact that $D^l(\alpha+\pi/2, \beta, \gamma)^*_{m0}$ is independent of γ. A consequence of equation (34) is the associated Legendre equation

$$\left[\frac{d}{dz}(1-z^2)\frac{d}{dz} + l(l+1) - \frac{m^2}{1-z^2}\right] P_l{}^m(z) = 0. \qquad (9.91)$$

The group representation property, or equation (69), gives rise to the identity known as the spherical harmonic addition theorem. In order to establish the result we first write $Y_{lm}(\theta,\phi)^* = e^{-im\phi} d^l{}_{0-m}(\theta) = e^{-im(\phi+\pi)} d^l{}_{0m}(\theta)$. Consider now

$$\sum_{m=-l}^{l} Y_{lm}(\theta,\phi)^* Y_{lm}(\theta',\phi')$$

$$= \sum_{m=-l}^{l} e^{-im(\phi+\pi)} d^l{}_{0m}(\theta)\, e^{im\phi'} d^l{}_{m0}(\theta')$$

$$= d^l{}_{00}(\Theta)$$

$$= P_l(\cos\Theta), \tag{9.92}$$

where $\cos\Theta = \cos\theta\cos\theta' - \sin\theta\sin\theta'\cos(\phi - \phi' + \pi)$. The importance of equation (92) stems from the fact that Θ is the angle between the directions whose spherical polar coordinates are (θ, ϕ) and (θ', ϕ'). Equation (92) is frequently of value in expanding a function of the angle between two directions in terms of the spherical harmonics for each separate direction.

It follows immediately from equation (63) with $n = n' = 0$, or from (64) that the spherical harmonics are orthogonal when integrated over the angles in a spherical polar coordinate system. The orthogonality relation is

$$\int_0^{2\pi} d\phi \int_0^{\pi} \sin\theta\, d\theta\, Y_{lm}(\theta,\phi)^* Y_{l'm'}(\theta,\phi) = \frac{4\pi}{2l+1}\,\delta_{ll'}\,\delta_{mm'}. \tag{9.93}$$

The orthogonality property and normalization integral for associated Legendre functions is now seen to be

$$\int_{-1}^{1} P_l{}^m(z)\, P_{l'}{}^m(z)\, dz = \frac{2}{2l+1}\,\frac{(l+m)!}{(l-m)!}\,\delta_{ll'}. \tag{9.94}$$

A very important property of the spherical harmonics is that they are complete with respect to continuous functions whose domain is the surface of a sphere, that is for functions of variables (θ, ϕ), $0 \le \theta \le \pi$, $0 \le \phi < 2\pi$. This completeness property can easily be seen to be a consequence of equation (65) with the function f restricted to be independent of γ. The completeness relation is

$$\sum_{lm} |c_{lm}|^2 = \int_0^{2\pi} d\phi \int_0^{\pi} \sin\theta\, d\theta\, |f(\theta,\phi)|^2 \tag{9.95a}$$

where

$$c_{lm} = \left[\frac{2l+1}{4\pi}\right]^{1/2} \int_0^{2\pi} d\phi \int_0^{\pi} \sin\theta\, d\theta\, Y_{lm}(\theta,\phi)^*\, f(\theta,\phi). \tag{9.95b}$$

This can also be demonstrated from the facts that the functions $e^{im\phi}$ are complete on $[0, 2\pi]$ and the functions $d^l{}_{m0}(\theta)$, m fixed, are complete on $[0, \pi]$.

Chapter 10

ROTATIONS IN FOUR DIMENSIONS

In this chapter the group $O(4)^+$ of proper rotations in a 4-dimensional space will be considered. This group is not of great interest in itself since, as will be shown in the first section, it has the same structure as $SU(2) \otimes SU(2)$. Results of some interest are obtained, however, if the representations are calculated in a form in which the representations of the subgroup $O(3)^+$ appear in reduced form. It will be found in Sections 3 and 4 that these representations give rise to representations of $O(3)^+$ expressed in terms of parameters χ, ξ, η where 2χ is the angle of rotation and ξ and η are the colatitude and azimuth of the axis of rotation. When expressed in this form the representations involve the special functions known as Gegenbauer polynomials and certain properties of these functions will be demonstrated in Section 5. In the last section the group representations will be applied to calculate the spherical harmonics in four dimensions and the relation of these functions to hydrogen atom wave functions will be discussed.

The fourth coordinate will be denoted by t, and will, when necessary, correspond to an index 4.

10-1 THE LIE ALGEBRA OF O(4)

It is known from the discussion of Section 4-7 that the Lie algebra of the orthogonal group O(4) is composed of all 4×4 real skew-symmetric matrices. These can be written as linear combinations of six matrices I_{kl}, $k > l$, which have elements 1 and -1 in row k and column l and row l and column k respectively, and zeros elsewhere. The matrix elements of I_{kl} are given explicitly by

$$(I_{kl})_{mn} = \delta_{km}\delta_{ln} - \delta_{kn}\delta_{lm}. \tag{10.1}$$

It is also convenient to define I_{kl} for $k \leq l$ by $I_{kl} = -I_{lk}$ and $I_{kk} = 0$.

The commutator of two elements I_{kl} and I_{st} can be calculated to be

$$[I_{kl}, I_{st}] = \delta_{ls}I_{kt} - \delta_{ks}I_{lt} - \delta_{lt}I_{ks} + \delta_{kt}I_{ls}. \tag{10.2}$$

This result is easily remembered by noting that $[I_{ij}, I_{jk}] = I_{ik}$ and that $[I_{ij}, I_{kl}] = 0$ if all four subscripts are different. These rules, with the property that $I_{ij} = -I_{ji}$, allow one to write down any commutator immediately.

It will now be shown that the Lie algebra of O(4) is isomorphic to the direct product of the Lie algebra of SU(2) with itself. By this we mean that the algebra is spanned by two ideals which intersect only in the zero element. We consider linear combinations of the I_{kl} defined by

$$I_1 = I_{23} - I_{14}, \qquad I_2 = I_{13} + I_{24}, \qquad I_3 = I_{12} - I_{34}$$

$$J_1 = I_{23} + I_{14}, \qquad J_2 = I_{13} - I_{24}, \qquad J_3 = I_{12} + I_{34}.$$

It is a simple matter to verify that the matrices I_k, J_l satisfy $[I_k, J_l] = 0$ and

$$[I_1, I_2] = 2I_3, \qquad [I_2, I_3] = 2I_1, \qquad [I_3, I_1] = 2I_2,$$

$$[J_1, J_2] = 2J_3, \qquad [J_2, J_3] = 2J_1, \qquad [J_3, J_1] = 2J_2.$$

It is obvious that the I_k and J_l span the Lie algebra and therefore effect the decomposition into a direct product.

A parametrization of the group as a direct product will be considered in the next section. It is fairly clear, however, that a rotation of the form $e^{\alpha J_1}$ is, for example, a rotation of the 2-3 plane into itself by α together with a rotation of the 1-4 plane into itself by α.

10-2 PARAMETRIZATION OF O(4)$^+$ AS A DIRECT PRODUCT

The parametrization of O(4)$^+$ as the direct product of SU(2) with itself can be achieved very conveniently as follows. We consider a matrix

$$X = \begin{pmatrix} t + iz & -y + ix \\ y + ix & t - iz \end{pmatrix} = tI + xI_x + yI_y + zI_z \tag{10.3}$$

where I_x, I_y, I_z are given by (8.7). It is easy to see that if the condition $x^2 + y^2 + z^2 + t^2 = 1$ is imposed, X belongs to SU(2). Let A and B be two arbitrary elements of SU(2) and consider the matrix $X' = AXB^{-1}$. If X ε SU(2), X' is also in SU(2). Moreover, any element of SU(2) can be written uniquely in the form

$$\begin{pmatrix} t' + iz' & -y' + ix' \\ y' + ix' & t' - iz' \end{pmatrix}$$

where $x'^2 + y'^2 + z'^2 = t'^2 = 1$.

The numbers x', y', z', t' are linear functions of x, y, z, t. If these sets of numbers are regarded as coordinates of points on the unit sphere in four dimensions, it is clear that the pair (A, B) generates a rotation of the unit sphere into itself; that is, a mapping has been established from SU(2) ⊗ SU(2) into O(4). Again the identity $A(A'XB'^{-1})B^{-1} = (AA')\, X\, (BB')^{-1}$ shows that the rotation generated by (A', B') followed by the rotation generated by (A, B) is the same as the rotation generated by (AA', BB'), that is, that the mapping is a homomorphism.

The kernel K of the homomorphism consists only of the pairs (I, I) and (-I, -I). In order that a pair (A, B) be in the kernel it is necessary that $AXB^{-1} = X$ for all X ε SU(2). The special case X = I demonstrates that A = B for elements in the kernel. Furthermore, it was shown in Section 9-3 that $AXA^{-1} = X$ for all X in which t = 0 implies A = ± I.

It is less obvious that any element of $O(4)^+$ can be generated by a suitable choice of A and B. It can be observed first that the subgroup for which B = A leaves t invariant and, in fact, according to Section 9-3, generates the subgroup of rotations in the 3-dimensional space orthogonal to the t axis.

Let $\boldsymbol{l}$ be a unit vector parallel to the t axis. It will be shown that there is a pair that rotates $\boldsymbol{l}$ into any direction. It is easy to verify by direct calculation that the pair (A, I), $A = \cos\phi + \sin\phi\, I_z$ generates a rotation in the x-y plane by ϕ plus a rotation in the t-z plane by ϕ. Following this rotation $\boldsymbol{l}$ has a component $\sin\phi$ along the z axis. By a suitable rotation in the x-y-z space, this component of $\boldsymbol{l}$ can be rotated into any direction leaving the component along the t axis fixed. Therefore $\boldsymbol{l}$ can be rotated to its final position by a pair of the form (RA, R). If this operation is preceded by a suitable rotation in the x-y-z space, leaving $\boldsymbol{l}$ invariant, unit vectors along these axes will also be rotated into the correct final position. It follows that any element of O(4) in which there is no reflection can be generated by a pair of the form (RAS, RS). Since any pair (X, Y) can be written in this form the mapping is onto $O(4)^+$;

there are no reflections since all the operations that have been carried out have unit determinant.

It can be concluded that the group $O(4)^+$ is isomorphic to $SU(2) \otimes SU(2)/K$. The parameters of A and B can be used as group parameters although the domain should be restricted so that the pairs (A, B) and (−A, −B) will not both be included. Since we are primarily interested in representations, this complication will be ignored and we will instead restrict our attention to representations in which (A, B) and (−A, −B) are represented by the same matrix.

10-3 REPRESENTATIONS OF $O(4)^+$

The irreducible representations of $O(4)^+$ can be written down immediately as the product of two representations of SU(2). We consider the matrices $\tilde{D}$ of dimension $(2j+1)(2j'+1)$ defined by

$$\tilde{D}^{jj'}(A, B)_{mm',nn'} = D^j(A)_{mn} D^{j'}(B)_{m'n'}. \tag{10.4}$$

The rows and columns of $\tilde{D}$ are indexed by the pairs (m, m') and (n, n') respectively where $-j \leq m \leq j$, $-j' \leq m' \leq j'$, and so on.

The matrices $\tilde{D}$ provide a representation of the direct product of SU(2) with itself. We will require that $j + j'$ be an integer to be denoted by Λ; it then follows that $\tilde{D}^{jj'}(-A, -B) = \tilde{D}^{jj'}(A, B)$ so that the representation is single-valued. It will be convenient, henceforth, to suppress the superscripts j and j' on $\tilde{D}$.

It can be shown, by considering the matrices $\tilde{D}(A, I)$ and $\tilde{D}(I, B)$, that any matrix that commutes with all the $\tilde{D}$ is of the form λI, and hence, that the representation (4) is irreducible. The details of this demonstration will be left to the reader. It can be also be shown that the representation is unitary.

The representations (4) are of negligible interest in themselves since they contain no more algebraic structure than do the D^j and $D^{j'}$ separately. We have seen, however, that they provide also a (in general reducible) representation of the group $O(3)^+$ of rotations in the x-y-z subspace provided by the matrices $\tilde{D}(A, A)$. It is of some interest to consider the problem of transforming $\tilde{D}$ so that the representations of this subgroup appear in reduced form.

The problem of reducing the representation $\tilde{D}(A, A)$ has in fact already been solved in Section 8-3 since this is just the direct product of $D^j(A)$ and $D^{j'}(A)$. It is known that the direct product is reduced by a real, unitary transformation whose matrix elements are simply related to the 3−j coefficients. We, therefore, consider a matrix D(A, B) whose elements are defined by

$$D(A,B)_{LM,JN} = \sum [L]^{1/2} \begin{pmatrix} j & j' & L \\ m & m' & M \end{pmatrix} D^j(A)_{mn}$$

$$\times D^{j'}(B)_{m'n'} [J]^{1/2} \begin{pmatrix} j & j' & J \\ n & n' & N \end{pmatrix} \tag{10.5}$$

where the sum is on m, m', n, n'. The rows of D are indexed by the pair of integers (L, M), $|j - j'| \leq L \leq j + j'$, $-L \leq M \leq L$ and the columns similarly.

The subgroup of rotations in the x-y-z space appears in D in reduced form; a direct calculation employing (8.36) and (8.38) shows that, as we should expect,

$$D(A,A)_{LM,JN} = \delta_{L,J} D^L(A)^*_{MN}, \tag{10.6}$$

showing that D(A, A) is in its reduced form. The remaining portion of this section will be devoted to obtaining a somewhat different form for D(A, B).

Since (A, B) = (A, I)(I, B), it is sufficient for many purposes to calculate D(A, I) and D(I, B). We, therefore, consider the special case D(A, I). If B = I, $D^{j'}(B)_{m'n} = \delta_{m'n'}$ and (5) becomes

$$D(A,I)_{LM,JN} = \sum ([L][J])^{1/2} \begin{pmatrix} j & j' & L \\ m & m' & M \end{pmatrix} \begin{pmatrix} j & j' & J \\ n & m' & N \end{pmatrix} D^j(A)_{mn}. \tag{10.7}$$

We will evaluate (7) first under the assumption that A is diagonal. In this case $D^j(A)_{mn} = e^{-2im\phi}\delta_{mn}$ and equation (7) becomes

$$D(A,I)_{LM,JN} = \sum ([L][J])^{1/2} \begin{pmatrix} j & j' & L \\ m & m' & M \end{pmatrix} \begin{pmatrix} j & j' & J \\ m & m' & N \end{pmatrix} e^{-2im\phi}. \tag{10.8}$$

The sum is on m and m'; it can be noted, however, that $m' = -m - M = -m - N$, and hence, that M = N if $D(A,I)_{LM,JN}$ is to be nonzero.

The product of 3−j symbols in (8) can be rewritten by the symmetry properties and (8.53) as

$$\begin{pmatrix} L & j & j' \\ M & m & m' \end{pmatrix} \begin{pmatrix} j & J & j' \\ -m & -N & -m' \end{pmatrix}$$

$$= \sum_K (-1)^{j'+K+M-m} [K] \begin{Bmatrix} L & j & j' \\ j & J & K \end{Bmatrix} \begin{pmatrix} j & j & K \\ -m & m & 0 \end{pmatrix} \begin{pmatrix} L & J & K \\ M & -M & 0 \end{pmatrix}.$$

It is now seen that

$$D(A, I)_{LM,JN} = \delta_{MN} \sum_K (-1)^{K+M+j+j'} [K]$$
$$\times ([L][J])^{1/2} \begin{Bmatrix} L & j & j' \\ j & J & K \end{Bmatrix} \begin{pmatrix} L & J & K \\ M & -M & 0 \end{pmatrix} H_{j,K}(\phi) \qquad (10.9)$$

where we define

$$H_{j,K}(\phi) = \sum_m (-1)^{-j-m} \begin{pmatrix} j & j & K \\ -m & m & 0 \end{pmatrix} e^{-2im\phi}. \qquad (10.10)$$

In the next section the problem of finding an explicit expression for $H_{j,K}$ will be considered. For the present we will calculate D(A, I) for arbitrary A. An arbitrary element A ε SU(2) can be diagonalized by an element R ε SU(2); that is, there exists an R such that $R^{-1}AR = A'$ where A' is diagonal. The identity $(A, I) = (R, R)(A', I)(R^{-1}, R^{-1})$ and the representation property give, from the known representations (6) and (9),

$$D(A, I)_{LM,JN} = \sum D(R, R)_{LM,PQ} D(A', I)_{PQ,ST} D(R^{-1}, R^{-1})_{ST,JN}$$
$$= \sum D^L(R)^*_{MQ} D(A', I)_{LQ,JQ} D^J(R^{-1})^*_{QN}. \qquad (10.11)$$

The fourfold sum reduces to a single sum because of the δ factors in (6) and (9).

Comparison of (9) and (11) shows that the sum on Q is of the form

$$\sum_Q (-1)^Q \begin{pmatrix} L & J & K \\ Q & -Q & 0 \end{pmatrix} D^L(R)^*_{MQ} D^J(R^{-1})^*_{QN}$$

which by straightforward manipulations using (8.18), (8.38), (9.38), and (9.81) can be shown to be equal to

$$(-1)^M \begin{pmatrix} L & J & K \\ M & -N & N-M \end{pmatrix} Y_{K,M-N}(\xi, \eta). \qquad (10.12)$$

The angles $\eta + \pi/2$ and ξ are the first two Euler angles of the rotation $\tilde{R}$ that corresponds to the element $R \in SU(2)$. The complete representation is therefore given by

$$D(A, I)_{LM,JN} = \sum_K (-1)^{K+M+\Lambda} [K]([L][J])^{1/2} \times \begin{Bmatrix} L & J & K \\ j & j & j' \end{Bmatrix} \begin{pmatrix} L & J & K \\ M & -N & N-M \end{pmatrix} H_{j,K}(\chi) Y_{K,M-N}(\xi, \eta) \qquad (10.13)$$

where $e^{i\chi}$, $0 \leq \chi \leq \pi$, is the eigenvalue of A in the upper half plane.

It is possible to give a geometric interpretation to the angles χ, ξ, η. For this purpose we consider rotations $\tilde{A}$, $\tilde{A}'$, $\tilde{R}$ in O(3) corresponding to the matrices A, A', R in SU(2). Since A' is diagonal, $\tilde{A}'$ is a rotation about the z axis by 2χ. Moreover, since $A' = R^{-1}AR$, $\tilde{A}' = \tilde{R}^{-1}\tilde{A}\tilde{R}$ and $\tilde{A}$ and $\tilde{A}'$ are in the same class; it follows that $\tilde{A}$ is a rotation by 2χ. The unit vector parallel to the axis of rotation will be denoted by $\mathbf{n}$. It can be shown that $\mathbf{n} = \pm\tilde{R}\mathbf{k}$ where $\mathbf{k}$ is the unit vector in the z direction. This is true if $\tilde{A}\mathbf{n} = \mathbf{n}$. Now $\tilde{A}(\tilde{R}\mathbf{k}) = \tilde{R}\tilde{A}'\tilde{R}^{-1} \times (\tilde{R}\mathbf{k}) = \tilde{R}\tilde{A}'\mathbf{k} = \tilde{R}\mathbf{k}$ since $\tilde{A}'$ is about the z axis, and therefore, $\mathbf{n} = \pm\tilde{R}\mathbf{k}$. It is known (cf. the discussion leading to (9.38)) that the rotation whose first two Euler angles are $\eta + \pi/2$ and ξ rotates $\mathbf{k}$ into the direction with polar angles ξ, η. It can be concluded that ξ and η are the colatitude and azimuth of the axis of rotation of the rotation $\tilde{A}$ corresponding to A.

It is interesting to note that if $j' = 0$, (13) reduces to

$$D(A, I)_{jm,jn} = (-1)^{j-m} \sum_K [K] \begin{pmatrix} j & j & K \\ m & -n & n-m \end{pmatrix} H_{j,K}(\chi) Y_{K,m-n}(\xi, \eta) \qquad (10.14)$$

where j is necessarily an integer. The 6−j coefficient for $j' = 0$ can be evaluated from (8.41) and (8.57) to be $(-1)^{2j+K}/[j]$. On the other hand, it is not difficult to show from (7) that in this case $D(A, I)_{jm,jn} = D^j(A)^*_{mn}$. It follows that the complex conjugate of (14) is the expression for the representations of the rotation group $O(3)^+$ when written in terms of the parameters χ, ξ, η determined from the axis and angle of rotation. The same result, but in a different form, has been recently calculated by Moses [1].

The representation of (I, B) can be written down immediately by using the symmetry properties of the 3−j coefficients. The result is

$$D(I, B)_{LM,JN} = \sum_K (-1)^{L+J+M+K+\Lambda} ([L][J])^{1/2} [K]$$

$$\times\begin{Bmatrix} L & J & K \\ j' & j' & j \end{Bmatrix}\begin{pmatrix} L & J & K \\ M & -N & N-M \end{pmatrix} H_{j',K}(\chi')Y_{K,M-N}(\xi',\eta'), \tag{10.15}$$

where χ', ξ', η' are the parameters of B. The complete representation can now be obtained by multiplying together the representations of (A, I) and (I, B). There is little point to this, however, since the complete group has no more interesting structure than that of each of its factors.

10-4 THE FUNCTIONS $H_{j,K}$

The functions $H_{j,K}$ defined by (10) have been calculated by Bander and Itzykson [2]; the method that will be followed here differs from theirs, somewhat, in detail.

Equation (10) can be rewritten as

$$H_{j,K}(\phi) = \sum (-1)^{j+m} \begin{pmatrix} j & K & j \\ m & 0 & -m \end{pmatrix} e^{-2im\phi}. \tag{10.16}$$

The 3−j symbol in (16) can be written explicitly, according to (8.35), as

$$\begin{pmatrix} j & K & j \\ m & 0 & -m \end{pmatrix} = (-1)^{2j-K}\left[\frac{(2j-K)!}{(2j+K+1)!}\right]^{1/2}$$

$$\times \quad \frac{(-1)^t(2j-t)!(K+t)!}{(j-m-t)!(t+K-j+m)!t!(2j-K-t)!}. \tag{10.17}$$

The sum can be taken over all integral values of t provided we define in the usual way $(n!)^{-1} = 0$, $n = -1, -2, \ldots$. With this definition the identity $[(n-1)!]^{-1} = n(n!)^{-1}$ is valid for all n.

The procedure is to substitute (17) into (16), interchange the order of summation, and put $m = \mu - K + j - t$. The allowed values for μ are then 0, 1, ..., K. The result is

$$H_{j,K}(\phi) = \left[\frac{(2j-K)!}{(2j+K+1)!}\right]^{1/2} \sum \frac{(-1)^{\mu}(2j-t)!(K+t)!\ e^{-2i(\mu-K+j-t)\phi}}{(K-\mu)!\mu!\ t!(2j-K-t)!}.$$

The sum on μ can now be performed by the binomial theorem and gives a factor $(1-e^{-2i\phi})^K/K!$ which can be conveniently written as $(2i \sin\phi)^K e^{-iK\phi}/K!$. We therefore obtain

$$H_{j,K}(\phi) = \frac{1}{K!}\left[\frac{(2j-K)!}{(2j+K+1)!}\right]^{1/2} [2i \sin \phi]^K f_K(\phi) \tag{10.18}$$

where

$$f_K(\phi) = \sum_{t=0}^{2j-K} \frac{(2j-t)!(K+t)!}{t!(2j-K-t)!} e^{i(K-2j+2t)\phi}. \tag{10.19}$$

The properties of the functions $f_K(\phi)$ can be established most easily by obtaining a generating function for them. This is done by multiplying equation (19) by y^{2j-K} and summing over all values of $2j \geq K$. We define

$$S(\phi, y) = \sum_{2j=K}^{\infty} y^{2j-K} f_K(\phi) = \sum_{2j=K}^{\infty} \sum_{t=0}^{2j-K} \frac{(2j-t)!(K+t)!}{t!(2j-K-t)!} y^{2j-K}$$

$$\times e^{i(K-2j+2t)\phi} = \sum_{t=0}^{\infty} \sum_{2j=K+t}^{\infty} \frac{(2j-t)!(K+t)!}{t!(2j-K-t)!} y^{2j-K} e^{i(K-2j+2t)\phi}. \tag{10.20}$$

The interchange in the order of summation is permissible provided $|y| < 1$. We now put $s = 2j - K - t$ and the sum becomes

$$S(\phi, y) = \sum_{t=0}^{\infty} \sum_{s=0}^{\infty} \frac{(s+K)!(t+K)!}{s!t!} y^{s+t} e^{-is\phi} e^{it\phi} = [K!]^2 [1 - ye^{-i\phi}]^{-K-1}$$

$$\times [1 - ye^{i\phi}]^{-K-1} = \frac{[K!]^2}{[1 - 2y \cos \phi + y^2]^{K+1}} . \tag{10.21}$$

The <u>Gegenbauer polynomial</u> $C_n^{\alpha}(x)$ of degree of n and order α is defined to be the coefficient of z^n in the power series expansion of $(1 - 2xz + z^2)^{-\alpha}$; that is,

$$(1 - 2xz + z^2)^{-\alpha} = \sum_{n=0}^{\infty} C_n^{\alpha}(x) z^n. \tag{10.22}$$

Comparison of (20), (21), and (22) shows that the functions $f_K(\phi)$ can be expressed in terms of Gegenbauer polynomials by

$$f_K(\phi) = [K!]^2 C_{2j-K}^{K+1}(\cos \phi). \tag{10.23}$$

and hence that

$$H_{j,K}(\phi) = K!\left[\frac{(2j-K)!}{(2j+K+1)!}\right]^{1/2} [2i\sin\phi]^K C_{2j-K}{}^{K+1}(\cos\phi). \tag{10.24}$$

It is possible to obtain an explicit Rodrigues-like expression for $f_K(\phi)$. If the identity

$$(1-2zx+z^2)^{-1} = \sum_{n=0}^{\infty} C_n{}^1(x)z^n$$

is differentiated p times with respect to x, it is found that

$$p!(2z)^p(1-2zx+z^2)^{-p-1} = \sum_{n=0}^{\infty} \frac{d^p}{dx^p} C_n{}^1(x)z^n$$

and hence that

$$C_n{}^{p+1}(x) = [2^p p!]^{-1} \frac{d^p}{dx^p} C_{n+p}{}^1(x) \tag{10.25}$$

or, in terms of the functions f_K,

$$f_K(\phi) = \frac{K!}{2^K} \frac{d^K}{d(\cos\phi)^K} f_0(\phi). \tag{10.26}$$

According to equation (19) the function $f_0(\phi)$ is given by

$$f_0(\phi) = \sum_{t=0}^{2j} e^{2i(t-j)\phi} = \frac{\sin(2j+1)\phi}{\sin\phi}. \tag{10.27}$$

We can write, therefore,

$$H_{j,K}(\phi) = i^K\left[\frac{(2j-K)!}{(2j+K+1)!}\right]^{1/2} \sin^K\phi \frac{d^K}{d(\cos\phi)^K} \frac{\sin(2j+1)\phi}{\sin\phi} \tag{10.28}$$

10-5 PROPERTIES OF GEGENBAUER POLYNOMIALS

In this section certain properties of Gegenbauer polynomials and the functions $H_{j,K}$ will be developed. For this purpose the representation (13) will be employed, primarily with $j' = 0$ as in (14), or with $J = N = 0$. These functions are particularly convenient since the 6−j coefficients are eliminated. The fact that D(A, I) represents SU(2) is the algebraic property of greatest significance rather than the fact that D(A, B) represents $O(4)^+$. In this connection it should be noted that the matrices defined in (14) provide a representation of SU(2) for each value of j; the restriction that j be an integer will, therefore, be ignored.

We will first relate the parameters χ, ξ, η to the parameters θ, ϕ, ψ of SU(2) defined through (8.6). It follows immediately from the invariance of the trace when A is diagonalized that

$$\cos \chi = \cos \theta \cos \phi. \tag{10.29}$$

In order to determine ξ and η it is necessary to determine the direction invariant under $\tilde{A}$. This is less difficult than it might appear, since we can observe that

$$A - \cos \theta \cos \phi \, I = \begin{pmatrix} i \cos \theta \sin \phi & i \sin \theta \, e^{i\psi} \\ i \sin \theta \, e^{-i\psi} & -i \cos \theta \sin \phi \end{pmatrix}$$

is skew-Hermitian, has zero trace, and obviously satisfies $A(A - \cos \theta \times \cos \phi \, I)A^{-1} = A - \cos \theta \cos \phi \, I$. The last result indicates that the point P identified with $A - \cos \theta \cos \phi \, I$ through (9.15) is invariant under $\tilde{A}$; P has coordinates $(\cos \psi \sin \theta, \sin \psi \sin \theta, \cos \theta \sin \phi)$. It follows from the interpretation of ξ and η as colatitude and azimuth of P that

$$\tan \xi = \tan \theta \csc \phi, \tag{10.30}$$

$$\eta = \psi. \tag{10.31}$$

The distance of P from the origin is $(\sin^2 \theta + \cos^2 \theta \sin^2 \phi)^{1/2} = (1 - \cos^2 \theta \cos^2 \phi)^{1/2} = \sin \chi$. From this we obtain two further useful relations:

$$\sin \chi \cos \xi = \cos \theta \sin \phi, \tag{10.32}$$

$$\sin \chi \sin \xi = \sin \theta. \tag{10.33}$$

A point which may cause some confusion arises in connection with (29)-(33). It is observed that the vector **n** left invariant by $\tilde{A}$ is undetermined as to sign and this in turn leaves the angles ξ, η ambiguous. This ambiguity is clearly associated with the fact that A and $-A$ generate the same rotation. In equations (30) and (31) a definite choice of ξ and η has been made. It is not difficult to see that with this choice distinct group elements are represented by distinct points in the parameter space if the parameter domain is given by $0 \leq \chi < \pi$,

$0 \leq \xi \leq \pi$, $0 \leq \eta < 2\pi$. For example, if A has coordinates χ, ξ, η, $-A$ has coordinates $\pi - \chi$, $\pi - \xi$, $\eta \pm \pi$.

The invariant weight function for SU(2) in terms of the parameters χ, ξ, η will be required. In the parameters θ, ϕ, ψ the weight function is $2 \sin \theta \cos \theta$ since the weight function on $O(3)^+$ is $\sin \beta$ and $\beta = 2\theta$. The factor 2 in the weight function is irrelevant and will be omitted. To express the weight function in the parameters χ, ξ, η it is necessary to multiply by $|\partial(\theta, \phi, \psi)/\partial(\chi, \xi, \eta)|$ which can be seen from (31) to be $|\partial(\theta, \phi)/\partial(\chi, \xi)|$. From (32) and (33)

$$\frac{\partial(\theta, \phi)}{\partial(\chi, \xi)} = \frac{1}{\cos^2 \theta \cos \phi} \begin{vmatrix} \cos \chi \sin \xi & \cos \chi \cos \xi \\ \sin \chi \cos \xi & -\sin \chi \sin \xi \end{vmatrix} = \frac{-\sin \chi \cos \chi}{\cos^2 \theta \cos \phi},$$

and hence

$$w(\chi, \xi, \eta) = \sin^2 \chi \sin \xi. \tag{10.34}$$

The group volume is readily calculated to be $2\pi^2$.

It will now be shown that $C_\lambda^\alpha(x)$ is a polynomial of degree λ in x and has the parity of λ, that is, $C_\lambda^\alpha(-x) = (-1)^\lambda C_\lambda^\alpha(x)$. It is observed that

$$\frac{\sin n\phi}{\sin \phi} = \frac{d}{d(\cos \phi)} \frac{\cos n\phi}{n},$$

and hence that

$$C_\lambda^\alpha(\cos \phi) = \frac{1}{2^{\alpha-1}(\alpha-1)!} \frac{d^\alpha}{d(\cos \phi)^\alpha} \frac{\cos(\lambda + \alpha)\phi}{\lambda + \alpha}. \tag{10.35}$$

It is easy to show inductively that $\cos(n\phi)$ is a polynomial of degree n in $\cos \phi$ and has the parity of n. (It is, in fact, a Tchebycheff polynomial in $\cos \phi$.) The desired result is then an immediate consequence of (35).

It is possible to obtain an orthogonality property for the Gegenbauer polynomials and calculate the corresponding normalization integral. It is necessary first to solve (14) for the $H_{j,K}$ by using the unitary property of the 3−j symbols in the familiar way. The result is

$$H_{j,K}(\chi) Y_{K,M}(\xi, \eta) = \sum (-1)^{j-m} \begin{pmatrix} j & j & K \\ m & n & -M \end{pmatrix} D(A, I)_{jm,jn} \tag{10.36}$$

where the sum is on m and $n = M - m$. We now consider rewriting (36) with j, m, n replaced by j', m', n' respectively, taking the complex conjugate, multiplying the equations and integrating over A. The result is

$$\frac{4\pi}{[K]}\int_0^\pi \sin^2\chi\, H_{j',K}(\chi)^* H_{j,K}(\chi)d\chi = \frac{2\pi^2}{[j]}\sum\begin{pmatrix} j & j & K \\ m & n & -M \end{pmatrix}^2 \delta_{jj'},$$

the sum again being on m. From (8.36) this gives

$$\int_0^\pi H_{j',K}(\chi)^* H_{j,K}(\chi)\sin^2\chi\, d\chi = \frac{\pi}{2[j]}\,\delta_{jj'}. \tag{10.37}$$

In terms of Gegenbauer polynomials this is

$$\int_{-1}^1 C_n^\alpha(x)C_{n'}^\alpha(x)(1-x^2)^{\alpha-1/2}dx$$

$$= \frac{\pi(n+2\alpha-1)!}{2^{2\alpha-1}n!(n+\alpha)[(\alpha-1)!]^2}\,\delta_{nn'}. \tag{10.38}$$

It is easy to demonstrate that the functions C_n^α for fixed α are complete with respect to continuous functions on $[-1, 1]$. The method is to apply the fact that the D(A, I) defined in (14) are complete on the group SU(2) with respect to a function of the form $g(\cos\chi)Y_{\alpha,0}(\xi,\eta)$ where g is any function continuous on $[-1, 1]$. The details of the proof will be left to the reader.

The group representation property implies a general addition theorem and various recurrence relations for the functions $H_{j,K}$ and the Gegenbauer polynomials. The general addition theorem is obviously quite complicated and is probably of limited interest; we will return, however, to a special case which is of some importance.

The reduction of the direct product of two of the representations of the form (5) has been discussed by Biedenharn [3] and the matrix that reduces the direct product given. Biedenharn has applied the result to obtain recurrence relations, using the method that was applied, for example, to obtain equation (9.83) and has also obtained the differential equations analogous to (9.59) and (9.60).

It appears to be simpler, however, to obtain the recurrence relations from the generating function (22). Differentiation of (22) with respect to x and t gives two recurrence relations:

$$\frac{d}{dx}C_n^\alpha(x) = 2\alpha C_{n-1}^{\alpha+1}(x) \tag{10.39}$$

$$2\alpha x C_n^{\alpha+1}(x) = (n+1)C_{n+1}^\alpha(x) + 2\alpha C_{n-1}^{\alpha+1}(x). \tag{10.40}$$

Multiplication by $(1 - 2xt + t^2)$ yields a third identity:

$$2xC_n^{\alpha}(x) = C_{n-1}^{\alpha}(x) - C_{n+1}^{\alpha-1}(x) + C_{n+1}^{\alpha}(x). \tag{10.41}$$

The two latter results can be combined to give a recurrence relation with α fixed:

$$2(\alpha+n)xC_n^{\alpha}(x) = (2\alpha+n-1)C_{n-1}^{\alpha}(x) + (n+1)C_{n+1}^{\alpha}(x). \tag{10.42}$$

It is also possible to obtain an identity in which the sum of the order and the degree is fixed; the result is

$$2(\alpha-1)(2\alpha-1)xC_n^{\alpha}(x) = 4\alpha(\alpha-1)(1-x^2)C_{n-1}^{\alpha+1}(x)$$

$$+ (2\alpha+n-1)(n+1)C_{n+1}^{\alpha-1}(x). \tag{10.43}$$

Equations (42) and (43) are essentially the results obtained by Biedenharn.

Equations (43) and (39) can be combined to show that

$$(2\alpha-2)(1-x^2)\frac{d}{dx}C_n^{\alpha}(x) = (2\alpha-2)(2\alpha-1)xC_n^{\alpha}(x)$$

$$-(2\alpha+n-1)(n+1)C_{n+1}^{\alpha-1}(x). \tag{10.44}$$

Differentiating (44) with respect to x and using (39) gives a second-order differential equation similar to the hypergeometric equation for C_n^{α}:

$$\frac{d}{dx}(1-x^2)\frac{dy}{dx} - (2\alpha-1)x\frac{dy}{dx} + n(n+2\alpha)y = 0. \tag{10.45}$$

If the Gegenbauer polynomials in (39) and (44) are expressed in terms of the $H_{j,K}$ recurrence relations of some interest in these functions are obtained; the results are

$$\frac{d}{d\phi}H_{j,K}(\phi) - K\cot\phi\, H_{j,K}(\phi)$$

$$= i[(2j-K)(2j+K+2)]^{1/2}H_{j,K+1}(\phi) \tag{10.46}$$

$$\frac{d}{d\phi}H_{j,K}(\phi) + (K+1)\cot\phi\, H_{j,K}(\phi)$$

$$= i[(2j-K+1)(2j+K+1)]^{1/2}H_{j,K-1}(\phi). \tag{10.47}$$

These two results can be combined to give a second-order differential equation for the $H_{j,K}$:

$$\frac{d^2H_{j,K}}{d\phi^2} + 2 \cot \phi \frac{dH_{j,K}}{d\phi} - \frac{K(K+1)}{\sin^2 \phi} H_{j,K} = -2j(2j+2)H_{j,K}. \tag{10.48}$$

10-6 SPHERICAL HARMONICS IN FOUR DIMENSIONS

The elements $D(A, I)_{LM,00}$ of the representation matrices (13) can be shown to be spherical harmonics in 4-dimensional space, a property analogous to the similar property of $D^l(\alpha, \beta, 0)^*_{mo}$ in three dimensions. In this section we will demonstrate this property and also discuss the significance of these functions for the treatment of the quantum-mechanical hydrogen atom problem.

It should first be observed that these functions are defined only if $j' = j$; the sum in (13) in this case consists only of a single term, $K = L$, and is, according to (8.57),

$$D(A, I)_{LM,00} = (-1)^L \left(\frac{[L]}{[j]}\right)^{1/2} H_{j,L}(\chi) Y_{LM}(\xi, \eta). \tag{10.49}$$

The function $D(A, I)^*_{LM,00}$ will, henceforth, be denoted by $\Psi_{nLM}(\chi, \xi, \eta)$ where $n = 2j$, and χ, ξ, η are the parameters of A defined by (29)-(31).

We will have occasion to use two simple properties of the functions $D(A, B)_{LM,00}$:

$$D(I, A)_{LM,00} = (-1)^L D(A, I)_{LM,00} \tag{10.50}$$

$$D(A^{-1}, I)_{LM,00} = (-1)^L D(A, I)_{LM,00}. \tag{10.51}$$

The former is a consequence of (15), in the special case $j = j'$. The latter follows from the facts that A^{-1} has parameters $2\pi - \chi$, ξ, η and that, from (24), $H_{j,L}(2\pi - \chi) = (-1)^L H_{j,L}(\chi)$.

In Section 2 it was shown that points on the unit sphere in four dimensions can be placed in 1-1 correspondence with elements of SU(2) by expressing

$$A(\theta, \phi, \psi) = \begin{pmatrix} \cos\theta\, e^{i\phi} & i \sin\theta\, e^{i\psi} \\ i \sin\theta\, e^{-i\psi} & \cos\theta\, e^{-i\phi} \end{pmatrix} = \begin{pmatrix} t + iz & -y + ix \\ y + ix & t - iz \end{pmatrix}$$

where $x^2 + y^2 + z^2 + t^2 = 1$. If A is expressed in the parameters χ, ξ, η, one finds from (29)-(33) that $t = \cos \chi$, $z = \sin \chi \cos \xi$, $x = \sin \chi \times \sin \xi \cos \eta$, $y = \sin \chi \sin \xi \sin \eta$. The angles χ, ξ, η are, therefore, the 4-dimensional polar coordinates of the point on the unit sphere associated with A. Moreover, the volume element in four dimensions can be determined to be $r^3 \sin^2 \chi \sin \xi$, which coincides with the group volume element on the unit sphere.

The above relations between the Cartesian and polar coordinates can be used to find the distance S between two points; S is found to be given by

$$S^2 = r^2 - 2rr' \cos \Phi + r'^2 \qquad (10.52)$$

where

$$\cos \Phi = \cos \chi \cos \chi' + \sin \chi \sin \chi' \cos \Theta \qquad (10.53a)$$

$$\cos \Theta = \cos \xi \cos \xi' + \sin \xi \sin \xi' \cos(\eta - \eta'). \qquad (10.53b)$$

The angle Φ is the angle between the χ, ξ, η and χ', ξ', η' directions and (53) can be viewed as the cosine law in four dimensions. The angle Θ is the angle between the projections of the χ, ξ, η and χ', ξ', η' directions into the x-y-z subspace.

It will now be shown that the function $r^n \Psi_{nLM}$ is a homogeneous polynomial of degree n in the variables t, x, y, and z and satisfies the 4-dimensional Laplace's equation. It will first be observed, however, that

$$\int \Psi_{n'L'M'}(A)^* \Psi_{nLM}(A)\, dA = \frac{2\pi^2}{(n+1)^2}\, \delta_{nn'} \delta_{LL'} \delta_{MM'}. \qquad (10.54)$$

This is not a direct consequence of Theorem 6—4, since D(A, I) is not irreducible, but follows readily from the orthogonality properties of the Y_{LM} and $H_{j,K}$. It is clear also that the Ψ_{nLM} constitute a complete set on the four-dimensional unit sphere.

The function $r^n \Psi_{nLM}$ contains the essential factors $r^{2j} \sin^L \chi \times C_{2j-L}{}^{L+1}(\cos \chi) Y_{LM}(\xi, \eta)^*$. The factors $r^L \sin^L \chi\, Y_{LM}(\xi, \eta)^*$ constitute a homogeneous polynomial of degree L in the variables x, y, z. The remaining factors are $r^{2j-L} C_{2j-L}{}^{L+1}(\cos \chi)$. The terms in $C_{2j-L}{}^{L+1}(\cos \chi)$ are of the form $\cos^{2j-L-2p} \chi$, p a positive integer; $r^{2j-L} \cos^{2j-L-2p} \chi$ then gives rise to a term of the form $r^{2p} t^{2j-L-2p} = (x^2 + y^2 + z^2 + t^2)^p t^{2j-L-2p}$. It is apparent that each term in $r^{2j-L} \times C_{2j-L}{}^{L+1}$ is homogeneous and of degree $2j - L$ and hence that $r^n \times \Psi_{nLM}$ is homogeneous of degree n.

To show that $r^n \Psi_{nLM}$ is harmonic we consider a special case of the general group addition theorem.

$$\sum D(A, I)^*_{LM,00} D(A', I)_{LM,00} = D(A^{-1}A', I)_{00,00}$$

or,

$$\sum \Psi_{nLM}(A)\Psi_{nLM}(A')^* = [j]^{-1/2} H_{j,0}(\chi''). \tag{10.55}$$

The angle χ'' is to be calculated as the angle of rotation corresponding to $A^{-1}A'$. The result can be obtained geometrically by the method described at the end of Section 9−1 but an algebraic approach is perhaps more straightforward. We can calculate, using (29)-(33)

$$\cos\chi'' = \frac{1}{2}\operatorname{Tr}(A^{-1}A') = \cos\theta\cos\theta'\cos(\phi-\phi') + \sin\theta\sin\theta'\cos(\psi-\psi')$$

$$= \cos\chi\cos\chi' + \sin\chi\sin\chi'\cos\xi\cos\xi'$$

$$+ \sin\chi\sin\chi'\sin\xi\sin\xi'\cos(\eta-\eta').$$

Comparison of this result with (53) reveals that χ'' is the angle between the χ, ξ, η and χ', ξ', η' directions.

The generating function (22) in the case $\alpha = 1$ and $x = \cos\chi''$ shows that, since $C_n^1(\cos\chi'') = [j]^{1/2} H_{j,0}(\chi'')$ by (24),

$$[1-2t\cos\chi'' + t^2]^{-1} = \sum_j t^{2j}[j]^{1/2} H_{j,0}(\chi'')$$

$$= \sum_{nLM} (n+1)\, t^n\, \Psi_{nLM}(A)\, \Psi_{nLM}(A')^*. \tag{10.56}$$

Equation (56) can be transformed to an integral equation for Ψ_{nLM} by multiplying by $\Psi_{n'L'M'}(A')$ and integrating over A'; the orthogonality property (54) can be invoked and the result is, dropping the primes,

$$t^n \Psi_{nLM}(A) = \frac{n+1}{2\pi^2}\int [1-2t\cos\chi'' + t^2]^{-1} \Psi_{nLM}(A')\, dA'. \tag{10.57}$$

Putting $t = r/r'$ and denoting $r^n\Psi_{nLM}(A)$ by $\Psi_{nLM}(\mathbf{r})$ where $\mathbf{r}$ is the vector with coordinates t, x, y, z gives, for $r < r'$,

$$\Psi_{nLM}(\mathbf{r}) = \frac{n+1}{2\pi^2}|\mathbf{r}'|^2 \int |\mathbf{r}-\mathbf{r}'|^{-2} \Psi_{nLM}(\mathbf{r}')\, d\Omega'. \tag{10.58}$$

The integral is over the direction of $\mathbf{r}'$. Equation (58) is, in fact, valid for all $\mathbf{r}$, since each side is a polynomial in the components of $\mathbf{r}$.

It can be shown without difficulty that

$$\Delta_{r,4}|\mathbf{r}-\mathbf{r}'|^{-2} = \left[\frac{\partial^2}{\partial x^2} + \frac{\partial^2}{\partial y^2} + \frac{\partial^2}{\partial z^2} + \frac{\partial^2}{\partial t^2}\right]|\mathbf{r}-\mathbf{r}'|^{-2} = 0 \tag{10.59}$$

for $\mathbf{r} \neq \mathbf{r}'$. Provided $|\mathbf{r}| \neq |\mathbf{r}'|$, equation (58) can be differentiated under the integral sign and it follows that

$$\Delta_4 \Psi_{nLM}(\mathbf{r}) = 0, \tag{10.60}$$

at least for $|\mathbf{r}| < |\mathbf{r}'|$. If a polynomial is harmonic in a sphere, however, it must be harmonic everywhere. It is clear that the Ψ_{nLM} are linearly independent, since they are orthogonal and that they exhaust the spherical harmonics, since they are complete on the unit sphere.

The functions Ψ_{nLM} satisfy a property analogous to (9.35) that

$$\sum D(A, B)_{JN,LM} \Psi_{nJN}(\chi, \xi, \eta) = \Psi_{nLM}(\chi', \xi', \eta') \tag{10.61}$$

where χ', ξ', η' are the coordinates of the point obtained from χ, ξ, η under the rotation (A^{-1}, B^{-1}). The result follows from the identity

$$\sum D(A, B)_{LM,JN} D(X, I)_{JN,00} = D(AXB^{-1}, I)_{LM,00},$$

which can be obtained easily from the group representation property and (50) and (51). Equation (61) is obtained by replacing A and B by A^{-1} and B^{-1} and taking the complex conjugate. It is recalled that $A^{-1}XB$ corresponds to the point on the unit sphere into which (A^{-1}, B^{-1}) rotates the point corresponding to X.

It has been shown by Fock [4], that the four-dimensional spherical harmonics are closely related to hydrogen atom wave functions in the momentum representation. The Schroedinger equation in this case is the integral equation

$$\frac{\mathbf{p}^2}{2m} \psi(\mathbf{p}) - \frac{Ze^2}{2\pi^2\hbar} \int |\mathbf{p} - \mathbf{p}'|^{-2} \psi(\mathbf{p}') \, d\mathbf{p}' = E \psi(\mathbf{p}),$$

or,

$$[\mathbf{k}^2 + k_0^2] \psi(\mathbf{k}) = \frac{\lambda}{2\pi^2} \int |\mathbf{k} - \mathbf{k}'|^{-2} \psi(\mathbf{k}') \, d\mathbf{k}' \tag{10.62}$$

where $\hbar\mathbf{k} = \mathbf{p}$, $\lambda = 2mZe^2/\hbar^2$, $k_0^2 = -2mE/\hbar^2$. Equation (62) is apparently singular; this is not the case, however, since the threefold integration removes the singularity.

Fock introduced new variables, angles α and α' related to $k = |\mathbf{k}|$ and $k' = |\mathbf{k}'|$ by

$$k = k_0 \tan\frac{\alpha}{2}, \qquad k' = k_0 \tan\frac{\alpha'}{2}. \tag{10.63}$$

It can be seen that

$$k'^2\, dk' = \frac{k_0^3}{2} \sec^2 \frac{\alpha'}{2} \tan^2 \frac{\alpha'}{2}\, d\alpha' = \left[\frac{k_0}{2}\right]^3 \left(\frac{\sin^2 \alpha'}{\cos^6 \frac{\alpha'}{2}}\right) d\alpha'. \tag{10.64}$$

If γ is the angle between $\mathbf{k}$ and $\mathbf{k}'$, we can write

$$|\mathbf{k}-\mathbf{k}'|^2 = k_0^2 \left[\tan^2 \frac{\alpha}{2} - 2 \tan \frac{\alpha}{2} \tan \frac{\alpha'}{2} \cos \gamma + \tan^2 \frac{\alpha'}{2}\right]$$

$$= \frac{\left[\frac{k_0}{2}\right]^2 [2 - 2 \cos \alpha \cos \alpha' - 2 \sin \alpha \sin \alpha' \cos \gamma]}{\cos^2 \frac{\alpha}{2} \cos^2 \frac{\alpha'}{2}}. \tag{10.65}$$

It is observed from (52) and (53) that the quantity $2 - 2 \cos \alpha \cos \alpha'$ $-2 \sin \alpha \sin \alpha' \cos \gamma$ is the distance between points $\mathbf{u}$ and $\mathbf{v}$ on a four-dimensional unit sphere with polar angles α, θ, ϕ and α', θ', ϕ' respectively.

Since $k^2 + k_0^2 = k_0^2/\cos^2(\alpha/2)$, equation (62) can be written

$$\sec^4 \frac{\alpha}{2}\, \psi(\mathbf{u}) = \frac{\lambda}{4\pi^2 k_0} \int |\mathbf{u}-\mathbf{v}|^{-2} \sec^4 \frac{\alpha'}{2}\, \psi(\mathbf{v})\, d\Omega \tag{10.66}$$

where $d\Omega = \sin^2 \alpha \sin \theta\, d\alpha\, d\theta\, d\phi$. Comparison of (66) and (58) shows that the eigenvalues of (66) are given by $\lambda = 2k_0(n+1)$, $n = 0, 1, \ldots$ and that the corresponding wave functions are proportional to $\cos^4 (\alpha/2) \Psi_{nLM}$. The normalization integral is

$$N^2 = \left(\frac{k_0}{2}\right)^3 \int \cos^2 \frac{\alpha}{2} |\Psi_{nLM}|^2 d\Omega = \left(\frac{2\pi^2 k_0^3}{16(n+1)^2}\right)$$

since $\cos^2(\alpha/2) = (1+\cos\alpha)/2$ and the term in $\cos\alpha$ does not contribute to the integral.

The complete wave function is

$$\psi_{nLM} = \left[\frac{2(n+1)(n-L)!}{\pi(n+L+1)!\, k_0^3}\right]^{1/2} (1+\cos\alpha)^2 \sin^L \alpha$$

$$\times \left[\frac{d^L}{d(\cos\alpha)^L} \frac{\sin(n+1)\alpha}{\sin\alpha}\right] Y_{LM}(\theta, \phi)^*. \tag{10.67}$$

The spherical harmonic in (67) is normalized, that is, Y_{LM} in (49) has been replaced by $(4\pi/[L])^{1/2}\, Y_{LM}$.

The energy levels in the hydrogen atom are given by $k_0 = \lambda/2(n+1)$ which leads to the familiar result

$$E_n = -\frac{mZ^2e^4}{2\hbar^2(n+1)^2}. \tag{10.68}$$

The energy level E_n exhibits the well-known $(n+1)^2$-fold degeneracy, with wave functions ψ_{nLM}, $|M| \leq L \leq n$.

It is possible to carry out the Fourier transformation of (67) and obtain the wave functions in configuration space [5]; the procedure is somewhat complicated, however, and will not be described here.

Chapter 11

EUCLIDEAN GROUP IN THE PLANE

In this chapter and the next the theory of the Euclidean groups E_2 and E_3 in two and three dimensions will be discussed. These are the groups of length preserving transformations of two- and three-dimensional spaces into themselves. The study of these groups is complicated by the fact that they are not compact so that many of the preceding results are not applicable. For this reason, the discussion here will be incomplete in that it will not be shown that the representations obtained exhaust the unitary irreducible representations. This is, in fact, true [1], but the demonstration of the fact is rather involved.

The representations of the Euclidean group in the plane will be found to involve the Bessel functions of integral order and a number of properties of these functions will be demonstrated group theoretically.

The inequivalent irreducible representations of E_2 are nondenumerable; that is, there is an index $p \geq 0$ such that for each p there is a unitary irreducible representation of E_2 which is inequivalent to each other such representation. The representations will be constructed by Frobenius' method of induced representations, which will be described in Section 2. They can also be constructed by finding representations of the Lie algebra of E_2 and constructing and solving the differential equations (6.52), but only the first part of this program will be carried out. A third construction, the method of contraction, will also be described briefly.

Bessel functions of nonintegral order can be interpreted as partner functions to the group representations. This will be discussed in the last section.

11-1 PROPERTIES OF THE GROUP E_2

The Euclidean group in the plane is defined to be the set of all transformations of the plane of the form $T(\mathbf{a})R(\theta)$ where $R(\theta)$ is a rotation of the plane about the origin by an angle θ, and $T(\mathbf{a})$ is a translation of the plane by the vector **a**. The coordinates of (x', y') of an arbitrary point (x, y) following the transformation are

$$x' = \cos\theta\, x - \sin\theta\, y + a \tag{11.1a}$$

$$y' = \sin\theta\, x + \cos\theta\, y + b \tag{11.1b}$$

where a and b are the components of **a**.

It is possible to obtain a faithful matrix representation of the group element $T(\mathbf{a})R(\theta)$. We associate with each point (x, y) in the plane a three-dimensional vector $(x, y, 1)$. The matrix

$$E(a, b, \theta) = \begin{pmatrix} \cos\theta & -\sin\theta & a \\ \sin\theta & \cos\theta & b \\ 0 & 0 & 1 \end{pmatrix} \tag{11.2}$$

has the property that multiplying $(x, y, 1)$ it yields $(x', y', 1)$ where x' and y' are given by (1). This implies that transformations of the form (1) can be associated in a 1-1 way with matrices of the form (2).

The Lie algebra of the group can be obtained by calculating, at the identity, the derivatives of the matrix E with respect to its three parameters; the results are

$$P_a = \frac{\partial E}{\partial a}(0) = \begin{pmatrix} 0 & 0 & 1 \\ 0 & 0 & 0 \\ 0 & 0 & 0 \end{pmatrix}$$

$$P_b = \frac{\partial E}{\partial b}(0) = \begin{pmatrix} 0 & 0 & 0 \\ 0 & 0 & 1 \\ 0 & 0 & 0 \end{pmatrix}.$$

$$M = \frac{\partial E}{\partial \theta}(0) = \begin{pmatrix} 0 & -1 & 0 \\ 1 & 0 & 0 \\ 0 & 0 & 0 \end{pmatrix} \tag{11.3}$$

These matrices define the algebra of equations (4.46) and (4.47) in the special case $\lambda = 0$. We can write, therefore,

$$[P_a, P_b] = 0, \quad [P_a, M] = -P_b, \quad [P_b, M] = P_a. \tag{11.4}$$

The general group element has been represented as the product of elements from two of its subgroups, the rotation group and the translation group. If these elements commuted, the group would be Abelian and of little more interest than the two subgroups separately. It is not difficult to see, however, that the two operations do not commute. We consider the product $R(\theta)T(\mathbf{a})$. The first operation translates the origin into the point with coordinates (a, b). The second operation rotates this point to the point with coordinates ($\cos\theta\ a - \sin\theta\ b$, $\sin\theta\ a + \cos\theta\ b$) and rotates directions by θ. The result is equivalent to the transformation $T(\tilde{\theta}\mathbf{a})R(\theta)$ where $\tilde{\theta}\mathbf{a}$ denotes the vector $\mathbf{a}$ rotated by θ. We can, therefore, write

$$R(\theta)T(\mathbf{a}) = T(\tilde{\theta}\mathbf{a})R(\theta). \tag{11.5a}$$

This equation is central to much of the theory. It can also be demonstrated by direct calculation with the matrices E defined by (2).

It can now be seen that the subgroup of translations is invariant. Let $T(\mathbf{a})$ be a translation and $T(\mathbf{b})R(\theta)$ be an arbitrary group element. The inverse of $T(\mathbf{b})R(\theta)$ is $R(2\pi - \theta)T(-\mathbf{b})$. It follows immediately from (5a) and the Abelian nature of the translations that

$$T(\mathbf{b})R(\theta)T(\mathbf{a})R(2\pi - \theta)T(-\mathbf{b}) = T(\mathbf{b})T(\tilde{\theta}\mathbf{a})T(-\mathbf{b}) = T(\tilde{\theta}\mathbf{a})$$

which is again a translation.

If the subgroup of rotations were also invariant the group would be a direct product. This is not the case, but the group has, however, the property that in can be written in the form NH, where N is a normal subgroup and H is a subgroup and $H \cap N = \{e\}$. Such a group is said to be a <u>semidirect product</u>.

The product of two group elements is defined by the relation

$$\begin{aligned} T(\mathbf{a})R(\theta)T(\mathbf{a}')T(\theta') &= T(\mathbf{a})T(\tilde{\theta}\mathbf{a}')R(\theta)R(\theta') \\ &= T(\mathbf{a} + \tilde{\theta}\mathbf{a}')R(\theta + \theta') \end{aligned} \tag{11.6a}$$

which is an immediate consequence of (5a).

The arguments that led to equations (5a) and (6a) are equally valid for the Euclidean group in a space of an arbitrary number of dimensions. The general group element is of the form $T(\mathbf{a})R$ where $T(\mathbf{a})$ is a translation by $\mathbf{a}$, and R is a rotation of the space into itself. If R and S are rotations, and $T(\mathbf{a})$ and $T(\mathbf{b})$ translations, equations (5a) and (6a) become

$$RT(\mathbf{a}) = T(R\mathbf{a})R \tag{11.5b}$$

$$T(\mathbf{a})RT(\mathbf{b})S = T(\mathbf{a} + R\mathbf{b})RS \tag{11.6b}$$

where $R\mathbf{a}$ denotes the vector $\mathbf{a}$ rotated by R.

11-2 THE FROBENIUS METHOD OF INDUCED REPRESENTATIONS

A representation D of a group G with a subgroup N also provides a representation of the subgroup. The latter may be reducible, however, even if D is irreducible as a representation of G since a subspace may be invariant under the operators $D(n)$, $n \in N$, but not under all the $D(g)$. The Frobenius method of induced representations applies to the case in which the subgroup N is normal; the representations are then constructed so that as representations of N they are in reduced form. The vector space H in which the representation is defined is then decomposed into the direct sum of vector spaces, each of which is invariant under the $D(n)$, $n \in N$.

In the case of the Euclidean groups the normal subgroup is the Abelian translation subgroup and the invariant subspaces are, therefore, one-dimensional. The irreducible representations of the translation subgroup are of the form $e^{i\mathbf{p}\cdot\mathbf{a}}$ where $\mathbf{a}$ is the translation vector and $\mathbf{p}$ is an arbitrary vector that labels the representation. Let $D(\mathbf{a}, R)$ be a representation of a Euclidean group in which the $D(\mathbf{a}, I)$ are reduced. It is then to be expected that there are vectors ψ in the representation space H that satisfy

$$D(\mathbf{a}, I)\psi = e^{i\mathbf{p}\cdot\mathbf{a}}\psi. \tag{11.7}$$

It will be found that equation (7) is, in fact, incorrect in that D(**a**, I) has a purely continuous spectrum and, therefore, has no eigenvectors. We will continue to use (7), however, to motivate some of the discussion. Let us consider the vector D(0, R)ψ. Equation (5b) shows that

$$D(\mathbf{a}, I)D(0, R)\psi = D(0, R)D(R^{-1}\mathbf{a}, I)\psi$$

$$= e^{i\mathbf{p}\cdot R^{-1}\mathbf{a}}D(0, R)\psi = e^{iR\mathbf{p}\cdot\mathbf{a}}D(0, R)\psi; \quad (11.8)$$

since the rotations are orthogonal, $\mathbf{p}\cdot R^{-1}\mathbf{a} = R\mathbf{p}\cdot\mathbf{a}$.

Equation (8) shows that if the representation $e^{i\mathbf{p}\cdot\mathbf{a}}$ occurs in the reduced form of D(**a**, I), then all the representations of the form $e^{i\mathbf{p}'\cdot\mathbf{a}}$ where $\mathbf{p}' = R\mathbf{p}$ also occur; **p**' can be any vector of the same length as **p**.

Since ψ and D(0, R)ψ are eigenvectors of D(**a**, I) corresponding to different eigenvalues, they are orthogonal. The vectors D(0, R)ψ are, however, not countable, contrary to the fact that a set of orthogonal vectors in a Hilbert space is countable. This proves the assertion that the spectrum of D(**a**, I) is continuous.

It is for this reason that the discussion becomes nonrigorous. We can argue as follows, however. Associated with each vector **p**, there is a vector space $H_{\mathbf{p}}$ such that all the vectors of $H_{\mathbf{p}}$ are transformed by D(**a**, I) according to equation (7), and D(0, R) maps $H_{\mathbf{p}}$ into $H_{R\mathbf{p}}$. We consider a family of vector spaces $H_{\mathbf{p}}$ for $|\mathbf{p}|$ fixed. These are isomorphic since one can be mapped into another by a suitably chosen D(0, R), which is invertible. The representation space H is apparently the direct sum of the $H_{\mathbf{p}}$. Any element of this direct sum is an arbitrary set of vectors obtained by selecting one vector from each of the $H_{\mathbf{p}}$; this can be regarded as a function **f** where **f**(**p**) is a vector in $H_{\mathbf{p}}$. (Although the argument of **f** is denoted by **p**, we are assuming that $|\mathbf{p}|$ is fixed, so that **f** is a function only of the direction of **p**.) The direct sum is then the set of all such functions. This is too general, however, since the set of all such functions is not a Hilbert space. It can be shown, though, that if the functions are restricted to those such that the integral over the direction of **p** of $|\mathbf{f}(\mathbf{p})|^2$ exists, the resulting space is a Hilbert space, which is known as the <u>direct integral</u> of the $H_{\mathbf{p}}$. In the examples with which we will be concerned, this space is the space of all square-integrable functions; it is a consequence of the Riesz-Fischer Theorem that it is a Hilbert space. Strictly speaking, the elements of the Hilbert space are not functions, but equivalence classes of functions, such that two functions are in the same class if they differ only on a set of measure zero.

The inner product is defined in the direct integral space by

$$(\mathbf{f}, \mathbf{g}) = \int (\mathbf{f}(\mathbf{p}), \mathbf{g}(\mathbf{p}))\, d\mathbf{p}. \tag{11.9}$$

The representations of the Euclidean groups will be constructed in these direct integral spaces.

The effect of D($\mathbf{a}$, I) is to multiply each vector of $H_{\mathbf{p}}$ by $e^{i\mathbf{p}\cdot\mathbf{a}}$. Therefore, D($\mathbf{a}$, I)$\mathbf{f}$ is defined by

$$[D(\mathbf{a}, I)\mathbf{f}](\mathbf{p}) = e^{i\mathbf{p}\cdot\mathbf{a}}\mathbf{f}(\mathbf{p}); \tag{11.10}$$

D($\mathbf{a}$, I) is a "local" operator that multiplies the value of $\mathbf{f}$ at each point $\mathbf{p}$ by $e^{i\mathbf{p}\cdot\mathbf{a}}$.

The effect of D(0, R) can be determined by considering a function of the form $\mathbf{a}\,\delta(\mathbf{p} - \mathbf{p}_0)$. This is a vector in $H_{\mathbf{p}_0}$ and D(0, R) $\mathbf{a}\,\delta(\mathbf{p} - \mathbf{p}_0)$ is, therefore, a vector $\mathbf{a}'$ in $H_{R\mathbf{p}_0}$. The corresponding function can be written $\mathbf{a}'\,\delta(\mathbf{p} - R\mathbf{p}_0) = \mathbf{a}'\,\delta(R^{-1}\mathbf{p} - \mathbf{p}_0)$. This shows that the value of D(0, R)$\mathbf{f}$ at $\mathbf{p}$ should be expressed in terms of the value of $\mathbf{f}$ at $R^{-1}\mathbf{p}$ and we write

$$[D(0, R)\mathbf{f}](\mathbf{p}) = m(R, \mathbf{p})\mathbf{f}(R^{-1}\mathbf{p}). \tag{11.11}$$

Since $\mathbf{f}(R^{-1}\mathbf{p}) \in H_{R^{-1}\mathbf{p}}$ and the left-hand side is in $H_{\mathbf{p}}$, it is necessary to include the factor m(R, $\mathbf{p}$), which is a mapping of $H_{R^{-1}\mathbf{p}}$ onto $H_{\mathbf{p}}$.

If equations (10) and (11) are to determine a representation, it is necessary that D(0, R)D(0, S) = D(0, RS). Now $[D(0, S)\mathbf{f}](\mathbf{p}) = m(S, \mathbf{p})\mathbf{f}(S^{-1}\mathbf{p})$. The value of D(0, R)D(0, S)$\mathbf{f}$ at $\mathbf{p}$ is the value of D(0, S)$\mathbf{f}$ at $R^{-1}\mathbf{p}$ multiplied by m(R, $\mathbf{p}$) and is, therefore, $m(R, \mathbf{p}) \times m(S, R^{-1}\mathbf{p})\mathbf{f}(S^{-1}R^{-1}\mathbf{p})$. On the other hand, the value of D(RS)$\mathbf{f}$ at $\mathbf{p}$ should be $m(RS, \mathbf{p})\mathbf{f}(S^{-1}R^{-1}\mathbf{p})$. It is, therefore, necessary that

$$m(RS, \mathbf{p}) = m(R, \mathbf{p})m(S, R^{-1}\mathbf{p}). \tag{11.12}$$

Geometrically, this states that the mapping m(RS, $\mathbf{p}$) from $H_{S^{-1}R^{-1}\mathbf{p}}$ to $H_{\mathbf{p}}$ is the same as the mapping m(S, $R^{-1}\mathbf{p}$) from $H_{S^{-1}R^{-1}\mathbf{p}}$ to $H_{R^{-1}\mathbf{p}}$ followed by the mapping m(R, $\mathbf{p}$) from $H_{R^{-1}\mathbf{p}}$ to $H_{\mathbf{p}}$. If (12) is satisfied, the operators D(0, R) defined by (11) are a representation of the subgroup of rotations. It is then possible to show that the operators defined by (10) and (11) constitute a representation of the Euclidean group. This will be the case if (5b) is satisfied. We calculate

$$
\begin{aligned}
[D(0, R)D(\mathbf{a}, I)\mathbf{f}](\mathbf{p}) &= D(0, R)e^{i\mathbf{p}\cdot\mathbf{a}}\mathbf{f}(\mathbf{p}) \\
&= e^{iR^{-1}\mathbf{p}\cdot\mathbf{a}}m(R, \mathbf{p})\mathbf{f}(R^{-1}\mathbf{p}) \\
&= e^{i\mathbf{p}\cdot R\mathbf{a}}m(R, \mathbf{p})\mathbf{f}(R^{-1}\mathbf{p}) \\
&= [D(R\mathbf{a}, I)D(0, R)\mathbf{f}](\mathbf{p}),
\end{aligned}
$$

which demonstrates the desired result.

It will now be shown that solutions of (12) can be constructed, thereby generating representations of the Euclidean groups. It is first necessary to note that, according to (11), $D(0, I)\mathbf{f}(\mathbf{p}) = m(I, \mathbf{p})\mathbf{f}(\mathbf{p})$ and hence

$$m(I, \mathbf{p}) = I \tag{11.13}$$

for all $\mathbf{p}$. If we put $S = R^{-1}$ in (12), it is seen that $m(R, \mathbf{p})m(R^{-1}, R^{-1}\mathbf{p}) = I$ and, therefore, that

$$m(R, \mathbf{p})^{-1} = m(R^{-1}, R^{-1}\mathbf{p}). \tag{11.14}$$

We consider now a particular vector $\mathbf{k}$. The set of all rotations that leave $\mathbf{k}$ fixed is readily seen to be a subgroup of the rotation group; this subgroup is known as the little group $L_\mathbf{k}$ of $\mathbf{k}$. If R and S are in $L_\mathbf{k}$, equation (12) shows that

$$m(RS, \mathbf{k}) = m(R, \mathbf{k})m(S, \mathbf{k}) \tag{11.15}$$

so that the function $m(R, \mathbf{k})$ restricted to $L_\mathbf{k}$ provides a representation of $L_\mathbf{k}$. It will now be shown that a representation of $L_\mathbf{k}$ can be used to construct a solution of (12), and hence, a representation of the complete group.

For each $\mathbf{p}$, we pick out a single rotation $\rho(\mathbf{p})$ that rotates $\mathbf{k}$ into $\mathbf{p}$, that is,

$$\rho(\mathbf{p})\mathbf{k} = \mathbf{p}. \tag{11.16}$$

The rotation $\rho(\mathbf{p})$ can be chosen, in general, in many different ways; it is only necessary that it be continuous in $\mathbf{p}$ and, in particular, that

$$\lim_{\mathbf{p}\to\mathbf{k}} \rho(\mathbf{p}) = I \tag{11.17}$$

regardless of the direction of $\mathbf{p}$.

It has been remarked that the subspaces $H_{\mathbf{p}}$ are isomorphic to one another. It is possible, therefore, to choose the basis in $H_{\mathbf{p}}$ so that a particular invertible mapping from the fixed space $H_{\mathbf{k}}$ to $H_{\mathbf{p}}$ is the identity. We define

$$m(\rho(\mathbf{p}), \mathbf{p}) = I; \qquad (11.18)$$

$m(\rho(\mathbf{p}), \mathbf{p})$ is a mapping from $H_{\mathbf{k}}$ to $H_{\mathbf{p}}$ and (18) essentially fixes the basis in $H_{\mathbf{p}}$ in terms of the basis in $H_{\mathbf{k}}$.

Consider now an arbitrary $m(R, \mathbf{p})$ which maps $H_{R^{-1}\mathbf{p}} \to H_{\mathbf{p}}$. If this is preceded by $m(\rho(R^{-1}\mathbf{p}), R^{-1}\mathbf{p})$, which maps $H_{\mathbf{k}} \to H_{R^{-1}\mathbf{p}}$ and followed by $m(\rho(\mathbf{p}), \mathbf{p})^{-1}$, which maps $H_{\mathbf{p}} \to H_{\mathbf{k}}$, the result is a mapping $H_{\mathbf{k}} \to H_{\mathbf{k}}$. The rotation corresponding to this sequence of mappings is $Q = \rho(\mathbf{p})^{-1}R\rho(R^{-1}\mathbf{p})$; Q is an element of $L_{\mathbf{k}}$ since $\rho(\mathbf{p})^{-1}$ $R\rho(R^{-1}\mathbf{p})\mathbf{k} = \rho(\mathbf{p})^{-1}RR^{-1}\mathbf{p} = \rho(\mathbf{p})^{-1}\mathbf{p} = \mathbf{k}$. Since, by definition, $m(\rho(R^{-1}\mathbf{p}), R^{-1}\mathbf{p}) = m(\rho(\mathbf{p}), \mathbf{p}) = I$, we put

$$m(R, \mathbf{p}) = m(Q, \mathbf{k}) = m(\rho(\mathbf{p})^{-1}R\rho(R^{-1}\mathbf{p}), \mathbf{k}) \qquad (11.19)$$

and anticipate that the result is a solution of (12). This can be demonstrated by a direct calculation using the fact that $m(R, \mathbf{k})$ is a representation of $L_{\mathbf{k}}$ for $R \in L_{\mathbf{k}}$:

$$\begin{aligned} m(R, \mathbf{p})m(S, R^{-1}\mathbf{p}) &= m(\rho(\mathbf{p})^{-1}R\rho(R^{-1}\mathbf{p}), \mathbf{k})m(\rho(R^{-1}\mathbf{p})^{-1}S\rho(S^{-1}R^{-1}\mathbf{p}), \mathbf{k}) \\ &= m(\rho(\mathbf{p})^{-1}R\rho(R^{-1}\mathbf{p})\rho(R^{-1}\mathbf{p})^{-1}S\rho(S^{-1}R^{-1}\mathbf{p}), \mathbf{k}) \\ &= m(\rho(\mathbf{p})^{-1}RS\rho(S^{-1}R^{-1}\mathbf{p}), \mathbf{k}) \\ &= m(RS, \mathbf{p}). \end{aligned}$$

It is possible to show [1] that an irreducible unitary representation of a Euclidean group must be equivalent to one of the type defined by (10), (11) and (19), where $|\mathbf{p}|$ is fixed, $\mathbf{f}$ is a function of the direction of $\mathbf{p}$, and $m(R, \mathbf{k})$, $R \in L_{\mathbf{k}}$, is an irreducible unitary representation of $L_{\mathbf{k}}$. Two such representations are equivalent if, and only if, $|\mathbf{p}| = |\mathbf{p}'|$ and the representations of $L_{\mathbf{k}}$ are equivalent. It is, furthermore, true that an arbitrary unitary representation is equivalent to a direct integral of such representations, that is, a representation in a direct integral of the spaces defined above.

It should be mentioned that in this case the little group $L_{\mathbf{k}}$ is isomorphic to that of every other vector of the same length, and that the construction is independent of the direction of $\mathbf{k}$. This is not the case in, for example, the inhomogeneous Lorentz group.

11-3 REPRESENTATIONS OF E_2

If the group under consideration is the Euclidean group in the plane, the little group of any vector $\mathbf{p} \neq 0$ contains only the identity. Therefore, $m(R, \mathbf{p}) = I$ for an irreducible representation. The functions $\mathbf{f}$ that define the representation have as domain the direction of a vector in a plane, which can be taken to be the polar coordinate ϕ, $0 \leq \phi < 2\pi$ of the vector, and as range a one-dimensional vector space, that is, the space of complex numbers. The representation is, therefore, given by

$$D(\mathbf{a}, 0)f(\phi) = e^{ipr\cos(\beta-\phi)}f(\phi), \tag{11.20a}$$

$$D(0, \theta)f(\phi) = f(\phi - \theta). \tag{11.20b}$$

The angle $\beta - \phi$ is the angle between $\mathbf{p}$ and $\mathbf{a}$ and $r = |\mathbf{a}|$; since ϕ is the polar angle of $\mathbf{p}$, β is the polar angle of $\mathbf{a}$. The number p is an arbitrary positive number and is the index for the representation. If $p = 0$, $L_\mathbf{p}$ is the rotation group, and the functions f are constant. The representations are then one-dimensional and are given by $D(\mathbf{a}, \theta) = e^{im\theta}$. Since this is constant over the cosets of the translation subgroup, it is actually a representation of the factor group of E_2 over the translation subgroup, that is, of the rotation group.

The complete representation is given, for $p \neq 0$, by

$$\begin{aligned}[D(\mathbf{a}, \theta)f](\phi) &= [D(\mathbf{a}, 0)D(0, \theta)f](\phi) \\ &= e^{ipr\cos(\beta-\phi+\theta)}f(\phi - \theta).\end{aligned} \tag{11.21}$$

It can be verified by explicit calculation that this is a representation.

The inner product (9) is in this case given by

$$(f, g) = \int_0^{2\pi} f(\phi)^* g(\phi)\, d\phi. \tag{11.22}$$

It is readily verified that the representation $D(\mathbf{a}, \theta)$ is unitary in this inner product.

The representation $D(\mathbf{a}, \theta)$ also provides a representation of the rotation subgroup. Since this subgroup is compact, it is known from Section 7-3 that the representation of this subgroup is expressible as a direct sum of the irreducible representations. More precisely, there exists in the representation space a complete set of functions $f_{n\alpha}$ satisfying

$$D(0, \theta)f_{n\alpha}(\phi) = e^{-in\theta}f_{n\alpha}(\phi). \tag{11.23}$$

The index α is included since there may be more than one function satisfying (23).

The functions $f_{n\alpha}$ can be determined from (20b) and (23) which require $f_{n\alpha}(\phi - \theta) = e^{-in\theta} f_{n\alpha}(\phi)$. Putting $\phi = 0$ gives $f_{n\alpha}(\theta) = e^{in\theta} f_{n\alpha}(0)$. There is no other solution of (23) linearly independent of $e^{in\theta}$ so that the index α is unnecessary. The functions f_n can be multiplied by an arbitrary constant factor. It is convenient to put $f_n(0) = i^{-n}(2\pi)^{-1/2}$ so that the f_n are normalized and the representation that they define is unitary. Then

$$f_n(\phi) = (2\pi)^{-1/2} i^{-n} e^{in\phi}. \tag{11.24}$$

If the vectors f_n are chosen as the basis in the representation space, the translation subgroup is no longer reduced. The matrix elements of the translation operators can, however, be readily calculated from equation (6.5), which in this case is

$$D(\mathbf{a}, 0) f_n = \sum_m \Delta_p(\mathbf{a}, 0)_{mn} f_m. \tag{11.25}$$

The value of (25) at ϕ, disregarding the $(2\pi)^{-1/2}$, is, according to (20a),

$$i^{-n} e^{ipr\cos(\beta-\phi)} e^{in\phi} = \sum_m \Delta_p(\mathbf{a}, 0)_{mn} i^{-m} e^{im\phi}.$$

This shows that $\Delta_p(\mathbf{a}, 0)_{mn}$ is the coefficient of $e^{im\phi}$ in the Fourier expansion of $e^{ipa\cos(\beta-\phi)} e^{in\phi}$, and therefore, that

$$\Delta_p(\mathbf{a}, 0)_{mn} = \frac{i^{m-n}}{2\pi} \int_0^{2\pi} e^{ipr\cos(\beta-\phi)} e^{i(n-m)\phi}\, d\phi.$$

If the variable of integration is changed to $\xi = \beta - \phi - \pi/2$, it is found that

$$\Delta_p(\mathbf{a}, 0)_{mn} = (-1)^{m-n} e^{i(n-m)\beta} J_{m-n}(pr) \tag{11.26}$$

where

$$J_n(x) = \frac{1}{2\pi} \int_0^{2\pi} e^{-ix\sin\xi} e^{in\xi}\, d\xi. \tag{11.27}$$

The function J_n is the familiar <u>Bessel</u> <u>function</u> of order n. The integral (26) defining it can also be written as

$$\frac{1}{\pi} \int_0^{\pi} \cos(x\sin\xi - n\xi)\, d\xi$$

showing that $J_n(x)$ is real for real values of x.

The complete representation can now be written, since $\Delta_p(0, \theta)$ is diagonal with matrix elements given by (23),

$$\Delta_p(\mathbf{a}, \theta)_{mn} = (-1)^{m-n} e^{-im\beta} J_{m-n}(pr) e^{in(\beta-\theta)}, \quad (11.28)$$

where (r, β) are the polar coordinates of **a**. In this representation, translations along the x axis are represented by real matrices.

It is not difficult to show that the representation (28) is irreducible in the sense that $\Delta_p(\mathbf{a}, \theta)S = S\Delta_p(\mathbf{a}, \theta) = 0$ implies $S = \lambda I$. In order that S commute with all the diagonal rotation matrices $\Delta_p(0, \theta)$, it is necessary that S be diagonal. It follows readily that the diagonal elements of S are all equal, since, for example, $\Delta_p(\mathbf{a}, 0)_{m,m-1} = -e^{-i\beta} J_1(pr)$ is not identically zero.

11-4 REPRESENTATIONS OF THE LIE ALGEBRA OF E_2

It is possible to construct the representations of the Euclidean group from the commutation relations (4) of the associated Lie algebra. The method is to calculate first the irreducible representations of the Lie algebra. Since we are interested in unitary group representations we will try to find skew-Hermitian representations of the algebra; it will be found that this requires the representations to be, except for a special case, infinite-dimensional. At the risk of some confusion the representation operators will also be denoted by M, P_a, and P_b.

We consider now operators P^+ and P^- defined by $P^+ = P_a + iP_b$ and $P^- = (-P^+)^\dagger = P_a - iP_b$. It can be readily determined from (4) that these operators commute and also satisfy

$$[M, P^+] = -iP^+ \qquad [M, P^-] = iP^-. \quad (11.29)$$

We also consider the operator $P^2 = P_a^{\,2} + P_b^{\,2} = P^+P^- = P^-P^+$. It can be verified that P^2 commutes with P_a, P_b and M and is, therefore, if the representation is irreducible, a (nonpositive) real constant which will be denoted by $-p^2$.

It is necessary to invoke certain group properties in order to guarantee that the representation of the algebra should correspond to a representation of E_2. This is necessary since various nonisomorphic groups may have the same Lie algebra. The property to be invoked is that E_2 has a compact subgroup, the rotation group. In the parametrization chosen, in which $R(2\pi) = I$, this requires that the eigenvalues of M be i n, n an integer, in order that $e^{2\pi M} = I$.

Suppose now that ψ_n is a normalized eigenvector of M satisfying

$$M\psi_n = -in\psi_n. \tag{11.30}$$

There are two different cases that should be considered. The first is $p^2 = 0$ which implies $P^+P^-\psi_n = P^-P^+\psi_n = 0$. This, however, implies that $(\psi_n, P^+P^-\psi_n) = -|P^-\psi_n|^2 = 0$ so that $P^-\psi_n = 0$, and similarly, $P^+\psi_n = 0$. In this case the complete representation is defined by ψ_n and is one-dimensional. The representation is essentially of the rotation subgroup, and is of little interest.

The second case is that in which $p^2 > 0$. In this case $P^+\mathbf{u}$ and $P^-\mathbf{u}$ are nonzero for all $\mathbf{u}$ in the domain of P^+ and P^- since otherwise p^2 would vanish. We consider now $P^+\psi_n$; equation (29) shows that

$$M(P^+\psi_n) = P^+M\psi_n - iP^+\psi_n = -i(n+1)P^+\psi_n.$$

Therefore, $P^+\psi_n$ is an eigenvector of M corresponding to the eigenvalue $-i(n+1)$. In the same way, it can be shown that $P^-\psi_n$ is an eigenvector of M corresponding to the eigenvalue $-i(n-1)$.

The vectors $P^+\psi_n$ and $P^-\psi_n$ are not normalized, but rather satisfy $|P^+\psi_n|^2 = -(\psi_n, P^-P^+\psi_n) = p^2$, and, similarly, $|P^-\psi_n|^2 = p^2$. We define normalized eigenvectors of M by

$$\psi_{n+1} = \frac{-P^+}{p}\psi_n$$

$$\psi_{n-1} = \frac{P^-}{p}\psi_n.$$

The phases of ψ_{n+1} and ψ_{n-1} can be fixed arbitrarily; they have been chosen so that the representation obtained will be compatible with equation (28).

We can define inductively

$$\psi_{n+m} = \left(\frac{-P^+}{p}\right)^m \psi_n \tag{11.31a}$$

$$\psi_{n-m} = \left(\frac{P^-}{p}\right)^m \psi_n \tag{11.31b}$$

and these are again eigenvectors of M corresponding to eigenvalues $-i(n+m)$ and $-i(n-m)$ respectively. It is evident from the definition that for $m > 0$, $(-P^+/p)\psi_{m+n} = \psi_{n+m+1}$, $(P^-/p)\psi_{n-m} = \psi_{n-m-1}$. It is also true, however, that for $m \geq 1$

$$\frac{P^-}{p}\psi_{n+m} = \frac{P^-}{p}\left(\frac{-P^+}{p}\right)^m \psi_n$$

$$= \frac{-P^-P^+}{p^2}\left(\frac{-P^+}{p}\right)^{m-1}\psi_n$$

$$= \psi_{n+m-1}.$$

In a similar way, it can be shown that $(-P^+/p)\psi_{n-m} = \psi_{n-m+1}$.

It can be concluded from this that the vectors ψ_m, $m = n, n \pm 1, \ldots$ provide a complete definition of the Lie algebra by

$$M\psi_m = -im\psi_m \tag{11.32a}$$

$$P^+\psi_m = -p\psi_{m+1} \tag{11.32b}$$

$$P^-\psi_m = p\psi_{m-1}\ . \tag{11.32c}$$

This construction is independent of the choice of the eigenvector ψ_n in (30); if another eigenvector of M had been chosen the same sequence of eigenvectors would have been generated. The eigenvectors of M are seen to be nondegenerate, since degenerate eigenvectors would lead to proper invariant subspaces and reducible representations. It is observed that the representations are necessarily infinite-dimensional since the vectors $\psi_{n\pm m}$ defined by (31) cannot vanish for any value of m and are necessarily linearly independent.

Since $P_a = (P^+ + P^-)/2$, we can write

$$P_a\psi_n = \frac{p}{2}[\psi_{n-1} - \psi_{n+1}]$$

$$= \sum_m \frac{p}{2}[\delta_{m,n-1} - \delta_{m,n+1}]\psi_m.$$

The matrix elements of P_a are, therefore, given by

$$(P_a)_{mn} = \frac{p}{2}[\delta_{m,n-1} - \delta_{m,n+1}]. \tag{11.33a}$$

It will now be shown that the Lie algebra defined by (32) is also the Lie algebra of the representation (28). In the representation (28), translations along the x axis by a distance a are represented by $(-1)^{m-n}J_{m-n}(pa)$. It can be verified from (27) that

$$(-1)^{m-n}J'_{m-n}(0) = \frac{(-1)^{m-n}}{2\pi}\int_0^{2\pi} (-i \sin \xi)e^{i(m-n)\xi}\, d\xi$$

$$= \frac{1}{2}[\delta_{m,n-1} - \delta_{m,n+1}]. \qquad (11.33b)$$

It is seen from this that P_a defined by (33a) is the corresponding element of the Lie algebra of equation (28). Moreover, comparison of (23) and (30) shows that M is also the corresponding element of the Lie algebra of (28). It is unnecessary to make the check for P_b since this is guaranteed by the identity $[M, P_a] = P_b$. The abstract vectors ψ_n correspond to the functions f_n, defined by (24), in the explicit representation of the previous section.

It is apparent that the representations of the Lie algebra could have been calculated by differentiation of the group representation. The calculation from the commutation relations may be somewhat instructive, however, and demonstrates explicitly why the representations must be infinite-dimensional.

It should be mentioned that, just as the discussion of Section 2 was not completely justifiable, the argument of this section is also not rigorous. The difficulty is that the operators P_a, P_b, and M may not be defined on all vectors of the Hilbert space; this is the case in particular if they are unbounded, as M is. The operators P^+ and P^- are bounded, as is shown by the identities $|P^+\mathbf{u}|^2 = |P^-\mathbf{u}|^2 = p^2|\mathbf{u}|^2$, and hence it can be assumed that they are defined for all **u**. We have assumed, and it can be shown to be true, that $P^+\psi_n$ and $P^-\psi_n$ are in the domain of M.

11-5 PROPERTIES OF BESSEL FUNCTIONS

The group representation property of Bessel functions will be applied in this section to obtain a number of properties of them. The index p that labels the representations is irrelevant for these properties and will, therefore, be taken to be 1.

The power series for J_n can be obtained by considering translations by a vector **a** parallel to the x axis. Equation (25) becomes in this case

$$D(\mathbf{a}, 0)\psi_n = \sum_m (-1)^{m-n}J_{m-n}(a)\psi_m. \qquad (11.34)$$

According to equation (6.55) a translation by a distance a in the x direction can be written as

$$D(\mathbf{a}, 0) = e^{P_a a}$$

$$= \sum_{s=0}^{\infty} \frac{1}{s!} (p^+ + P^-)^s \left(\frac{a}{2}\right)^s$$

$$= \sum_{s=0}^{\infty} \sum_{r=0}^{\infty} \frac{1}{r!(s-r)!} \left(\frac{a}{2}\right)^s (P^+)^r (P^-)^{s-r}.$$

This expansion can be substituted for $D(\mathbf{a}, 0)$ in (34) in the special case $n = 0$. The result is, since, according to (32b) and (32c), $(P^+)^r (P^-)^{s-r}\psi_o = (-1)^r \psi_{2r-s}$,

$$m\ (-1)^m J_m(a)\psi_m = \sum_{s=0}^{\infty} \sum_{r=0}^{\infty} \frac{(-1)^r}{r!(s-r)!} \left(\frac{a}{2}\right)^s \psi_{2r-s}$$

$$= \sum_{r=0}^{\infty} \sum_{s=r}^{\infty} \frac{(-1)^r}{r!(s-r)!} \left(\frac{a}{2}\right)^s \psi_{2r-s}$$

$$= \sum_{r=0}^{\infty} \sum_{s=0}^{\infty} \frac{(-1)^r}{r!s!} \left(\frac{a}{2}\right)^{r+s} \psi_{r-s}.$$

The series for J_m is obtained by equating coefficients of ψ_n on each side of the identity. It is desirable to distinquish the cases $m \geq 0$ and $m < 0$. If $m \geq 0$, the terms on the right-hand side for which $r = s + m$ give the desired result:

$$J_m(a) = \sum_{s=0}^{\infty} \frac{(-1)^s}{s!(s+m)!} \left(\frac{a}{2}\right)^{2s+m}. \tag{11.35a}$$

For $m < 0$, the terms for which $s = r - m$ give the result

$$J_m(a) = (-1)^m \sum_{r=0}^{\infty} \frac{(-1)^r}{r!(r-m)!} \left(\frac{a}{2}\right)^{2r-m} = (-1)^m J_{-m}(a). \tag{11.35b}$$

These power series are convergent for all values of the argument.

The group representation property gives rise to a general addition theorem for Bessel functions. The most general addition theorem is

$$\Delta(\mathbf{a} + \tilde{\theta}\mathbf{a}', \theta + \theta')_{mn} = \sum_p \Delta(\mathbf{a}, \theta)_{mp} \Delta(\mathbf{a}', \theta')_{pn}.$$

There is no loss in generality, however, if we put $\theta = \theta' = 0$, since the rotations of the plane can only give rise to the identity $e^{im\theta} e^{im\theta'} = e^{im(\theta+\theta')}$ and rotate $\mathbf{a}'$, whose direction is already arbitrary. Similarly, it can be assumed that $\mathbf{a}$ is parallel to the x axis, since this can be achieved by a simultaneous rotation of $\mathbf{a}$ and $\mathbf{a}'$.

The addition theorem can be conveniently expressed in Cartesian coordinates. To this end we write $e^{-i\beta'} = \cos\beta' - i\sin\beta' = (a' - ib')/r'$ and

$$\Delta(\mathbf{a}', 0)_{mn} = (-1)^{m-n}\left[\frac{a' - ib'}{r'}\right]^{m-n} J_{m-n}(r'). \tag{11.36}$$

Since $\mathbf{a}$ is along the x axis, so that $\beta = 0$, $\mathbf{a} + \mathbf{a}'$ has components $r + a', b'$, where $r = |\mathbf{a}|$. We note that $\Delta(\mathbf{a}, 0)_{mp} = (-1)^{m-p}J_{m-p}(r)$. Then we have, in the special case $n = 0$,

$$\left[\frac{r + a' - ib'}{R}\right]^m J_m(R) = \sum_p \left[\frac{a' - ib'}{r'}\right]^p J_{m-p}(r)J_p(r') \tag{11.37a}$$

where $r'^2 = a'^2 + b'^2$ and $R^2 = (r + a')^2 + b'^2$. The sum is over all integral values of p. The restriction $n = 0$ does not produce any loss in generality.

In polar coordinates, equation (37a) is

$$e^{-imB}J_m(R) = \sum_p e^{-ip\beta'}J_{m-p}(r)J_p(r') \tag{11.37b}$$

where $R^2 = r^2 + 2rr'\cos\beta' + r'^2$, $\cos B = (r + a')/R$, $\sin B = b'/R$.

In the special case $b' = 0$, corresponding to the product of translations along the x axis, equation (37a) reduces to

$$J_m(a + a') = \sum_p J_{m-p}(a)J_p(a'). \tag{11.38a}$$

Similarly, if $a' = 0$, the identity is, replacing b' with b,

$$\left[\frac{a - ib}{\sqrt{a^2 + b^2}}\right]^m J_m(\sqrt{a^2 + b^2}) = \sum_p (-i)^p J_{m-p}(a)J_p(b). \tag{11.38b}$$

Equations (38a) and (38b) lead to the two standard recurrence relations for Bessel functions. If (38a) is differentiated with respect to a', and the result evaluated at $a' = 0$, it is found that

$$2J_m'(a) = J_{m-1}(a) - J_{m+1}(a) \tag{11.39}$$

since $J_p'(0) = [\delta_{p,1} - \delta_{p,-1}]/2$. Similarly, (38b) can be differentiated with respect to b and evaluated at $b = 0$. The derivative of the left-hand side at $b = 0$ is $(-im/a)J_m(a)$ and the result can be written

$$\frac{2m}{a}J_m(a) = J_{m-1}(a) + J_{m+1}(a). \tag{11.40}$$

It is perhaps evident from the method of derivation of the last two identities that they are essentially the partial differential equations (6.52) for the group E_2; these equations arise from the identity $\Delta(\mathbf{a}, 0)\Delta(\mathbf{a}', 0) = \Delta(\mathbf{a} + \mathbf{a}', 0)$ by differentiating with respect to a' and b' and evaluating the result at $\mathbf{a}' = 0$. They are

$$\frac{\partial \Delta}{\partial a}(\mathbf{a}) = \Delta(\mathbf{a})P_a, \qquad \frac{\partial \Delta}{\partial b}(\mathbf{a}) = \Delta(\mathbf{a})P_b. \tag{11.41}$$

Because of the fact that $P_a{}^2 + P_b{}^2 = -p^2 = -1$, these two equations can be combined in the same way that (9.55) was derived to show that

$$\frac{\partial^2 \Delta}{\partial a^2} + \frac{\partial^2 \Delta}{\partial b^2} + \Delta = 0. \tag{11.42}$$

This equation is the two-dimensional Helmholtz equation and is satisfied by each matrix element of the representation. In polar coordinates the equation is

$$\frac{\partial^2 \Delta}{\partial r^2} + \frac{1}{r}\frac{\partial \Delta}{\partial r} + \frac{1}{r^2}\frac{\partial^2 \Delta}{\partial \beta^2} + \Delta = 0.$$

It is seen from this and (26) that the Bessel functions satisfy Bessel's equation:

$$J_m''(r) + \frac{1}{r}J_m'(r) + \left[1 - \frac{m^2}{r^2}\right]J_m(r) = 0. \tag{11.43}$$

Equations (39) and (40) can be combined to show that

$$J_{m-1}(r) = J_m'(r) + \frac{m}{r}J_m(r) \tag{11.44a}$$

$$J_{m+1}(r) = -J_m'(r) + \frac{m}{r}J_m(r). \tag{11.44b}$$

These two relations provide the factorization of Bessel's equation.

The functions $\Delta(\mathbf{a}, 0)_{mn}$ were defined to be the coefficients of $i^{-m}e^{im\phi}$ in the Fourier expansion of $e^{ir\cos(\beta-\phi)}i^{-n}e^{in\phi}$. In the special case $\beta = \pi/2$, for which $\Delta(\mathbf{a}, 0)_{mn} = i^{m-n}J_{m-n}(r)$, by (26), this property is

$$i^{-n}e^{ir\sin\phi}e^{in\phi} = \sum_m i^{m-n}J_{m-n}(r)i^{-m}e^{im\phi}.$$

We put $z = e^{i\phi}$, so that $\sin\phi = (z - z^{-1})/2i$, and $n = 0$ and obtain

$$e^{r(z-z^{-1})/2} = \sum_m z^m J_m(r). \tag{11.45}$$

The function $e^{r(z-z^{-1})/2}$ is known as the generating function for Bessel functions.

This result has only been demonstrated for $|z| = 1$. If it can be shown that the series converges for other values of z, the result can be extended to these values by analytic continuation. It can be seen from the series representation (35) that $J_m(r) \sim \pm(r/2)^{|m|}/|m|!$ for $|m| \to \infty$. The series (45), which is a Laurent series, therefore, converges for all z such that $|z| \neq 0$, so that (45) is valid for all nonzero z.

It can be shown that the results of this section can be extended to complex values of the arguments of the Bessel functions. It is sufficient for this purpose to show that (37) is valid for complex translation vectors **a** and **a**'. This will be proved by showing that the function $\Delta(a, b, 0)$ is an entire function of a and b. In fact, equations (35a) and (36) can be combined to show that for $m \geq n$.

$$\Delta(a, b, 0)_{mn} = (-1)^{m-n}(a - ib)^{m-n} \sum_{s=0}^{\infty} \frac{(-1)^s}{s!(s+m-n)!}\left[\frac{a^2+b^2}{2}\right]^s \tag{11.46}$$

which shows that $\Delta(a, b, 0)_{mn}$ is analytic for all a and b. A similar result is valid for $n > m$. The series in (37) converges for all values of **a** and **a**' by the above estimate of $J_m(r)$ for large $|m|$. Therefore, since (37) is valid for all real values of **a** and **a**', it is valid, by analytic continuation, for all complex values.

If r and θ are complex, the matrices $\Delta(\mathbf{a}, \theta)$ provide a representation of the Euclidean group in a two-dimensional complex vector space. The representation of this enlarged group is not, however, unitary.

11-6 THE METHOD OF CONTRACTION

It is possible to construct the representations of the group E_2 from the known representations of the group O(3) of rotations in space. The method can be described heuristically as follows. Consider a point P close to the north pole of a unit sphere and the tangent plane to the sphere at the north pole, as shown in Fig. 11-1. The point P is almost in the tangent plane. Under a rotation by θ about the z axis, P is rotated in the tangent plane by θ. Under a small rotation by $\delta\beta$ about the x axis, P is translated in the tangent

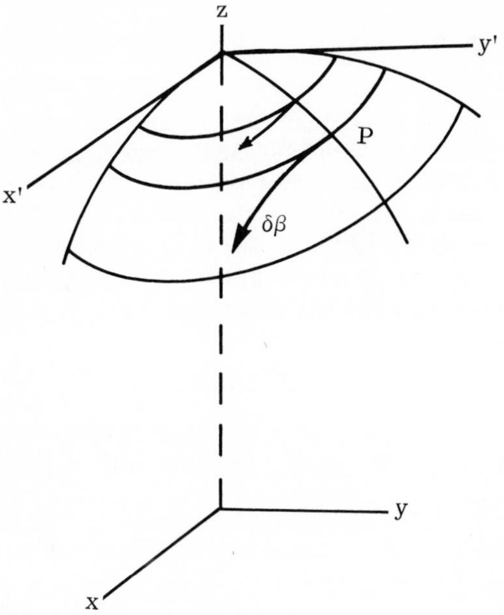

Fig. 11-1
A point P close to the north pole of the unit sphere and the tangent plane at the north pole. The tangent plane has x'-y' coordinate axes parallel to the x-y coordinate axes. Under a rotation $\delta\beta$ about the y axis, P is translated almost parallel to the x' axis by $\delta\beta$.

plane a distance $-\delta\beta$ along the y axis and under a rotation by $\delta\beta'$ about the y axis, P is translated a distance $\delta\beta'$ along the x axis. We may, therefore, expect that the representations of E_2 may be obtained by taking a suitable limit of the representations of O(3).

The limit in question must involve letting the Euler angle β become small. We therefore replace β by β/c and define a new function, similar to $D^l(\alpha, \beta, \gamma)$, by

$$D^l{}_c(\alpha, \beta, \gamma)_{mn} = i^{m-n} e^{im\alpha}\, d^l{}_{mn}\left(\frac{\beta}{c}\right) e^{-in\gamma}. \qquad (11.47)$$

This function would represent the rotation group if β were measured in c^{-1} radians.

The substitution β/c for β causes the matrices J_x and J_y of the Lie algebra of O(3) to be multiplied by c^{-1}. That is, the elements of the Lie algebra of $D^l{}_c$ are $J_x' = J_x/c$, $J_y' = J_y/c$, $J_z' = J_z$. It follows from (9.40) that

$$[J_x', J_y'] = \frac{J_z'}{c^2}, \quad [J_y', J_z'] = J_x', \quad [J_z', J_x'] = J_y'.$$

In the limit $c \to \infty$, these commutators are the same as (4) if J_z' is identified with M, J_x' with $-P_b$ and J_y' with P_a.

As $c \to \infty$, the matrices that represent J_x' and J_y' also approach zero. If, however, as c varies, the index l that labels the representation is also permitted to vary, it is possible to obtain a finite limit as $c \to \infty$. Consider matrices $M' = J_x' + iJ_y'$ and $N' = J_x' - iJ_y'$ which have elements given, from (9.49), by

$$M'_{mn} = -\frac{i}{c}[(l - n)(l + n + l)]^{1/2}\delta_{m,n+1}$$

$$N'_{mn} = -\frac{i}{c}[(l + n)(l - n + 1)]^{1/2}\delta_{m,n-1}.$$

If we choose for l the integer closest to pc, for p an arbitrary positive number, it is found that

$$\lim_{c\to\infty} M' = iP^+, \qquad \lim_{c\to\infty} N' = -iP^-.$$

Hence, $J_x' = (M' + N')/2 \to i(P^+ - P^-)/2 = -P_b$ and $J_y' = (M' - N')/2i \to (P^+ + P^-)/2 = P_a$. Comparison of (9.41) and (32a) shows that $J_z' = J_z \to M$ as $l \to \infty$.

It can be concluded that if the scale of the Euler angle β is decreased and the dimension of the representation matrices of O(3) simultaneously increased, the representations of the Lie algebra of O(3) go over into the representations of the Lie algebra of E_2.

We can take the same limit in the group representations. It is sufficiently general to consider rotations about the y axis, which go over into translations along the x axis. Rotations about the y axis are represented by (9.23c). We therefore obtain

$$\lim_{l\to\infty} d^l{}_{mn}\left(\frac{p\beta}{l}\right) = (-1)^{m-n} J_{m-n}(p\beta) \tag{11.48}$$

as an alternate expression for the Bessel function of integral argument. Equation (48) is a consequence of the fact that each side represents a one-parameter subgroup of E_2, and the tangent at zero of each side is the same.

This construction of representations of a group as a limit of representations of another group is known as <u>contraction</u>. It was first considered by Segal [2] and Inönü and Wigner [3] and has been investigated in detail by Saletan [4]. The above derivation of equation (48) was given by Inönü and Wigner.

11-7 PARTNER FUNCTIONS FOR THE REPRESENTATIONS Δ_p

In this section we will investigate the functions defined on the Euclidean plane that satisfy equation (6.44) which will be rewritten

$$f_n(A^{-1}\mathbf{x}) = \sum_m \Delta_p(A)_{mn} f_m(\mathbf{x}). \tag{11.49}$$

In the following discussion points in the Euclidean plane will be denoted by boldface letters and group elements will be denoted by upper case letters. It is also convenient to introduce a <u>row</u> vector **f** whose elements are the f_n; equation (49) can then be written as

$$\mathbf{f}(A^{-1}\mathbf{x}) = \mathbf{f}(\mathbf{x})\Delta_p(A). \tag{11.50}$$

It will be found that the Bessel functions of noninteger order arise in a fairly natural way as solutions of equation (49).

One solution to (49) can be written down quite readily. If A is replaced by A^{-1} and the unitary property of Δ_p used, equation (49) becomes

$$f_n(A\mathbf{x}) = \sum_m \Delta_p(A)^*_{nm} f_m(\mathbf{x}).$$

If $A = T(\mathbf{a})R(\theta)$, $A\mathbf{x} = \tilde{\theta}\mathbf{x} + \mathbf{a}$ and we obtain the equation

$$f_n(\tilde{\theta}\mathbf{x} + \mathbf{a}) = \sum_m \Delta_p(\mathbf{a}, \theta)^*_{nm} f_m(\mathbf{x}). \tag{11.51}$$

We now refer to equation (28) and note that $\Delta_p(\mathbf{a}, \theta)_{mo} = e^{-im\beta} \cdot (-1)^m J_m(pr)$ is independent of θ. Putting $\theta' = 0$ in equation (6a) and using the representation property of the matrices Δ, one can write

$$\begin{aligned}\sum_s \Delta_p(\mathbf{a}, \theta)^*_{ms} \Delta_p(\mathbf{a}', 0)^*_{so} &= \Delta_p(\mathbf{a} + \tilde{\theta}\mathbf{a}', \theta)^*_{mo} \\ &= \Delta_p(\mathbf{a} + \tilde{\theta}\mathbf{a}', 0)^*_{mo}.\end{aligned}$$

Comparison of this result with (51) indicates that the functions

$\Delta_p(\mathbf{x}, 0)^*_{mo} = e^{im\psi}(-1)^m J_m(pr)$ satisfy (51); r and ψ are the polar coordinates of **x**. It may be recognized that the functions $\Delta_p(\mathbf{x}, 0)^*_{mo}$ play a role analogous to that of the spherical harmonics in the theory of the rotation group.

The question of whether there are other solutions of (49) will now be investigated. It will be assumed that the functions f_n are differentiable functions of the coordinates. The method that will be followed is to obtain a differential equation for the f_n, or **f**, and to show that a solution of the differential equation satisfies (49).

It is necessary to introduce auxiliary functions $g^\mu(A, \mathbf{x})$ which are defined to be the μth coordinate of $A^{-1}\mathbf{x}$. It will be assumed, and it is clearly valid in this case, that the functions g^μ are differentiable in the group parameters. Since the coordinates of the point $A^{-1}(B^{-1}\mathbf{x})$ are the same as the coordinates of $(A^{-1}B^{-1})\mathbf{x} = (BA)^{-1}\mathbf{x}$ the g^μ satisfy the identity

$$g^\mu(BA, \mathbf{x}) = g^\mu(A, B^{-1}\mathbf{x}). \tag{11.52}$$

The partial derivative of g^μ with respect to the λth group parameter will be denoted by $\partial g^\mu/\partial a^\lambda$, again regardless of the point at which the derivative is evaluated. If equation (52) is differentiated with respect to a^β the result is

$$\frac{\partial g^\mu}{\partial a^\alpha}(BA, \mathbf{x})\frac{\partial f^\alpha}{\partial y^\beta}(B, A) = \frac{\partial g^\mu}{\partial a^\beta}(A; B^{-1}\mathbf{x}),$$

where f^α is the familiar group product function. If this is evaluated at $A = I$, the result is

$$\frac{\partial g^\mu}{\partial a^\alpha}(B, \mathbf{x})v^\alpha{}_\beta(B) = \Psi^\mu{}_\beta(B^{-1}\mathbf{x}) \tag{11.53}$$

where

$$\Psi^\mu{}_\beta(\mathbf{x}) = \frac{\partial g^\mu}{\partial a^\beta}(I, \mathbf{x}). \tag{11.54}$$

We now differentiate (50) with respect to a^β and evaluate the result at $A = I$ to obtain

$$\frac{\partial \mathbf{f}}{\partial x^\mu}(A^{-1}\mathbf{x})\frac{\partial g^\mu}{\partial a^\beta}(A, \mathbf{x}) = \mathbf{f}(\mathbf{x})\frac{\partial \Delta_p}{\partial a^\beta}(A)$$

and,

$$\frac{\partial \mathbf{f}}{\partial x^\mu}(\mathbf{x})\Psi^\mu{}_\beta(\mathbf{x}) = \mathbf{f}(\mathbf{x})J_\beta \tag{11.55}$$

where J_β is defined by (6.50). Equation (55) is the desired differential equation for **f**; it will now be shown that if **f** is a solution of (55) it also satisfies (50).

The method of proof is to show that each side of (50), where **f** is a known solution of (55), satisfies the same differential equation, in this case (6.52). Since the solutions of (6.52) are known to be uniquely determined by initial conditions at the identity and (50) is clearly satisfied at A = I, the desired result will follow. In the present notation (6.52) is

$$v^{\alpha}{}_{\beta}(A)\frac{\partial \Delta}{\partial a^{\alpha}}(A) = \Delta(A)J_{\beta}.$$

This equation is linear in $\Delta(A)$ and hence, if $\Delta(A)$ is a solution, $\mathbf{f}(x)\Delta(A)$ is also a solution; this is, however, the right-hand side of (50). We now consider

$$v^{\alpha}{}_{\beta}(A)\frac{\partial}{\partial a^{\alpha}}\mathbf{f}(A^{-1}\mathbf{x}) = v^{\alpha}{}_{\beta}(A)\frac{\partial \mathbf{f}}{\partial x^{\mu}}(A^{-1}\mathbf{x})\frac{\partial g^{\mu}}{\partial a^{\alpha}}(A, \mathbf{x})$$

$$= \Psi^{\mu}{}_{\beta}(A^{-1}\mathbf{x})\frac{\partial \mathbf{f}}{\partial x^{\mu}}(A^{-1}x)$$

$$= \mathbf{f}(A^{-1}\mathbf{x})J_{\beta}.$$

The first step follows from (53) and the second from (55), (with **x** replaced by $A^{-1}\mathbf{x}$). It is observed that the last equation is in fact the same as (6.52); since (50) is satisfied at A = I the desired result follows. This proof is valid in any region in which (6.52) can be integrated along a one-parameter subgroup continuously from I; if the product functions are discontinuous at some point the result may be valid only locally.

It should be remarked that the derivation of (55) may be invalid for infinite-dimensional representations since the term-by-term differentiation of the right-hand side of (50) may not be justifiable. On the other hand, the preceding argument is valid provided the integration of equation (6.52) is valid.

In order to apply these considerations to the Euclidean group in the plane it is necessary to compute the functions g and Ψ. The inverse of the group element $T(\mathbf{a})R(\theta)$ is $R(2\pi - \theta)\ T(-\mathbf{a})$ which transforms a point **x** with coordinates (x, y) to $\tilde{\theta}^{-1}(\mathbf{x} - \mathbf{a})$ with coordinates

$$g^x = \cos\theta(x - a) + \sin\theta(y - b)$$

$$g^y = -\sin\theta(x - a) + \cos\theta(y - b)$$

where (a, b) are the components of **a**. It can be immediately determined from (54) that the functions ψ are given by

$$\Psi^x_a = -1 \qquad \Psi^x_b = 0 \qquad \Psi^x_\theta = y$$
$$\Psi^y_a = 0 \qquad \Psi^y_b = -1 \qquad \Psi^y_\theta = -x. \tag{11.56}$$

Equation (55) provides a set of three differential equations corresponding to the three group parameters. The first of these is

$$\Psi^x_a \frac{\partial \mathbf{f}}{\partial x} + \Psi^y_a \frac{\partial \mathbf{f}}{\partial y} = \mathbf{f}P_a.$$

In component form this is, from (33a) and (56),

$$\frac{\partial f_n}{\partial x} = \frac{p}{2}[f_{n+1} - f_{n-1}]. \tag{11.57}$$

In a similar way two further equations can be obtained:

$$\frac{\partial f_n}{\partial y} = -\frac{ip}{2}[f_{n+1} + f_{n-1}], \tag{11.58}$$

$$x\frac{\partial f_n}{\partial y} - y\frac{\partial f_n}{\partial x} = inf_n. \tag{11.59}$$

It is convenient to introduce differential operators

$$D^+ = \frac{1}{p}\left(\frac{\partial}{\partial x} + i\frac{\partial}{\partial y}\right)$$

$$D^- = -\frac{1}{p}\left(\frac{\partial}{\partial x} - i\frac{\partial}{\partial y}\right)$$

in terms of which (57) and (58) become $D^\pm f_n = f_{n\pm1}$. We also introduce plane polar coordinates (r, ψ) in terms of which the differential operators are given by

$$\frac{\partial}{\partial x} = \frac{x}{r}\frac{\partial}{\partial r} - \frac{y}{r^2}\frac{\partial}{\partial \psi}$$

$$\frac{\partial}{\partial y} = \frac{y}{r}\frac{\partial}{\partial r} + \frac{x}{r^2}\frac{\partial}{\partial \psi}.$$

Equation (59) then becomes

$$\frac{\partial f_n}{\partial \psi} = inf_n \tag{11.60}$$

indicating that f_n is necessarily of the form $q_n(r)e^{in\Psi}$.

It can now be verified that the equations $D^{\pm}f_n = f_{n\pm1}$ involve only the q_n and are

$$\frac{dq_n}{dr} - \frac{n}{r}q_n = pq_{n+1}, \tag{11.61a}$$

$$-\frac{dq_n}{dr} - \frac{n}{r}q_n = pq_{n-1}. \tag{11.61b}$$

It is of interest to discuss the solution of equations (60) and (61) without making the assumption that n in (30) is an integer. It will be noted that equations (32) define a representation of the Lie algebra (4) regardless of the value of n; it is necessary only that there be an infinite set of vectors ψ_n, $\psi_{n\pm1}$, $\psi_{n\pm2}$, ... satisfying (32).

It will be recalled that the requirement that n be an integer was imposed by the fact that the Euclidean group contains the compact rotation subgroup. If n is not an integer the representation (32) cannot correspond to a representation of the Euclidean group but rather corresponds to a representation of some group locally isomorphic to the Euclidean group. A solution of (60) and (61) will then satisfy (49) at least locally.

If n is not an integer it is necessary to specify how the function $e^{-in\psi}$ is to be defined. It is convenient to restrict ψ by $-\pi < \psi \leq \pi$, that is, to cut the plane along the negative x axis.

It can be verified by direct substitution that one solution of equations (61) is given by $q_n = (-1)^n J_n$ where the Bessel function J_n of arbitrary order is defined, for $x \geq 0$, by

$$J_n(x) = \sum_{p=0} \frac{(-1)^p}{p!\,\Gamma(n+p+1)}\left(\frac{x}{2}\right)^{2p+n}. \tag{11.62}$$

Here Γ denotes the well-known gamma function which satisfies $\Gamma(x+1) = x\Gamma(x)$. One solution of (49) is, therefore, given by

$$f_n(\mathbf{x}) = e^{in\psi}(-1)^n J_n(pr). \tag{11.63}$$

It can now be seen that equation (51) with $\theta = 0$ and **a** along the x axis provides a generalization of the addition theorem (37).

Equation (51) can be written, on taking the complex conjugate and putting p = 1,

$$e^{-im\Psi} J_m(R) = \sum_p J_{m-p}(a) e^{-ip\psi} J_p(r) \tag{11.64}$$

where $R^2 = (x + a)^2 + y^2 = a^2 + 2ar \cos \psi + r^2$, $\cos \Psi = (r \cos \psi + a)/R$, $\sin \Psi = r \sin \psi / R$. The angles ψ and Ψ are both in $[0, \pi)$ or both in $(-\pi, 0]$. With this convention, the integration of equations (57)-(59) can be performed without crossing the cut and equation (64) thereby established. If $\psi = 0$ or π, the integration of equations (57)-(59) cannot be carried through the branch point at the origin; equation (64) is then valid only if $re^{i\psi}$ and $a + re^{i\psi}$ have the same sign.

It is apparent that (64) is the generalization of (37b) to Bessel functions of arbitrary order m. It should be emphasized that the sum in (64) is over values of p such that $m - p$ is an integer.

The functions defined in (63) are only a particular solution of (57) and (58); the most general solution is provided by the general solution of equations (61). It can be verified readily that these equations together require that each q_n satisfy

$$q_n''(r) + \frac{1}{r} q_n'(r) + \left[p^2 - \frac{n^2}{r^2}\right] q_n(r) = 0.$$

In the special case p = 1, which we will consider henceforth, this is Bessel's equation.

Suppose now that a function y_n is some solution of Bessel's equation for a fixed value of n. Then we can define $y_{n\pm m}$ inductively by

$$y_{n+m+1}(r) = -y'_{n+m}(r) + \frac{n+m}{r} y_{n+m}(r) \tag{11.65a}$$

$$y_{n-m-1}(r) = y'_{n-m}(r) + \frac{n-m}{r} y_{n-m}(r). \tag{11.65b}$$

It is possible to prove inductively that the functions $y_{n\pm m}$ each satisfy Bessel's equation and that the functions $(-1)^n y_n$ are solutions of (61).

The functions $e^{im\psi}(-1)^m y_m(r)$ are then partner functions for the representation by matrices $\Delta(a, \theta)$ and therefore, satisfy a generalization of (64):

$$e^{-im\Psi} y_m(R) = \sum_p J_{m-p}(a) e^{ip\psi} y_p(r) \tag{11.66}$$

Equation (66) is valid for any set of solutions of Bessel's equation satisfying (65), provided the phase of $e^{-im\psi}$ is chosen correctly.

Chapter 12
THE EUCLIDEAN GROUP IN SPACE

In this chapter the group E_3 of rotations and translations in three dimensions will be considered. It will be found that the matrix elements of the group representations involve spherical Bessel functions, as might be expected, and the group representation property will be applied to derive some of the important properties of these functions.

The representations can be found by the Frobenius method in much the same way that they were calculated for E_2. It will be found that the irreducible representations are labeled by two indices, a continuous, nonnegative index p analogous to the continuous index in the theory of E_2, and an integer Q. The representations obtained by the Frobenius method will be transformed so that they are reduced as representations of the rotation subgroup. The representations in this form have been obtained explicitly by Miller [1] who used a method much the same as is followed here.

The representations can also be obtained by making a suitable contraction of the known representations of the group O(4). This method will be used to obtain the representation matrix elements explicitly, since it leads to the closed expression for the spherical Bessel functions.

Among the results that can be obtained from the representations of E_3 is the expansion of a spherical wave $j_l(kr)Y_{lm}(\theta, \phi)$ in one coordinate system in terms of spherical waves in another coordinate system. This expansion can also be employed to derive a similar expansion theorem for the harmonic functions $r^l Y_{lm}(\theta, \phi)$.

It is possible to extend the theory to include the spherical Neumann and Hankel functions by the method that was used in Section 11-7. The expansion theorems for spherical waves and harmonic functions will also be extended to these more general functions.

12-1 REPRESENTATIONS OF E_3 BY THE FROBENIUS METHOD

In order to construct the representations of E_3 by the Frobenius method described in Section 11-2, it is necessary to pick out a three-dimensional vector **k**, choose an irreducible representation of the little group $L_{\mathbf{k}}$ of **k**, and construct some rotation $\rho(\mathbf{p})$ that rotates **k** into an arbitrary vector **p**.

It is most natural to select **k** to be a vector parallel to the z axis. The group $L_{\mathbf{k}}$ is then the one-parameter group of rotations about the z axis. The irreducible representations of $L_{\mathbf{k}}$ are one-dimensional and are of the form $e^{iQ\phi}$, $Q = 0, \pm 1, \ldots$. The irreducible representations are, therefore, labeled by two indices, p, $0 \le p < \infty$, and Q where p is analogous to the continuous index that labeled the representations of E_2. The representations of the group with index $p = 0$ are, as in the case of E_2, the representations of the rotation subgroup.

The vector space H in which the representation is defined is composed of all square-integrable functions whose domain is the direction of a vector **p** in three-dimensional space and whose range is a one-dimensional complex vector space, that is, the complex plane. A function f in H can, therefore, be taken as a complex-valued function of variables (θ, ϕ), the colatitude and azimuth of **p**.

We consider now the question of constructing the functions $m(R, \mathbf{p})$. These will be defined in terms of the Euler angles α, β, γ of R and the polar coordinates of **p**. We note first that for $R \in L_{\mathbf{k}}$, $\beta = 0$,

$$m(R, \mathbf{k}) = e^{iQ(\alpha+\gamma)} \tag{12.1}$$

since $\alpha + \gamma$ is the angle of rotation about the z axis.

The rotation $\rho(\mathbf{p})$ that rotates **k** into **p** will be defined to be a rotation about an axis **n** in the x-y plane as shown in Fig. 12-1. If θ, ϕ are the colatitude and azimuth of **p**, the angle of rotation is θ and the azimuth of the rotation axis is $\phi + \pi/2$. The Euler angles of $\rho(\mathbf{p})$ are $\phi + \pi/2$, θ, $-\phi - \pi/2$ since $Z(\phi + \pi/2)X(\theta)Z(-\phi - \pi/2)$ first rotates the axis of rotation in the x-y plane into the x axis, then rotates about the x axis by θ, and then rotates the axis of rotation back to its original position and **k** into **p**. We therefore write

$$\rho(\theta, \phi) = Z\left(\phi + \frac{\pi}{2}\right)X(\theta)Z\left(-\phi - \frac{\pi}{2}\right). \tag{12.2}$$

It is observed that

$$\lim_{\theta \to 0} \rho(\theta, \phi) = I$$

independently of ϕ as we require. The rotation $\rho(\theta, \phi)$ is not uniquely determined for $\theta = \pi$; it will be argued, however, that this does not matter.

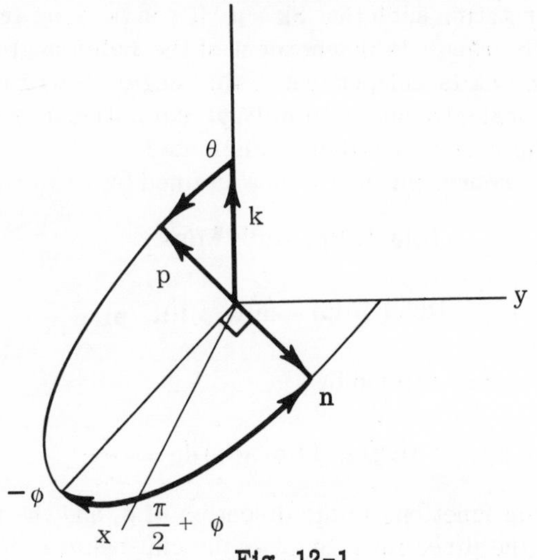

Fig. 12-1

The vector **n** is in the x-y plane, in the direction $\mathbf{k}\times\mathbf{p}$. A rotation about **n** by θ rotates **k** into **p**.

We can calculate now $m(R,\mathbf{k})$ for R an arbitrary rotation and **k** along the z axis. For this purpose we use equation (11.19) which in this case gives

$$m(R,\mathbf{k}) = m(R\rho(R^{-1}\mathbf{k}),\mathbf{k})$$

since $\rho(\mathbf{k}) = I$. If R has Euler angles α, β, γ, R^{-1} has Euler angles $\pi-\gamma, \beta, \pi-\alpha$; $R^{-1}\mathbf{k}$, therefore, has polar coordinates β, $\pi/2-\gamma$. The rotation $\rho(R^{-1}\mathbf{k})$ is then $Z(\pi-\gamma)X(\beta)Z(\gamma-\pi)$ and $R\rho(R^{-1}\mathbf{k}) = Z(\alpha)X(\beta) \times Z(\gamma)Z(\pi-\gamma)X(\beta)Z(\gamma-\pi) = Z(\alpha)X(\beta)Z(\pi)X(\beta)Z(\gamma-\pi) = Z(\alpha)Z(\pi) \times Z(\gamma-\pi) = Z(\alpha+\gamma)$. We have used the fact that $X(\beta)Z(\pi)X(\beta) = Z(\pi)$. It can be concluded from (1) and (11.19) that

$$m(R,\mathbf{k}) = e^{iQ(\alpha+\gamma)} \tag{12.3}$$

for arbitrary R. It should be noted from this that $m(R^{-1},\mathbf{k}) = e^{-iQ(\alpha+\gamma)} = m(R,\mathbf{k})^{-1}$.

The function $m(R,\mathbf{p})$ can now be calculated in general by writing, from (11.12),

$$m(R,S\mathbf{k}) = m(S^{-1},\mathbf{k})^{-1}m(S^{-1}R,\mathbf{k}) = m(S,\mathbf{k})m(S^{-1}R,\mathbf{k}), \tag{12.4}$$

where S is any rotation such that $S\mathbf{k} = \mathbf{p}$. It can be seen from inspection of (4) that the result is independent of the Euler angle γ of S as it should be since $S\mathbf{k}$ is independent of this angle. It will be unnecessary for our purposes to calculate $m(R, \mathbf{p})$ explicitly; it is apparent, however, that the result is rather complicated.

The complete representation is now defined by

$$[D(\mathbf{a}, I)f](\mathbf{p}) = e^{i\mathbf{p}\cdot\mathbf{a}} f(\mathbf{p}) \tag{12.5a}$$

$$[D(0, R)f](\mathbf{p}) = m(R, \mathbf{p}) f(R^{-1}\mathbf{p}) \tag{12.5b}$$

with the inner product defined by

$$(f, g) = \int f(\mathbf{p})^* g(\mathbf{p})\, d\mathbf{p}. \tag{12.6}$$

The domain of the functions is the direction of $\mathbf{p}$, and the integral in (6) is only over the directions, or over the unit sphere. It is observed that the representation defined by (5) is unitary in the inner product (6).

The function $m(R, \mathbf{p})$ is not continuous at the south pole, $\mathbf{p} = -p\mathbf{k}$, since the rotation $\rho(\mathbf{p})$ is not unique in this case. The function $D(0, R)f$ is, therefore, not unique at this point. The function $D(0, R)f$, which is defined for all $\mathbf{p} \neq -p\mathbf{k}$, is still square-integrable, however, so that $D(0, R)$ is defined in the space of square-integrable functions.

We consider now the problem of transforming the representation defined by (5) so that the rotation subgroup is reduced. It will be convenient to denote a point $\mathbf{p}$ on the unit sphere by the rotation P that rotates $\mathbf{k}$ into $\mathbf{p}$, that is, $\mathbf{p} = P\mathbf{k}$. The rotation P is not unique, but rather has arbitrary Euler angle γ. We will, however, define functions of P that are independent of γ and such a function can be considered either a function of α and β, or a function of points on the unit sphere (where β is the colatitude and $\alpha - \pi/2$ is the azimuth).

We consider the set of orthonormal functions F_{lm} defined on the unit sphere by

$$F_{lm}(P) = \left(\frac{[l]}{4\pi}\right)^{1/2} m(P, \mathbf{k}) D^l(P)_{mQ}. \tag{12.7}$$

It can be observed from (3) and (9.19) that $F_{lm}(P)$ is independent of the third Euler angle γ of P, since $m(P, \mathbf{k}) = e^{iQ(\alpha+\gamma)}$ and $D^l(P)_{mQ} = i^{m-n} e^{-im\alpha} d^l_{mQ}(\beta)\, e^{-iQ\gamma}$. Therefore, $F_{lm}(P)$ can be regarded as a function on the unit sphere.

It is apparent that if P rotates $\mathbf{k}$ into $\mathbf{p}$, $R^{-1}P$ rotates $\mathbf{k}$ into $R^{-1}\mathbf{p}$. We can, therefore, calculate from the definition (5b) and (4)

$$[D(0, R)F_{ln}](P) = \left(\frac{[l]}{4\pi}\right)^{1/2} m(R, P\mathbf{k})\, m(R^{-1}P, \mathbf{k}) D^l(R^{-1}P)_{nQ}$$

$$= \left(\frac{[l]}{4\pi}\right)^{1/2} m(P, \mathbf{k}) m(P^{-1}R, \mathbf{k}) m(R^{-1}P, \mathbf{k}) D^l(R^{-1}P)_{nQ}.$$

Since, as was shown from (3), $m(R, \mathbf{k})^{-1} = m(R^{-1}, \mathbf{k})$, $m(P^{-1}R, \mathbf{k}) \times m(R^{-1}P, \mathbf{k}) = I$. We can now use the representation property and unitarity of D^l to write

$$[D(0, R)F_{ln}](P) = \left(\frac{[l]}{4\pi}\right)^{1/2} m(P, \mathbf{k}) \sum_m D^l(R)^*_{mn} D^l(P)_{mQ}$$

$$= \sum_m D^l(R)^*_{mn} F_{lm}(P). \tag{12.8}$$

Equation (8) shows that the function subspace spanned by the functions F_{lm}, $-l \le m \le l$ is invariant under the rotations, and is, in fact, transformed by $D^l(R)^*$. It follows from the completeness properties of the $d^l{}_{mn}$ and exponential functions that the functions F_{lm} are complete on the unit sphere. They therefore effect the complete reduction of the rotation subgroup.

The reduced representation matrices, which will be denoted by Δ, have rows and columns indexed by a pair (l, m) of subscripts. The matrix elements of $\Delta(0, R)$ are, therefore, given by

$$\Delta(0, R)_{lm,jn} = \delta_{lj} D^l(R)^*_{mn}. \tag{12.9}$$

The elements of the matrix $\Delta(\mathbf{a}, I)$ that represents the translation subgroup are given, from (5a), by

$$e^{i\mathbf{p}\cdot\mathbf{a}} F_{jn}(\mathbf{p}) = \sum_{lm} \Delta(\mathbf{a}, I)_{lm,jn} F_{lm}(\mathbf{p}) \tag{12.10}$$

so that

$$\Delta(\mathbf{a}, I)_{lm,jn} = \int F_{lm}(\mathbf{p})^* e^{i\mathbf{p}\cdot\mathbf{a}} F_{jn}(\mathbf{p})\, d\mathbf{p}, \tag{12.11}$$

the integral being over the direction of $\mathbf{p}$. Since the functions F_{lm} are orthonormal, the transformation to the matrices Δ is unitary, and the matrices Δ are, therefore, a unitary representation.

It will not be necessary to evaluate (11) explicitly, since this will be done in the next section by another method. It is necessary, however, to calculate one element of the Lie algebra of Δ, in order to identify the representation of (9) and (11) with the representation to obtained.

We will calculate the element P_z tangent to the subgroup of translations along the z axis. In this case $e^{i\mathbf{p}\cdot\mathbf{a}} = e^{ipa\cos\theta}$ is independent of the azimuth of $\mathbf{p}$. It follows from this that the integral in (11) vanishes unless m = n, or, substituting (7) into (11)

$$\Delta(a\mathbf{k}, I)_{lm,jn} = \delta_{mn}\sqrt{[l][j]}\, Z_{lj,mQ}(a) \tag{12.12}$$

where

$$Z_{lj,mQ}(a) = \frac{1}{2}\int_0^\pi d^l{}_{mQ}(\theta)e^{ipa\cos\theta}\, d^j{}_{mQ}(\theta)\sin\theta\, d\theta. \tag{12.13}$$

We can now calculate

$$(P_z)_{lm,jn} = \frac{\partial\Delta_{lm,jn}}{\partial a_z}(0) = \delta_{mn}\sqrt{[l][j]}\,\frac{ip}{2}\int_0^\pi d^l{}_{mQ}(\theta)\cos\theta\, d^j{}_{mQ}(\theta)$$

$$\times \sin\theta\, d\theta = \frac{ip}{2}\delta_{mn}\sqrt{[l][j]}\,(-1)^{m+Q}\int_0^\pi d^l{}_{mQ}(\theta)\, d^1{}_{00}(\theta)\, d^j{}_{-m-Q}(\theta)$$

$$\times \sin\theta\, d\theta = ip\delta_{mn}(-1)^{m+Q}\sqrt{[l][j]}\begin{pmatrix} l & j & 1 \\ m & -m & 0\end{pmatrix}\begin{pmatrix} l & j & 1 \\ Q & -Q & 0\end{pmatrix}. \tag{12.14}$$

We have used the facts that $d^1{}_{00}(\theta) = \cos\theta$ and $d_{lmn}(\theta) = (-1)^{m+n} \times d^l{}_{-m-n}(\theta)$. The last step is a straightforward consequence of (8.28).

To conclude this section, it should be remarked that we have shown that the representation D(0, R) of the rotation subgroup contains $D^l(R)^*$ exactly once if $l \geq |Q|$ and not at all if $l < |Q|$. We can write, formally,

$$D(0, R) = \sum_{l=|Q|}^{\infty} D^l(R)^*. \tag{12.15}$$

12-2 EXPLICIT CONSTRUCTION OF THE REPRESENTATIONS OF E_3

In this section the representations of E_3 will be constructed by the method of contraction applied to the representations of O(4). The procedure is similar to the method described briefly in the discussion of E_2, namely of letting the elements of some rotation subgroup approach zero and simultaneously letting the dimension of the representation become large. The reasons for doing this are twofold. Physically, it is plausible that an "infinitesimal" rotation in the z-t plane should generate an infinitesimal translation along the z axis. Mathematically, it is known that the representation of O(4) labeled by j, j' contains the representation $D^L(R)^*$ of the rotation subgroup once if $|j - j'| \leq L \leq j + j'$ and not at all if $L < |j - j'|$. This strongly suggests that the representation j, j' of O(4) should be identified in some way with the representation $Q = j' - j$ of E_3. In the following we consider, therefore, the representations j, j' of O(4) for large j and j' but with the difference $j' - j = Q$, a constant.

In order to carry out the identification of representations of O(4) with those of E_3 it is necessary to employ the representations of the corresponding Lie algebras, as in the derivation of (11.48). The Lie algebra of E_3 is six-dimensional and is spanned by elements P_x, P_y, P_z, M_x, M_y, M_z where P_α is tangent to the subgroup of translations along the α axis, and M_α is the tangent to the subgroup of rotations about the α axis. Since the translations commute we have

$$[P_\alpha, P_\beta] = 0. \tag{12.16a}$$

It is obvious that a translation along and a rotation about a given axis commute, and hence

$$[P_\alpha, M_\alpha] = 0. \tag{12.16b}$$

The elements M_α satisfy

$$[M_x, M_y] = M_z, \qquad [M_y, M_z] = M_x, \qquad [M_z, M_x] = M_y. \tag{12.16c}$$

The remaining commutators can be obtained by considering (11.4) in each of the three coordinate planes. This gives

$$\begin{aligned} [P_x, M_z] &= -P_y & \qquad [P_y, M_z] &= P_x \\ [P_z, M_y] &= -P_x & \qquad [P_x, M_y] &= P_z \\ [P_y, M_x] &= -P_z & \qquad [P_z, M_x] &= P_y \ . \end{aligned} \tag{12.16d}$$

Consider now the matrices T_x, T_y, T_z and S_x, S_y, S_z related to the I_{kl} of equation (10.1) by

$$T_x = \frac{I_{41}}{\sigma}, \qquad T_y = \frac{I_{42}}{\sigma}, \qquad T_z = \frac{I_{43}}{\sigma} \tag{12.17a}$$

$$S_x = I_{32}, \qquad S_y = I_{13}, \qquad S_z = I_{21}. \tag{12.17b}$$

It is easy to verify that if T_α is identified with P_α and S_α is identified with M_α, the T_α and S_α satisfy all of equations (16) with the exception of (16a) which is instead

$$[T_x, T_y] = \frac{S_z}{\sigma^2}, \qquad [T_y, T_z] = \frac{S_x}{\sigma^2}, \qquad [T_z, T_x] = \frac{S_y}{\sigma^2}.$$

In the limit $\sigma \to \infty$, the S_α and T_α satisfy (16), if the limit can be taken in such a way that the T_α remain finite.

We will now fix our attention on T_z and I_{43}. This is sufficient since the identities $I_{42} = [I_{43}, I_{32}]$ and $I_{41} = [I_{43}, I_{31}]$ show that if I_{43} is multiplied by a constant, I_{41} and I_{42} are multiplied by the same constant. The element I_{43} is tangent to the subgroup of rotations in the z-t plane which leave the x-y plane fixed. It is easy to show that the pair $(A^{-1/2}, A^{1/2})$, $A^{\pm 1/2} = \cos(\varphi/2) \pm \sin(\varphi/2) I_z$, gives rise to such a rotation. The matrix that represents I_{43} in the representation of the Lie algebra is, therefore, the derivative with respect to ϕ, evaluated at I, of the matrix that represents $(A^{-1/2}, A^{1/2})$.

It is convenient to write $(A^{-1/2}, A^{1/2}) = (A^{1/2}, A^{1/2})(A^{-1}, I)$ where $A = \cos\phi + \sin\phi\, I_z$. The pair $(A^{1/2}, A^{1/2})$ corresponds to a rotation in the x-y-z subspace and is, in the desired limit, I.

The procedure now is to replace ϕ/σ in the matrix that represents $D(A^{-1}, I)$ and to calculate the derivative with respect to φ of this matrix at $\varphi = 0$. From (10.9) we obtain

$$D_\sigma(A^{-1}, I)_{LM,JN} = \delta_{MN} \sum_K (-1)^{K+M+j+j'} [K]([L][J])^{1/2}$$

$$\times \begin{Bmatrix} L & J & K \\ j & j & j' \end{Bmatrix} \begin{pmatrix} L & J & K \\ M & -M & 0 \end{pmatrix} H_{j,K}\left(\frac{-\phi}{\sigma}\right). \tag{12.18}$$

This matrix would represent a rotation in the z-t plane if the angle of rotation were measured in units of σ^{-1} radians.

Inspection of (10.24) shows that when the derivative of D_σ is evaluated at $\phi = 0$, the only nonvanishing term is that for which $K = 1$. The value of $H'_{j,1}(0)$ is most readily found by putting $\xi = 0$ and $m = n = j$ in (10.14) and evaluating the derivative with respect to χ at $\chi = 0$. Since $D(A, I)_{jj,jj} = e^{2ij\chi}$ in this case, we find

$$2ij = 3\begin{pmatrix} j & j & 1 \\ j & -j & 0 \end{pmatrix} H'_{j,1}(0)$$

or, from the known value of the $3-j$ coefficient,

$$H'_{j,1}(0) = \frac{i}{3}[2j(2j+1)(2j+2)]^{1/2}.$$

From (18) we obtain

$$\frac{\partial D_\sigma}{\partial \phi}(I, I)_{LM,JN} = \delta_{MN}(-1)^{M+j+j'} i([L][J])^{1/2}$$

$$\times \begin{Bmatrix} L & J & 1 \\ j & j & j' \end{Bmatrix} \begin{pmatrix} L & J & 1 \\ M & -M & 0 \end{pmatrix} \frac{1}{\sigma} [2j(2j+1)(2j+2)]^{1/2}. \qquad (12.19)$$

It is shown in the appendix to this chapter that if l_1, l_2, l_3 are large, but the differences $l_i - l_j$ are fixed,

$$\begin{Bmatrix} j_1 & j_2 & j_3 \\ l_1 & l_2 & l_3 \end{Bmatrix} \sim \frac{(-1)^{2(j_2+l_2)}}{(2l_1)^{1/2}} \begin{pmatrix} j_1 & j_2 & j_3 \\ m_1 & m_2 & m_3 \end{pmatrix} \qquad (12.20)$$

where $m_1 = l_3 - l_2$, $m_2 = l_1 - l_3$, $m_3 = l_2 - l_1$.

It is now seen that if we put $\sigma = 2j/p$

$$\lim_{j\to\infty} \frac{\partial D_\sigma}{\partial \phi} (I, I)_{LM,JN} = ip\delta_{MN}([L][J])^{1/2}(-1)^{M+Q}$$

$$\times \begin{pmatrix} L & J & 1 \\ Q & -Q & 0 \end{pmatrix} \begin{pmatrix} L & J & 1 \\ M & -M & 0 \end{pmatrix}. \qquad (12.21)$$

It is observed that this result is identical to (14). We can now draw the following conclusions. If the subgroup of O(4) of rotations in the z-t plane is considered in the variable $-p\phi/2j$ and the limit $j\to\infty$ calculated, the corresponding matrix in the Lie algebra approaches a finite limit. The same remark applies to the subgroups of rotations in the x-t and y-t planes. The limiting elements satisfy the commutation relations (16) with the matrices S_x, S_y, S_z generated by the representation of the rotation subgroup. Furthermore, the representation of the Lie algebra so constructed is identical with the representation of the Lie algebra generated by the matrices Δ. It should be noted that the representation of the rotation subgroup is the same in each case, being the direct sum of the $D^l(R)^*$, $l \geq |Q|$. If the same limit is taken in the representation of O(4), a representation of E_3 is obtained, and, moreover, this representation is identical to the matrices Δ.

In order to obtain the explicit group representations it is necessary to discuss the behavior of $H_{j,K}(-p\phi/2j)$ for large values of j. It is quite easy to show that $(2j)^{-1/2} H_{j,K}(-p\phi/2j)$ approaches a finite limit as $j\to\infty$. Since in the limit ϕ determines the length of the translation along the z axis, it is natural to replace it by a. It is observed first, from (10.27) and (10.18), that

$$\lim_{j\to\infty} (2j)^{-1/2} H_{j,0}\left(\frac{-pa}{2j}\right) = \lim_{j\to\infty} \frac{1}{2j} \frac{\sin[(2j+1)pa/2j]}{\sin(pa/2j)} = \frac{\sin pa}{pa} .$$

The limit in the general case can be obtained by making the following estimates in (10.28).

$$\left[\frac{(2j-K)!}{(2j+K+1)!}\right]^{1/2} \sim (2j)^{-K-1/2} .$$

$$\sin^K \phi \sim \left(\frac{-pa}{2j}\right)^K .$$

$$\frac{d}{d\cos\phi} = -\frac{1}{\sin\phi}\frac{d}{d\phi} \sim -\frac{(2j)^2}{pa}\frac{d}{d(pa)} .$$

Assembling the various factors in (10.28) one easily finds

$$\lim_{j\to\infty} (2j)^{-1/2} H_{j,K}\left(\frac{-pa}{2j}\right) = (-i)^K j_K(pa) \tag{12.22}$$

where we define

$$j_K(x) = x^K \left[\frac{-1}{x}\frac{d}{dx}\right]^K \left[\frac{\sin x}{x}\right]. \tag{12.23}$$

The function j_K is immediately recognized as the spherical Bessel function of order K.

It is now possible to write down the representation of the translation subgroup. For this we need only remark that a translation by $aR\mathbf{k}$ is obtained by multiplying the translation by $a\mathbf{k}$ on the right by R^{-1} and on the left by R; this is, however, the way in which (10.13) was obtained from (10.9). It follows that in the appropriate limit (10.13) represents a translation by a distance a in the direction whose polar angles are ξ, η. We obtain from (20) and (22)

$$\Delta(\mathbf{a}, I)_{LM,JN} = \sum_K i^K (-1)^{M+Q} [K]([L][J])^{1/2}$$

$$\times \begin{pmatrix} L & J & K \\ Q & -Q & 0 \end{pmatrix} \begin{pmatrix} L & J & K \\ M & -N & N-M \end{pmatrix} j_K(pa) Y_{K,M-N}(\xi, \eta). \tag{12.24}$$

The general element of the representation can now be obtained as the product $\Delta(\mathbf{a}, I)\Delta(0, R)$. Again, the complete representation is not of too much interest and will not be written down explicitly. The major result of this section is equation (24), which gives the matrix elements of the translation subgroup in the representation in which the rotation subgroup appears in reduced form.

12-3 PROPERTIES OF SPHERICAL BESSEL FUNCTIONS

In this section the previous results will be applied to derive some of the important properties of the spherical Bessel functions. Since it is not relevant to this work, we will, henceforth, assume for the most part that p = 1.

It is easy to obtain a power series for j_K from equation (23) and the power series for sin x. The result is

$$j_K(x) = (-x)^K \sum_n \frac{(2n)(2n-2)\ldots(2n-2K+2)}{(2n+1)!} (-1)^n x^{2n-2K}$$

$$= \sum_{n=K}^{\infty} \frac{(-1)^{n+K} 2^K n!}{(2n+1)!\,(n-K)!} x^{2n=K} . \tag{12.25}$$

It is a straightforward matter to derive from (25) and (11.62) the familiar relation

$$j_n(x) = \left(\frac{\pi}{2x}\right)^{1/2} J_{n+1/2}(x). \tag{12.26}$$

It follows readily from (25) that for x fixed and large values of K

$$j_K(x) \sim \frac{K!\,(2x)^K}{(2K+1)!} . \tag{12.27}$$

It is seen that for K large $j_K(x)$ approaches zero more rapidly than K^{-n} for any n. It is not difficult to see from (24) that a similar statement also holds for $\Delta(\mathbf{a}, I)_{LM,JN}$.

Perhaps the most important property of the spherical Bessel functions is the fact that they are the coefficients in the partial wave expansion of a plane wave. This result can be derived as follows. We put J = N = 0 in (24); this requires also that Q = 0. In this case

$$\Delta(\mathbf{a}, I)_{LM,00} = i^L [L]^{1/2} j_L(a) Y_{LM}(\xi, \eta). \tag{12.28}$$

It is seen, on the other hand, from (11) and since $F_{00} = (4\pi)^{-1/2}$, that

$$\Delta(\mathbf{a}, I)_{LM,00} = (4\pi)^{-1/2} \int F^*_{LM}(\mathbf{p}) e^{i\mathbf{p}\cdot\mathbf{a}}\, d\mathbf{p}. \tag{12.29}$$

The integral in (29) is, however, the Fourier coefficient of $F_{LM}(\mathbf{p})$ in the Fourier expansion of $e^{i\mathbf{p}\cdot\mathbf{a}}$; we can write, therefore, using (7)

$$e^{i\mathbf{p}\cdot\mathbf{a}} = \sum_L i^L [L]\, j_L(pa) Y_{LM}(\theta, \phi)^* Y_{LM}(\xi, \eta) \tag{12.30}$$

where θ, ϕ are the polar angles of $\mathbf{p}$. It should be noted, however, that the spherical harmonics in (30) are not normalized. The spherical harmonic addition theorem, (9.92), gives the important result

$$e^{ipa\cos\theta} = \sum_L i^L [L]\, j_L(pa) P_L(\cos\theta). \tag{12.31}$$

Recurrence relations for the spherical Bessel functions can be obtained from the group representation property, or by differentiating (31) with respect to pa or cos θ. It is perhaps evident that these two methods are, in fact, equivalent. It is simpler, however, to take the appropriate limit in equations (10.46) and (10.47), divided by $(2j)^{3/2}$. The results are easily seen to be

$$j'_K(x) - \frac{K}{x} j_K(x) = -j_{K+1}(x), \tag{12.32}$$

$$j'_K(x) + \frac{K+1}{x} j_K(x) = j_{K-1}(x). \tag{12.33}$$

These can be combined to give the more usual identities

$$\frac{2K+1}{x} j_K(x) = j_{K-1}(x) + j_{K+1}(x), \tag{12.34}$$

$$(2K+1) j'_K(x) = K j_{K-1}(x) - (K+1) j_{K+1}(x). \tag{12.35}$$

Equations (32) and (33) can also be written as

$$x^K \frac{d}{dx} [x^{-K} j_K(x)] = -j_{K+1}(x), \tag{12.36}$$

$$x^{-K-1} \frac{d}{dx} [x^{K+1} j_K(x)] = j_{K-1}(x). \tag{12.37}$$

It can be immediately demonstrated by taking the correct limit in (10.48) that the j_K satisfy the <u>spherical Bessel equation</u>

$$\frac{d^2 j_K}{dx^2} + \frac{2}{x}\frac{dj_K}{dx} + \left(1 - \frac{K(K+1)}{x^2}\right) j_K = 0. \tag{12.38}$$

This equation could also have been obtained by combining (32) and (33), which provide the factorization of the equation.

The group representation property implies an addition theorem involving spherical Bessel functions and spherical harmonics. The general addition theorem

$$\sum_{ST} \Delta(\mathbf{a}, I)_{LM,ST} \Delta(\mathbf{x}, I)_{ST,JN} = \Delta(\mathbf{x}', I)_{LM,JN}, \tag{12.39}$$

where $\mathbf{x}' = \mathbf{x} + \mathbf{a}$, is rather complicated and involves a summation on each side of the identity. It is not hard to convince oneself that (39) is the most general addition theorem, that is, that no essentially new content is obtained by including rotations in the representation matrices.

A special case of some importance is obtained by putting $J = N = 0$. The result is

$$j_L(r')Y_{LM}(\theta', \phi') = \sum i^{K+S-L}(-1)^M [K][S] \begin{pmatrix} L & S & K \\ 0 & 0 & 0 \end{pmatrix} \begin{pmatrix} L & S & K \\ M & -T & T-M \end{pmatrix}$$

$$\times\, j_K(a)Y_{K,M-T}(\xi, \eta)\, j_S(r)Y_{ST}(\theta, \phi). \tag{12.40}$$

The sum is on K, S, and T and the points whose spherical polar coordinates are (r', θ', ϕ'), (a, ξ, η), and (r, θ, ϕ) correspond respectively to $\mathbf{x}'$, $\mathbf{a}$, and $\mathbf{x}$. Equation (40) is of some practical significance in that it gives the expansion of a partial wave centered at $-\mathbf{a}$ in terms of partial waves centered at the origin. This result has been obtained previously by Friedman and Russek [2] and by Danos and Maximon [3] using a different method.

Danos and Maximon have also applied (40) to calculate the expansion of the harmonic functions $r^L Y_{LM}$ centered at one point in terms of the harmonic functions centered at another point. For this purpose we consider (40) with the parameter p reinstated. Each side of (40) is then a power series in p, with initial term proportional to p^L. Equating the coefficients of p^L on each side of the equation gives the desired result. It is not difficult to see that the only terms that contribute on the right-hand side are those for which $K + S = L$. The result is then, using (27),

$$r'^L Y_{LM}(\theta', \phi') = \sum_{KT} (-1)^M [K][L-K] \left[\frac{K!(L-K)!(2L+1)!}{(2K+1)!(2L-2K+1)!L!}\right]$$

$$\times \begin{pmatrix} L & L-K & K \\ 0 & 0 & 0 \end{pmatrix} \begin{pmatrix} L & L-K & K \\ M & -T & T-M \end{pmatrix}$$

$$\times\ a^K Y_{K,M-T}(\xi,\eta) r^{L-K} Y_{L-K,T}(\theta,\phi). \tag{12.41}$$

It is possible to obtain a simple expression for the 3−j coefficients in (41) which are said to be in the stretched configuration in which one j is equal to the sum of the other two. The expression follows from (8.35) and is

$$\begin{pmatrix} L & L-K & K \\ M & N & P \end{pmatrix} = (-1)^{2K-L+M} \left[\frac{(2K)!(2L-2K)!(L+M)!(L-M)!}{(2L+1)!(K+P)!(K-P)!(L-K-N)!(L-K-N)!}\right]^{1/2}$$

provided of course that M + N + P = 0. If this expression is employed in (41), we obtain the surprisingly simple result

$$Z_{LM}(\mathbf{x}+\mathbf{a}) = \sum_{ST} Z_{ST}(\mathbf{a}) Z_{L-S,M-T}(\mathbf{x}) \tag{12.42a}$$

where the functions Z are defined in terms of spherical harmonics by

$$Z_{LM}(\mathbf{x}) = [(L+M)!(L-M)!]^{-1/2} r^L Y_{LM}(\theta,\phi). \tag{12.42b}$$

Another type of addition theorem can be obtained by putting L = M = 0 in (40) which then becomes

$$j_0(r') = \sum_{KT} (-1)^{K+T} [K]\, j_K(a) Y_{K,-T}(\xi,\eta) j_K(r) Y_{KT}(\theta,\phi)$$

$$= \sum_{KT} [K]\, j_K(-a) j_K(r) Y_{KT}(\xi,\eta)^* Y_{KT}(\theta,\phi).$$

The length r' is given by $r'^2 = r^2 + 2ar\cos\chi + a^2$ where χ is the angle between the ξ, η and θ, ϕ directions. Changing the sign of a, and using the spherical harmonic addition theorem (9.92) shows that

$$j_0(r') = \sum_K [K] j_K(r) j_K(a) P_K(\cos\chi), \tag{12.43}$$

where $r'^2 = r^2 - 2ar\cos\chi + a^2$.

Equation (43) is a special case of a more general addition theorem:

$$\frac{j_L(r')}{r'^L} = \sum_{K=L}^{\infty} \frac{[K] j_K(a) j_K(r) P_K^L(\cos\chi)}{[ar\sin\chi]^L}. \tag{12.44}$$

It is easy to derive this result from (43) by differentiating L times with respect to cos χ, using (23), (9.78), and the fact that

$$\frac{d}{d(\cos\chi)} = -\frac{ar}{r'}\frac{d}{dr'}.$$

12-4 SPHERICAL NEUMANN AND HANKEL FUNCTIONS

This chapter will be concluded with some remarks on the spherical Neumann and spherical Hankel functions. This discussion will be analogous to that of Section 11-7 in which partner functions to the representations of E_2 were considered. We turn now to the problem of finding partner functions to those representations of E_3 for which $Q = 0$.

We consider the identity

$$\sum_{JN} \Delta(-R^{-1}\mathbf{a}, R^{-1})_{LM,JN}\Delta(\mathbf{x}, I)_{JN,00} = \sum_{JN} \Delta(R^{-1}(\mathbf{x}-\mathbf{a}), I)_{LM,JN}$$

$$\times \Delta(0, R^{-1})_{JN,00} = \Delta(R^{-1}(\mathbf{x}-\mathbf{a}), I)_{LM,00} \qquad (12.45)$$

since $\Delta(0, R^{-1})_{JN,00} = \delta_{J0}\delta_{N0}$. Taking the complex conjugate of (45) gives

$$\sum_{JN} \Delta(\mathbf{a}, R)_{JN,LM}\Delta(\mathbf{x}, I)^*_{JN,00} = \Delta(R^{-1}(\mathbf{x}-\mathbf{a}), I)^*_{LM,00}. \qquad (12.46)$$

Since $(T(\mathbf{a}), R)^{-1}$ transforms $\mathbf{x}$ to $R^{-1}(\mathbf{x}-\mathbf{a})$, equation (46) implies that the functions

$$\Delta(\mathbf{x}, I)^*_{LM,00} = (-i)^L[L]^{1/2} j_L(r) Y_{LM}(\theta, \phi)^* \qquad (12.47)$$

constitute a set of partner functions for the representation Δ.

The partner functions to a representation must satisfy a set of six first-order partial differential equations derived from (11.55). We do not wish to go through the procedure of calculating and solving these equations, since it is evident that any set of functions of the form

$$G_{LM}(\mathbf{x}) = (-i)^L[L]^{1/2} f_L(r) Y_{LM}(\theta, \phi)^* \qquad (12.48)$$

in which the functions f_L satisfy the same first-order equations as the j_L, namely (32) and (33), will constitute a set of partner functions.

A second solution to the pair (32) and (33) is given by the functions n_K, the spherical Neumann functions, defined by

$$n_0(x) = -\frac{\cos x}{x} \qquad (12.49a)$$

$$n_K(x) = x^K \left[-\frac{1}{x}\frac{d}{dx} \right]^K n_0(x). \tag{12.49b}$$

It is readily apparent that the n_K satisfy (36) (and hence (32)), but less so that they satisfy (37). This can be proved by induction. One can first calculate

$$x^{-2}\frac{d}{dx}\, x^2\, n_1(x) = x^{-2}\frac{d}{dx}\,[-x \sin x - \cos x] = n_0(x),$$

demonstrating the result for K = 1. If we now operate on (37) with $x^{K-1}(d/dx)x^{-K+1}$ we obtain, since (36) is satisfied, $-n_K(x)$ on the right-hand side. The left-hand side is

$$x^{K-1}\frac{d}{dx}\, x^{-2K}\frac{d}{dx}\, x^{K+1} n_K(x) = n_K''(x) + \frac{2}{x} n_K'(x) - \frac{K(K+1)}{x^2} n_K(x).$$

This is, however, equal to

$$x^{-K-2}\frac{d}{dx}\, x^{2K+2}\frac{d}{dx}\, x^{-K} n_K(x) = -x^{-K-2}\frac{d}{dx}\, x^{K+2} n_{K+1}(x),$$

again since (36) is satisfied. This demonstrates that (37), and hence (33) is valid for K = 1, 2, ...

The functions n_K can be expressed by a real Laurent series in x as

$$n_K(x) = -\sum_{n=0}^{\infty} \frac{(2n-1)(2n-3)\ldots(2n-2K+1)}{(2n)!}(-1)^{n+K} x^{2n-K-1} \tag{12.50}$$

for $x \neq 0$. It can be seen from this that for x fixed and large K the first term is dominant, and hence that

$$n_K(x) \sim (-1)(-3)\ldots(-2K+1)(-x)^{-K-1} = -\frac{(2K)!}{2^K K!\, x^{K+1}}. \tag{12.51}$$

Any linear combination of the form $A\,j_L(x) + B\,n_L(x)$ also satisfies (32) and (33). In particular the spherical Hankel functions

$$h_L^1(x) = x^L \left[-\frac{1}{x}\frac{d}{dx} \right]^L \frac{e^{ix}}{ix} = j_L(x) + i n_L(x) \tag{12.52}$$

$$h_L^2(x) = x^L \left[-\frac{1}{x}\frac{d}{dx} \right]^L \frac{e^{-ix}}{-ix} = j_L(x) - i n_L(x) \tag{12.53}$$

are also solutions of (32) and (33).

If $f_L(x)$ is any solution of (32) and (33) we can write, in analogy to (46) and (47),

$$\sum_{JN} \Delta(\mathbf{a}, R)_{JN,LM}(-i)^J [J]^{1/2} f_J(r) Y_{JN}(\theta, \phi)^*$$

$$= (-i)^L [L]^{1/2} f_L(r') Y_{LM}(\theta', \phi')^*$$

where (x', θ', ϕ') are the spherical polar coordinates of the point $R^{-1} \times (\mathbf{x} - \mathbf{a})$. If we put $R = I$, replace $\mathbf{a}$ by $-\mathbf{a}$ and take the complex conjugate it is easy to see that a generalization of (40) is obtained:

$$f_L(r') Y_{LM}(\theta', \phi') = \sum_{KST} i^{K+S-L} (-1)^M [K][S] \begin{pmatrix} L & S & K \\ 0 & 0 & 0 \end{pmatrix} \begin{pmatrix} L & S & K \\ M & -T & T-M \end{pmatrix}$$

$$\times j_K(a) Y_{K,M-T}(\xi, \eta) f_S(r) Y_{ST}(\theta, \phi). \qquad (12.54)$$

The question of convergence now becomes rather pressing. In fact, since the n_L are singular at the origin, the series in (54) cannot converge for $\mathbf{a} = -\mathbf{x}$. It will be shown, however, that the series converges for $|\mathbf{a}| < |\mathbf{x}|$.

The spherical harmonics in (54) are elements of unitary matrices and are, therefore, bounded by 1. For the same reason, the $3-j$ coefficients in (54) are each bounded by $[K]^{-1/2}$. It is, therefore, sufficient to study the convergence of

$$[S]^2 j_K(a) f_S(r).$$

An extra factor of $(2S+1)$ is included to account for the fact that there are $(2S+1)$ possible values of T in the summation. The difference $K-S$ can assume only a finite number, $2L+1$, of values. We can therefore study terms in the series for which this difference is fixed and show that each such subseries converges separately. From (27) and (51) we have, since the behavior of f_S is essentially that of n_S,

$$[S]^2 j_K(a) f_S(x) \sim B(2S+1)^2 \frac{K!\,2^K (2S)!}{(2K+1)!\,2^S S!} \frac{a^K}{x^{S+1}}.$$

It can be seen from this that the series converges geometrically in (a/x).

Equation (54) may be useful in that it permits the expansion of an arbitrary partial wave, that is, one with some phase shift, in partial waves in a different coordinate system. This result has also been obtained by Maximon and Danos.

Equation (54) also provides an addition theorem for the harmonic functions $r^{-L-1}Y_{LM}(\theta,\phi)$. The method consists of replacing f_K by n_K and r', a, r by pr', pa, pr in (54) and equating coefficients of p^{-L-1}. The only terms on the right-hand side that contribute are those for which $S-K=L$. A straightforward calculation shows that

$$Z_{LM}(\mathbf{x}+\mathbf{a}) = \sum_{ST} Z_{ST}(\mathbf{a})\, Z_{L+S,M-T}(\mathbf{x}) \tag{12.55a}$$

where we define

$$Z_{LM}(\mathbf{x}) = [(L+M)!\,(L-M)!]^{1/2}(-1)^{L-M} r^{-L-1} Y_{LM}(\theta,\phi). \tag{12.55b}$$

Equation (55a) has been derived by Rose [4], who has also obtained equations (42).

In the special case $L=M=0$, equations (55) become the generating function for Legendre polynomials. In this case $Z_{00}(\mathbf{x}+\mathbf{a}) = |\mathbf{x}+\mathbf{a}|^{-1}$ and (55a) can be written

$$\frac{1}{|\mathbf{x}+\mathbf{a}|} = \sum_{ST} (-1)^{S+T} \frac{a^S}{r^{S+1}} Y_{ST}(\xi,\eta)\, Y_{S-T}(\theta,\phi)$$

$$= \sum_{S} (-1)^S \frac{1}{r}\left(\frac{a}{r}\right)^S P_S(\cos\chi)$$

where χ is the angle between the ξ,η direction and the θ,ϕ direction. This is usually written, with $\cos\chi = -t$ and $(a/r) = y$, as

$$[1-2yt+y^2]^{-1/2} = \sum_{l=0}^{\infty} y^l P_l(t), \tag{12.56}$$

since $|\mathbf{x}+\mathbf{a}| = [r^2+2ar\cos\chi + a^2]^{1/2}$.

Equation (56) can be generalized to give a generating function for the associated Legendre functions by differentiating m times with respect to t. The result is, using (9.78)

$$\frac{(2m)!}{2^m m!}\left[\frac{y\sqrt{1-t^2}}{1-2yt+y^2}\right]^m [1-2yt+y^2]^{-1/2} = \sum_{l=m} y^m P_l^m(t). \tag{12.57}$$

To conclude this discussion we note that equation (54) can be applied to derive generalizations of (43) and (44) to the functions f_L. The results are

$$f_0(r') = \sum_K [K]\, j_K(a) f_K(r) P_K(\cos\chi) \tag{12.58}$$

$$\frac{f_L(r')}{r'^L} = \sum_{K=L}^{\infty} \frac{[K]\, j_K(a) f_K(r) P_K{}^L(\cos\chi)}{[ar\sin\chi]^L}, \tag{12.59}$$

where $r'^2 = a^2 - 2ar\cos\chi + r^2$.

12-5 APPENDIX

The purpose of this appendix is to demonstrate equation (20). To do this, Racah's explicit expression (8.56) for the 6 −j coefficient will be employed. We are considering the case in which j_1, j_2, j_3 and $m_1 = l_3 - l_2$, $m_2 = l_1 - l_3$, $m_3 = l_2 - l_1$ are fixed finite numbers, but $l_i \to \infty$. We will make use of the estimate

$$\frac{(n+p)!}{(n+q)!} \sim n^{p-q} \tag{12.60}$$

for $n \to \infty$. The quotient in (60) can be seen to contain $(p-q)$ factors, each of which is asymptotically equal to n.

It can be seen from (8.56b) that

$$\Delta(l_1 l_2 j_3) = \left[\frac{(l_1+l_2-j_3)!\,(l_2+j_3-l_1)!\,(j_3+l_1-l_2)!}{(l_1+l_2+j_3+1)!}\right]^{1/2}$$

$$\sim (2l_1)^{-j_3-1/2}\,[(j_2+m_3)!\,(j_3-m_3)!]^{1/2}.$$

Similar results are valid for $\Delta(l_1 j_2 l_3)$ and $\Delta(j_1 l_2 l_3)$. We can in the same way approximate the quotient $(l_1+l_2+j_1+j_2-t+1)!/(l_1+l_2-j_3-t)!$ in (56c) by $(2l_1)^{j_1+j_2+j_3+1}$. This is only valid if t is not too large; t is, however, bounded by $j_1 + j_2 - j_3$, which is fixed. Substituting these estimates into (8.56a) gives

$$\begin{Bmatrix} j_1 & j_2 & j_3 \\ l_1 & l_2 & l_3 \end{Bmatrix} \sim (2l_1)^{-1/2}(-1)^{2l_2}(-1)^{j_1+j_2-m_3}\Delta(j_1 j_2 j_3)\sum_t (-1)^t$$

$$\times \frac{[(j_1+m_1)!\,(j_1-m_1)!\,(j_2+m_2)!\,(j_2-m_2)!\,(j_3+m_3)!\,(j_3-m_3)!]^{1/2}}{t!\,(j_1+j_2-j_3)!\,(j_1-m_1-t)!\,(j_2+m_2-t)!\,(j_3-j_1-m_2+t)!\,(j_3-j_2+m_1+t)!}$$

$$= (2l_1)^{-1/2}(-1)^{2(l_2+j_2)}\begin{pmatrix} j_1 & j_2 & j_3 \\ m_1 & m_2 & m_3 \end{pmatrix}. \tag{12.61}$$

The last expression is a consequence of (8.40).

Chapter 13

THE QUANTUM–MECHANICAL GROUP

In this chapter the algebra defined by the quantum-mechanical position and momentum operators will be considered. A group that has this algebra will be constructed explicitly. Although this group appears to be of little interest in itself, its irreducible unitary representations are of interest. It will be found that these involve associated Laguerre polynomials and various properties of these functions will be derived from the group representation property. It will also be shown that the representation matrix elements are eigenfunctions of the two-dimensional harmonic oscillator problem and are closely related to hydrogen atom radial wave functions.

A set of partner functions for the group representation will also be constructed. These partner functions are eigenfunctions of the harmonic oscillator problem, and certain properties of Hermite polynomials can be demonstrated from their transformation properties. A function space representation of the group can be given using the harmonic oscillator wave functions as basis vectors in the function space. From this the Born-Jordan representation of the operators can be derived.

The group to be considered here is a subgroup of a four-parameter group whose representations have been calculated by W. Miller [1]. This is the group corresponding to the algebra defined by the boson creation, annihilation and number operators, together with the identity operator. The representations will be calculated here using a method quite different from that of Miller.

13-1 THE QUANTUM-MECHANICAL GROUP

A fundamental axiom of quantum mechanics is that the position and momentum operators q and p satisfy $qp - pq = i$ (if the units are chosen so that $\hbar = 1$). Since q and p commute with i, the three operators q, p, i satisfy

$$[q, i] = 0 \qquad [p, i] = 0 \qquad [q, p] = i. \tag{13.1}$$

This is the algebra described by equations (4.36) with **j** identified with q, **k** with p, and **i** with i. It has been shown by Von Neumann [2] that, except for possible scale changes, there is only one irreducible skew-Hermitian representation of these commutation relations (up to equivalences). This result will not be demonstrated here.

The group G corresponding to this algebra can be constructed from the matrices given in equation (4.37). It is convenient to obtain the group in canonical coordinates. We consider

$$A(x, y, z) = e^{[x\mathbf{j} + y\mathbf{k} + z\mathbf{i}]} = \begin{matrix} 1 & 0 & x \\ -y & 1 & z - \frac{xy}{2} \\ 0 & 0 & 1 \end{matrix} . \tag{13.2}$$

This expression for the group element is a simple consequence of equations (3.24) and (4.37).

It can be verified directly by matrix multiplication that A(x, y, z) A(x', y', z') = A(X, Y, Z) where

$$X = x + x' \tag{13.3a}$$

$$Y = y + y' \tag{13.3b}$$

$$Z = z + z' + \frac{xy' - x'y}{2}. \tag{13.3c}$$

Equations (3) define the product functions for the group and are central to the entire development.

It should be observed that the set of elements of the algebra of the form c**i** is both the center and the derived subalgebra of the algebra. Corresponding to this, the set of group elements of the form A(0, 0, z) is both a central normal subgroup of G and the commutator subgroup of G. In an irreducible representation A(0, 0, z) must be represented by a multiple of I. Since this subgroup is isomorphic to R, A(0, 0, z) must be represented by e^{icz} for c some real number. It will be found that there is an irreducible representation of G corresponding to each value of c. While these representations are inequivalent, they are not significantly different since they can be generated one from another by changing the scale of the parameters. The index c is, therefore, somewhat analogous to the index p in the representations of the Euclidean groups.

The method of contraction can be applied to find representations of G by taking a suitable limit of the known representations of the rotation group. This will be demonstrated first for the representations of the Lie algebra. Consider matrices J_x, J_y, J_z satisfying equations (9.40) and new matrices $J_x' = J_x/\sqrt{M}$, $J_y' = J_y/\sqrt{M}$, $J_z' = J_z/M$ where M is some positive number. It is observed that the new matrices satisfy

$$[J_x', J_y'] = J_z', \qquad [J_y', J_z'] = \frac{J_x'}{M}, \qquad [J_z', J_x'] = \frac{J_y'}{M}. \tag{13.4}$$

In the limit $M \to \infty$ the matrices J_x', J_y', J_z' satisfy equation (1) if J_x', J_y', J_z' are identified with q, p, i respectively. Unfortunately, J_x', J_y', J_z' themselves approach zero as $M \to \infty$. This difficulty can be avoided if the dimension of the matrices is allowed to increase as M increases; it turns out that if we put $M = l$, where $(2l + 1)$ is the dimension of the representation, and consider the limit $l \to \infty$, a representation of (1) is obtained. A further explanation of how the limit is to be taken is, however, necessary. The matrices will be considered to spread out from the $(-l, -l)$ element in the positive directions, rather than as spreading out from the (0,0) element in both directions as might appear more natural at first sight. The matrix elements will, therefore, be relabeled so that the $(-l, -l)$ element has indices (0, 0), and so on.

It is an easy matter to take the desired limit in the matrices defined by equations (9.42) and (9.50). The results are

$$\lim_{l\to\infty} \frac{J_z}{l} = iI \tag{13.5}$$

$$\lim_{l\to\infty} \frac{J_x}{\sqrt{l}} = Q = -\frac{i}{\sqrt{2}} \begin{pmatrix} 0 & 1 & 0 & 0 \cdots \\ 1 & 0 & \sqrt{2} & 0 \cdots \\ 0 & \sqrt{2} & 0 & \sqrt{3} \cdots \\ \cdot & \cdot & \cdot & \cdots\cdot \end{pmatrix} \tag{13.6}$$

$$\lim_{l\to\infty} \frac{J_y}{\sqrt{l}} = P = \frac{1}{\sqrt{2}} \begin{pmatrix} 0 & 1 & 0 & 0 & \cdots \\ -1 & 0 & \sqrt{2} & 0 & \cdots \\ 0 & -\sqrt{2} & 0 & \sqrt{3} & \cdots \\ \cdot & \cdot & \cdot & \cdots & \end{pmatrix} \tag{13.7}$$

where I is an infinite-dimensional unit operator. It can be verified by direct calculation that, as anticipated, $QP - PQ = iI$.

We turn now to the more difficult problem of calculating the representation of G corresponding to the matrices Q and P. For this purpose it is necessary to change the scale of the parameters in the representation of the rotation group so that J_x, J_y, J_z become J_x', J_y', J_z'. To this end we introduce a matrix $\bar{D}^l(\phi, z, t)$ defined in terms of $D^l(R)$ by

$$\bar{D}^l(\phi, z, t) = \left(D^l \ \phi + \frac{z}{2l}, \frac{t}{\sqrt{l}}, -\phi + \frac{z}{2l}\right). \tag{13.8}$$

It is observed that if $t = 0$, $\bar{D}^l$ corresponds to a rotation about the z axis by z/l, that if $\phi = z = 0$, $\bar{D}^l$ is a rotation about the x axis by $t/\sqrt{l}$, and that if $z = 0$, $\phi = \pi/2$, $\bar{D}^l$ is a rotation about the y axis by $t/\sqrt{l}$. It follows that

$$\frac{\partial \bar{D}^l}{\partial z}(0, 0, 0) = \frac{J_z}{l} = J_z'$$

$$\frac{\partial \bar{D}^l}{\partial t}(0, 0, 0) = \frac{J_x}{\sqrt{l}} = J_x'$$

$$\frac{\partial \bar{D}^l}{\partial t}\left(\frac{\pi}{2}, 0, 0\right) = \frac{J_y}{\sqrt{l}} = J_y'.$$

It is more generally true that $\bar{D}^l(\phi, 0, t) = Z(\phi)X(t/\sqrt{l})Z(-\phi)$ is a rotation by $t/\sqrt{l}$ about an axis in the x-y plane forming an angle ϕ with the x axis. It can, therefore, be seen geometrically that

$$\frac{\partial \bar{D}^l}{\partial t}(\phi, 0, 0) = \cos\phi J_x' + \sin\phi J_y'.$$

This can also be verified directly from equation (9.6).

The matrices $\bar{D}^l(\phi, 0, t)$ define a one-parameter subgroup in the parameter t with tangent vector $\cos\phi J_x' + \sin\phi J_y'$ at the identity. In the limit $l \to \infty$, $\bar{D}^l(\phi, 0, t)$ must be a one-parameter subgroup with tangent vector $\cos\phi Q + \sin\phi P$. The resulting matrices, therefore, represent the group elements $e^{t[\cos\phi \mathbf{j} + \sin\phi \mathbf{k}]} = A(t\cos\phi, t\sin\phi, 0)$.

We consider now the question of evaluating the desired limit, which will be denoted by $\bar{\Delta}_{\mu\nu}(z, \phi, t)$. Specifically,

$$\bar{\Delta}_{\mu\nu}(z, \phi, t) = \lim_{l\to\infty} D^l\left(\phi + \frac{z}{2l}, \frac{t}{\sqrt{l}}, -\phi + \frac{z}{2l}\right)_{\mu-l,\,\nu-l} \tag{13.9}$$

$$= \lim_{l\to\infty} i^{\mu-\nu} e^{-i(\mu-l)(\phi+z/2l)}$$

$$d^l_{\mu-l,\,\nu-l}\left(\frac{t}{\sqrt{l}}\right) e^{-i(\nu-l)(-\phi+z/2l)}$$

$$= i^{\mu-\nu} e^{iz} e^{i(\nu-\mu)\phi} F_{\mu\nu}(t) \tag{13.10}$$

where

$$F_{\mu\nu}(t) = \lim_{l\to\infty} d^l_{\mu-l,\,\nu-l}\left(\frac{t}{\sqrt{l}}\right). \tag{13.11}$$

The indices μ and ν can assume the values 0, 1, ...

The matrix $\bar{\Delta}_{\mu\nu}(0, \phi, t)$ represents the group element $A(t\cos\phi, t\sin\phi, 0)$. Furthermore, it is clear that $\bar{\Delta}_{\mu\nu}(z, \phi, 0) = e^{iz}\delta_{\mu\nu}$ represents the one-parameter subgroup A(0, 0, z) since the tangent at the identity of this matrix is iI. It can be concluded that the general matrix $\bar{\Delta}_{\mu\nu}(z, \phi, t)$ represents the group element $A(t\cos\phi, t\sin\phi, z)$ since this can be factored into the form $A(t\cos\phi, t\sin\phi, 0)$ A(0, 0, z).

It still remains to calculate the functions $F_{\mu\nu}$ defined by equation (11). This can be done by taking the limit $l \to \infty$ in $d^l_{\mu-l,\nu-l}(t/\sqrt{l})$ with this function expressed explicitly through equation (9.61).

It is convenient to introduce a new variable $\theta = t^2/2$ and it is necessary to observe that for large values of l, $\cos\beta$ is approximately $(1 - \theta/l)$; it is inadequate to approximate $\cos\beta$ by 1. The various factors in (9.61) can now be estimated for large values of l as follows.

$$\sin^{n-m}\beta \sim \left(\frac{t}{\sqrt{l}}\right)^{\nu-\mu}$$

$$(1+\cos\beta)^m \sim \left(2 - \frac{\theta}{l}\right)^{\mu-l} \sim 2^{\mu-l} e^{\theta/2}.$$

$$[(l+m)!(l-m)!]^{-1/2}\left[\frac{(l-n)!}{(l+n)!}\right]^{1/2} = [\mu!\,\nu!]^{-1/2}\left[\frac{(2l-\nu)!}{(2l-\mu)!}\right]^{1/2}$$

$$\sim [\mu!\,\nu]^{-1/2}(2l)^{(\mu-\nu)/2}$$

$$\frac{d^{l+n}}{d(\cos\beta)^{l+n}} \sim (-l)^{\nu}\frac{d^{\nu}}{d\theta^{\nu}}$$

$$(\cos\beta-1)^{l+m}(\cos\beta+1)^{l-m} \sim \left(\frac{-\theta}{l}\right)^{\mu}\left(2-\frac{\theta}{l}\right)^{2l-\mu}$$

$$\sim (-1)^{\mu}2^{2l-\mu}l^{-\mu}\theta^{\mu}e^{-\theta}.$$

It can now be seen that when these estimates are substituted into (9.61) the factors of l and 2^{l} disappear and that the limit is given by

$$F_{\mu\nu}(t) = (-1)^{\mu+\nu}[\mu!\,\nu!]^{-1/2}\left[\frac{t}{\sqrt{2}}\right]^{\nu-\mu} e^{\theta/2}\frac{d^{\nu}}{d\theta^{\nu}}\theta^{\mu}e^{-\theta}, \quad (13.12)$$

with $\theta = t^2/2$.

The associated Laguerre polynomial of degree m and index n is defined by

$$L_m^{\ n}(x) = \frac{e^x}{m!\,x^n}\frac{d^m}{dx^m}x^{m+n}e^{-x}. \quad (13.13)$$

Equation (12) can, therefore, be written

$$F_{\mu\nu}(t) = (-1)^{\mu+\nu}\left[\frac{\nu!}{\mu!}\right]^{1/2}\left[\frac{t}{\sqrt{2}}\right]^{\mu-\nu}e^{-t^2/4}L_{\nu}^{\ \mu-\nu}\left(\frac{t^2}{2}\right). \quad (13.14)$$

The complete representation is given, from (10) and (14), by

$$\bar{\Delta}_{\mu\nu}(\phi, z, t) = (-i)^{\mu-\nu}e^{iz}\left[\frac{x-iy}{\sqrt{2}}\right]^{\mu-\nu}e^{-(x^2+y^2)/4}$$

$$\times\left[\frac{\nu!}{\mu!}\right]^{1/2}L_{\nu}^{\ \mu-\nu}\left(\frac{x^2+y^2}{2}\right). \quad (13.15)$$

The last expression is the representation in terms of the group parameters x, y, z since $te^{-i\phi} = x - iy$ and $t^2 = x^2 + y^2$.

Other inequivalent representations may be obtained from (15) by changing the scale of the parameters; that is, it is possible to multiply x by α, y by β and z by $\alpha\beta$ without affecting the form of either equations (3) or the commutation relations of the corresponding Lie algebra. We can use this observation to simplify (15) slightly by removing various factors of $\sqrt{2}$; we put $\alpha = \beta = \sqrt{2}$ and obtain

$$\Delta_{\mu\nu}(x, y, z) = i^{\mu-\nu} e^{2iz} e^{i(\nu-\mu)\phi} F_{\mu\nu}(\sqrt{2}t)$$

$$= (-i)^{\mu-\nu} e^{2iz}(x - iy)^{\mu-\nu} e^{-(x^2+y^2)/2}$$

$$\times \left[\frac{\nu!}{\mu!}\right]^{1/2} L_{\nu}^{\mu-\nu}(x^2 + y^2) \tag{13.16}$$

as a representation for A(x, y, z). Equation (16) gives rise to the slightly paradoxical result that i is represented by 2iI.

13-2 PROPERTIES OF LAGUERRE POLYNOMIALS

Since the representation (16) has been constructed as a limit of unitary representations, it is itself unitary; that is,

$$\Delta_{\mu\nu}(-x, -y, -z) = \Delta_{\nu\mu}(x, y, z)^* . \tag{13.17a}$$

In terms of the functions $F_{\mu\nu}$ this is

$$F_{\nu\mu}(t) = (-1)^{\mu-\nu} F_{\mu\nu}(t) \tag{13.17b}$$

and in terms of Laguerre polynomials it is

$$L_{\nu}^{\mu-\nu}(t) = (-1)^{\mu-\nu} \frac{\mu!}{\nu!} t^{\nu-\mu} L_{\mu}^{\nu-\mu}(t); \tag{13.17c}$$

in other words, the function $(-1)^{\mu} \mu!\, t^{-\mu} L_{\mu}^{\nu-\mu}(t)$ is symmetric in μ and ν.

The group representation property implies an addition theorem for the functions Δ, and hence for the Laguerre polynomials. The general theorem is

$$\sum_{\lambda} \Delta_{\mu\lambda}(x, y, z)\Delta_{\lambda\nu}(x', y', z') = \Delta_{\mu\nu}(X, Y, Z) \tag{13.18}$$

where X, Y, Z are given by equation (3). The parameters z and z' do not play a significant role, so that we put z = z' = 0. Equation (18) is explicitly, using (16) and rearranging the result,

$$\sum_\lambda \left[\frac{x' - iy'}{x - iy}\right]^\lambda L_\lambda^{\mu-\lambda}(x^2 + y^2) L_\nu^{\lambda-\nu}(x'^2 + y'^2)$$
$$= \left[\frac{X - iY}{x - iy}\right]^\mu \left[\frac{x' - iy'}{X - iY}\right]^\nu e^{2iZ} e^{-xx'-yy'} L_\nu^{\mu-\nu}(X^2 + Y^2).$$

Since $Z = (xy' - x'y)/2$, $2iZ - xx' - yy' = -(x + iy)(x' - iy')$, and the addition theorem is

$$\sum_\lambda \left[\frac{x' - iy'}{x - iy}\right]^\lambda L_\lambda^{\mu-\lambda}(x^2 + y^2) L_\nu^{\lambda-\nu}(x'^2 + y'^2)$$
$$= \left[1 + \frac{x' - iy'}{x - iy}\right]^\mu \left[1 + \frac{x - iy}{x' - iy'}\right]^{-\nu} e^{-(x+iy)(x'-iy')}$$
$$\times L_\nu^{\mu-\nu}((x + x')^2 + (y + y')^2). \tag{13.19}$$

We have also used the facts that $X = x + x'$ and $Y = y + y'$.

The special cases $y = y' = 0$ and $x' = y = 0$ may be of more interest than the general equation (19). They are

$$\sum_\lambda \left(\frac{x'}{x}\right)^\lambda L_\lambda^{\mu-\lambda}(x^2) L_\nu^{\lambda-\nu}(x'^2)$$
$$= \left[1 + \frac{x'}{x}\right]^\mu \left[1 + \frac{x}{x'}\right]^{-\nu} e^{-xx'} L_\nu^{\mu-\nu}((x + x')^2) \tag{13.20}$$

$$\sum_\lambda \left(\frac{-iy'}{x}\right)^\lambda L_\lambda^{\mu-\lambda}(x^2) L_\nu^{\lambda-\nu}(y'^2)$$
$$= \left[1 - \frac{iy'}{x}\right]^\mu \left[1 + \frac{ix}{y'}\right]^{-\nu} e^{ixy'} L_\nu^{\mu-\nu}(x^2 + y'^2). \tag{13.21}$$

Equation (20) can be applied to find a generating function, which is not, however, the most familiar one, for the associated Laguerre polynomials. It is seen from (13) that $L_0^n(x) = 1$ for all x and n. We put $\nu = 0$ in (20) and also $x'/x = \theta$, $x^2 = y$. Equation (20) becomes

$$\sum_\lambda \theta^\lambda L_\lambda^{\mu-\lambda}(y) = (1 + \theta)^\mu e^{-\theta y}. \tag{13.22}$$

Various identities involving associated Laguerre polynomials can be obtained from equation (22) in a straightforward way. Differentiation of (22) with respect to y yields the result

$$\frac{d}{dy} L_\lambda^\sigma(y) = -L_{\lambda-1}^{\sigma+1}(y) \quad \lambda \geq 1, \tag{13.23}$$

and differentiation with respect to θ gives

$$yL_\lambda^{\sigma}(y) = (\lambda + \sigma)L_\lambda^{\sigma-1}(y) - (\lambda + 1)L_{\lambda+1}^{\sigma-1}(y). \tag{13.24}$$

Multiplication by $(1 + \theta)$ gives a third identity:

$$L_\lambda^{\sigma}(y) = L_\lambda^{\sigma+1}(y) - L_{\lambda-1}^{\sigma+1}(y), \qquad \lambda \geq 1. \tag{13.25}$$

The orthogonality property of the Laguerre polynomials can now be demonstrated in a rather heuristic fashion. We consider equation (9.64) which can be rewritten as

$$\int_0^{\pi} d^{l}_{\mu-l,\,\nu-l}(\beta)\, d^{l'}_{\mu'-l',\nu'-l'}(\beta) \sin\beta\, d\beta = \frac{2}{2l+1}\delta_{ll'}$$

provided $\mu - l = \mu' - l'$ and $\nu - l = \nu' - l'$. We put $l' - l = \lambda$ and change the variable of integration to $y = \sqrt{l}\beta$; then $\mu' = \mu + \lambda$ and $\nu' = \nu + \lambda$. The orthogonality relation is then

$$\int_0^{\sqrt{l}\pi} d^{l}_{\mu-l,\nu-l}\left(\frac{y}{\sqrt{l}}\right) d^{l'}_{\mu+\lambda-l,\,\nu+\lambda-l}\left(\frac{\rho y}{\sqrt{l'}}\right) \sin\frac{y}{\sqrt{l}}\frac{dy}{\sqrt{l}} = \frac{2}{2l+1}\delta_{\lambda o}$$

where

$$\rho = \sqrt{(l'/l)}\,.$$

In the limit $l \to \infty$ this becomes

$$\int_0^{\infty} F_{\mu\nu}(t)F_{\mu+\lambda,\nu+\lambda}(t)\, t\, dt = \delta_{\lambda o}. \tag{13.26a}$$

In terms of Laguerre polynomials and the variable $\theta = t^2/2$ this is

$$\int_0^{\infty} \theta^{\mu-\nu} e^{-\theta} L_\nu^{\mu-\nu}(\theta) L_{\nu+\lambda}^{\mu-\nu}(\theta)\, d\theta = \frac{\mu!}{\nu!}\delta_{\lambda o}. \tag{13.26b}$$

We can conclude that the functions L_m^n for fixed n are orthogonal on the interval $(0, \infty)$ with respect to the weight function $x^n e^{-x}$.

Equations (9.59) and (9.60) can be applied to give two recurrence relations for the functions $F_{\mu\nu}(t)$, and hence for the associated Laguerre polynomials. In taking the limit $l \to \infty$ in these equations a little care is required in treating the term $m \csc\beta - n \cot\beta = [(\mu - l) - (\nu - l)\cos\beta]/\sin\beta$, where $\beta = t/\sqrt{l}$. To obtain the correct answer, it is necessary to approximate $\cos\beta$ by $1 - t^2/2l$, which gives

$$m \csc \beta - n \cot \beta \sim \sqrt{l}\left[\frac{\mu - \nu}{t} - \frac{t}{2}\right].$$

In the limit $l \to \infty$ equations (9.59) and (9.60) (multiplied by $l^{-1/2}$) become

$$F'_{\mu\nu}(t) + \left[\frac{\mu - \nu}{t} - \frac{t}{2}\right]F_{\mu\nu}(t) = -\sqrt{2}(\nu + 1)\, F_{\mu,\nu+1}(t). \tag{13.27}$$

$$F'_{\mu\nu}(t) - \left[\frac{\mu - \nu}{t} - \frac{t}{2}\right]F_{\mu\nu}(t) = \sqrt{(2\nu)}\, F_{\mu,\nu-1}(t). \tag{13.28}$$

In terms of Laguerre polynomials these are equation (23) and

$$yL'^{\sigma}_{\lambda}(y) + (\sigma - y)L^{\sigma}_{\lambda}(y) = (\lambda + 1)L^{\sigma-1}_{\lambda+1}(y). \tag{13.29}$$

This is not a new identity, but can be derived from equations (23)-(25).

Equations (27) and (28) can be combined to give a second-order differential equation for the $F_{\mu\nu}$:

$$F''_{\mu\nu}(t) + \frac{1}{t}F'_{\mu\nu}(t) - \left[\frac{(\nu - \mu)^2}{t^2} - (\mu + \nu + 1) + \frac{t^2}{4}\right]F_{\mu\nu} = 0. \tag{13.30}$$

Equations (27) and (28) provide the factorization for this equation. Similarly, equations (29) and (23) can be combined, by differentiating (29) with respect to y, to give the differential equation for Laguerre polynomials.

$$yL''^{\sigma}_{\lambda}(y) + (\sigma + 1 - y)L'^{\sigma}_{\lambda}(y) + \lambda L^{\sigma}_{\lambda}(y) = 0. \tag{13.31}$$

It is interesting to observe that equation (30) is essentially the same as the radial wave equation for the two-dimensional isotropic harmonic oscillator. The equation is, in units in which the mass, $\hbar$ and the spring constant are 1,

$$-\frac{1}{2r}\frac{d}{dr}r\frac{d\psi}{dr} + \left[\frac{m^2}{2r^2} + \frac{1}{2}r^2\right]\psi = E\psi. \tag{13.32}$$

The parameter m^2 is the separation constant for the equation; if ψ satisfies equation (32), $\psi(r)e^{im\phi}$ is the solution of the complete wave equation. It is, therefore, necessary that $m = 0, \pm 1, \ldots$.

It is observed that equation (30) implies that $\psi(r) = F_{\mu\nu}(\sqrt{2}r)$ is a solution of equation (32), with $m = \nu - \mu$ and $E = \mu + \nu + 1 = n$. This shows that the energy of the system is $n\hbar\omega$, $n = 1, 2, \ldots$ where ω is the natural frequency $\sqrt{(k/M)}$, M being the mass and k the spring constant. For a particular n, m can assume the n values $n - 1, n - 3, \ldots, -n + 1$, so that the nth energy level is n-fold degenerate. This corresponds to the possibility of sharing $n - 1$ quanta of energy between the x and y directions in n ways. (The zero-point energy of 1/2 in each direction cannot be shared.)

The complete harmonic oscillator wave function is $e^{im\phi}\psi(r)$. Equation (16) shows, therefore, that the wave function is $\pi^{-1/2}$ $\Delta_{\mu\nu}(x, y, 0)$, where the factor $\pi^{-1/2}$ is included to normalize the wave function. Equation (26a) shows that a factor $\sqrt{2}$ is required to normalize the radial factor, and a factor $(2\pi)^{-1/2}$ normalizes the angular factor.

The function $F_{\mu\nu}$ are also related to hydrogen atom radial wave functions. This can be seen by putting $\theta = t^2/2$ in (30); the differential operator in (30), which can be expressed as $(1/t)(d/dt)t(d/dt)$ is then given by $(1/t)(d/dt)t^2(d/d\theta) = 2(d/d\theta)\theta(d/d\theta)$ since $(d/dt) = t(d/d\theta)$. Equation (30) can, therefore, be written

$$\frac{1}{\theta}\frac{d}{d\theta}\,\theta\frac{d}{d\theta}\,F_{\mu\nu} - \left[\frac{(\nu - \mu)^2}{4\theta^2} - \frac{(\mu + \nu + 1)}{2\theta} + \frac{1}{4}\right]F_{\mu\nu} = 0.$$

The function $w = \theta^{-1/2} F_{\mu\nu}$ satisfies

$$\frac{d^2w}{d\theta^2} + \frac{2}{\theta}\frac{dw}{d\theta} - \left[\frac{(\nu - \mu)^2 - 1}{4\theta^2} - \frac{(\mu + \nu + 1)}{2\theta} + \frac{1}{4}\right]w = 0.$$

If the scale of the independent variable is now changed by putting $r = (\mu + \nu + 1)\theta/4$, the equation can be written

$$\frac{1}{2}\frac{1}{r^2}\frac{d}{dr}\,r^2\frac{dw}{dr} + \frac{l(l + 1)}{2r^2}w - \frac{1}{r}w = -\frac{2}{(\mu + \nu + 1)^2}w. \tag{13.33}$$

where $l = (\nu - \mu - 1)/2$. It will be assumed that $\nu > \mu$. Equation (33) is the radial Schroedinger wave equation for the hydrogen atom in units in which $e = m = \hbar = 1$. The energy, which in the present units is measured in 2 Rydbergs, is $-1/2n^2$ where $n = (\mu + \nu + 1)/2$. In order that l be an integer it is necessary that $\nu - \mu$ be odd; $(\mu + \nu + 1)$ is, therefore, necessarily even, and n, the principal quantum number, can be any integer satisfying $n \geq l + 1$.

The radial wave function $R_{nl}(r)$ is proportional to $t^{-1}F_{n-l-1,l+n}(t)$ where $t = 2(r/n)^{1/2}$; explicitly, from (14)

$$R_{nl}(r) = A\left(\frac{2r}{n}\right)^{l} e^{-r/n} L_{n-l-1}^{2l+1}\left(\frac{2r}{n}\right) \tag{13.34a}$$

where A is a normalization constant which must satisfy

$$A^2 \int_0^{\infty} \left(\frac{2r}{n}\right)^{2l} e^{-2r/n} \left[L_{n-l-1}^{2l+1}\left(\frac{2r}{n}\right)\right]^2 r^2\, dr = 1.$$

The integral can be evaluated from equation (26) if we put $2r/n = y$ and use equation (24) and (25) to write a factor $y\, L_{n-l-1}^{2l+1}(y)$ as $-(n+l)L_{n-l-2}^{2l+1}(y) + (2n)L_{n-l-1}^{2l+1}(y) - (n-l)L_{n-l}^{2l+1}(y)$. It is then found that

$$A = \pm\frac{2}{n^2}\left[\frac{(n-l-1)!}{(n+l)!}\right]^{1/2}. \tag{13.34b}$$

In terms of the functions $F_{\mu\nu}$ the wave function is

$$R_{nl}(r) = \frac{2\sqrt{2}}{n^2} t^{-1} F_{n+l,n-l-1}(t), \qquad t = 2\left(\frac{r}{n}\right)^{1/2}. \tag{13.35}$$

13-3 HARMONIC OSCILLATOR WAVE FUNCTIONS

It was found in Section 9-5 that the functions $D^l(\alpha, \beta, 0)^*_{m0}$ play a special role in the theory of the rotation group. These are, within a normalization constant, the spherical harmonics, which constitute a set of partner functions for the group representations. It is natural to attempt to take the limit of these functions as discussed in the first section, and see if one obtains partner functions for the quantum-mechanical group. It will be found that if this is done in the correct way, we do find a set of partner functions, and that these are the eigenfunctions of the quantum-mechanical harmonic oscillator problem.

We are interested in the behavior of $d^l_{\mu-l,0}(\beta)$ for large values of l. These functions approach zero in this limit for all values of β. It will be found, however, that they are largest for β close to $\pi/2$ and that $d^l_{\mu-l,0}(\pi/2) \sim l^{-1/4}$. In order to obtain a finite limit, it is necessary to evaluate $d^l_{\mu-l,0}$ at values close to $\pi/2$; it turns out that β must be of the order of $l^{-1/2}$ from $\pi/2$.

It will now be shown that

$$G_\mu(\xi) = \lim_{l\to\infty} l^{1/4}\, d^l_{\mu-l,0}\left(\frac{\pi}{2} - \frac{\xi}{\sqrt{l}}\right) \tag{13.36}$$

exists, and is a harmonic oscillator wave function. We will use equations (9.76) and (9.79) with $m = \mu - l$ and $z = \cos\beta = \sin(\xi/\sqrt{l})$, or for large values of l, $z = \xi/\sqrt{l}$. Equation (36) becomes

$$G_\mu(\xi) = \lim_{l\to\infty} \frac{(-1)^{\mu-l}\, l^{1/4}}{2^l\, l!}\left[\frac{(2l-\mu)!}{\mu!}\right]^{1/2} \times \left(1-\frac{\xi^2}{l}\right)^{(\mu-l)/2} l^{\mu/2}\frac{d^\mu}{d\xi^\mu}\left(\frac{\xi^2}{l}-1\right)^l$$

$$= \lim_{l\to\infty} (-1)^\mu \frac{l^{\mu/2+1/4}}{2^l\, l!}\left[\frac{(2l-\mu)!}{\mu!}\right]^{1/2} e^{\xi^2/2}\frac{d^\mu}{d\xi^\mu}e^{-\xi^2}.$$

The limit of the remaining factors must be calculated from Stirling's formula: $x! \sim (2\pi x)^{1/2}(x/e)^x$. It can be seen that $l^{\mu/2}[(2l-\mu)!]^{1/2} \sim 2^{-\mu/2}[(2l)!]^{1/2}$. Stirling's formula now shows that $l^{1/4}[(2l)!]^{1/2} \sim 2^l |l!| \pi^{-1/4}$. We therefore obtain

$$G_\mu(\xi) = (-1)^\mu [2^\mu \mu! \sqrt{\pi}]^{-1/2} e^{\xi^2/2}\frac{d^\mu}{d\xi^\mu}e^{-\xi^2}$$

$$= [2^\mu \mu! \sqrt{\pi}]^{-1/2} e^{-\xi^2/2} H_\mu(\xi) \tag{13.37}$$

where

$$H_\mu(\xi) = (-1)^\mu e^{\xi^2}\frac{d^\mu}{d\xi^\mu}e^{-\xi^2}. \tag{13.38}$$

The function H_μ, which is a polynomial of degree μ, is known as a <u>Hermite polynomial</u>.

It may be recognized that the functions G_μ are the wave functions for the quantum-mechanical harmonic oscillator problem. This can be demonstrated by taking the correct limit in equation (9.62) which is, for $n = 0$ and $m = \mu - l$,

$$(1-z^2)^2 f'' - 2z(1-z^2)f' - (\mu - l)^2 f + l(l+1)(1-z^2)f = 0.$$

In this case $z = \sin(\xi/\sqrt{l}) \sim \xi/\sqrt{l}$ and the limit is easily taken by retaining only terms proportional to l. The limit can be expressed as

$$-\frac{1}{2}f'' + \frac{\xi^2}{2}f = \left(\mu + \frac{1}{2}\right)f \tag{13.39}$$

which is the Schroedinger equation for the harmonic oscillator, expressed in units such that the mass, ħ, and the spring constant are 1. The energy eigenvalue in these units is, therefore, $\mu + 1/2$.

It is possible to verify also, using arguments similar to those that led to equation (26), that the functions G_μ satisfy

$$\int_{-\infty}^{\infty} G_\mu(\xi)G_\nu(\xi)\, d\xi = \delta_{\mu\nu} \tag{13.40}$$

and hence that the Hermite polynomials satisfy

$$\int_{-\infty}^{\infty} e^{-\xi^2}H_\mu(\xi)H_\nu(\xi)\, d\xi = \pi^{1/2}2^\mu \mu!\,\delta_{\mu\nu}. \tag{13.41}$$

We will now investigate the role that the functions G_μ play as partner functions for the representation. To this end, let us consider equation (9.69) which can be rewritten in a form convenient for the present purpose, with $n = 0$, as

$$\begin{aligned} &l^{1/4} \sum_{\rho=0}^{2l} e^{-i(\rho-l)\alpha}\, d^l_{\mu-l,\rho-l}\left(\frac{t}{\sqrt{l}}\right) d^l_{\rho-l,0}\left(\frac{\pi}{2} - \frac{\xi}{\sqrt{l}}\right) \\ &= l^{1/4} e^{-i(\mu-l)A}\, d^l_{\mu-l,0}(B). \end{aligned} \tag{13.42}$$

It is now desired to take the limit $l \to \infty$ in this equation. To this end, it is necessary to establish the behavior of A and B for l large; it is in fact necessary to determine the limiting behavior of $l(A - \alpha)$ and $\pi/2 - B$.

Equation (9.9c) shows that $\cos B = \cos(t/\sqrt{l})\cos[(\pi/2) - (\xi/\sqrt{l})] - \sin(t/\sqrt{l})\sin[(\pi/2) - (\xi/\sqrt{l})]\cos\alpha \sim (\xi - t\cos\alpha)/\sqrt{l}$. Since $\cos B = \sin(\pi/2 - B)$, $\pi/2 - B \sim (\xi - t\cos\alpha)/\sqrt{l}$ and B is given, to the necessary degree of approximation, by $\pi/2 - (\xi - t\cos\alpha)/\sqrt{l}$. Hence, in the limit $l \to \infty$, $l^{1/4} d^l_{\mu-l,0}(B) = G_\mu(\xi - t\cos\alpha)$.

The behavior of $l(A - \alpha)$ can be determined from equations (9.9) by making the approximations $\sin\beta = t/\sqrt{l}$, $\cos\beta = (1 - t^2/2l)$, $\sin\beta' = (1 - \xi^2/2l)$, $\cos\beta' = \xi/\sqrt{l}$.

$$\begin{aligned} \sin B \sin(A - \alpha) &= \cos\alpha \sin B \sin A - \sin\alpha \sin B \cos A \\ &= \cos\alpha \sin\alpha\left(1 - \frac{\xi^2}{2l}\right) \\ &\quad - \sin\alpha\left[\cos\alpha\left(1 - \frac{t^2}{2l}\right)\left(1 - \frac{\xi^2}{2l}\right) + \frac{\xi t}{l}\right] \\ &= \frac{1}{2}[t^2\cos\alpha - 2\xi t]\,\frac{\sin\alpha}{l} \end{aligned}$$

where terms in l^{-2} have been ignored. As $l \to \infty$, $\sin B \to 1$, and $\sin(A - \alpha) \sim A - \alpha$. Therefore,

$$l\,(A - \alpha) \to R = \frac{1}{2}[t^2 \cos \alpha - 2\xi\, t] \sin \alpha. \qquad (13.43)$$

In the limit $l \to \infty$, equation (42) becomes

$$\sum_{\rho=0}^{\infty} e^{i(\mu-\rho)\alpha} F_{\mu\rho}(t) G_\rho(\xi) = e^{iR} G_\mu(\xi - t \cos \alpha),$$

or, using (17b),

$$\sum_{\rho=0}^{\infty} (-1)^\rho e^{i(\mu-\rho)\alpha} F_{\rho\mu}(t) G_\rho(\xi) = e^{iR} (-1)^\mu G_\mu(\xi - t \cos \alpha). \qquad (13.44)$$

Equation (44) implies an addition theorem involving Laguerre and Hermite polynomials. The result is (if t is replaced by 2t and the complex conjugate taken)

$$\sum_{\rho=0}^{\infty} \frac{1}{\rho!} [t\, e^{i\alpha}]^\rho L_\mu^{\rho-\mu}(2t^2) H_\rho(\xi)$$

$$= \frac{1}{\mu!} [te^{i\alpha}]^\mu \exp[2\xi\, te^{i\alpha} - t^2 e^{2i\alpha}] H_\mu(\xi - 2t \cos \alpha). \qquad (13.45)$$

Equation (45) is probably of little more than academic interest. In the special case $\alpha = \mu = 0$ it reduces, however, to give the familiar generating function for Hermite polynomials. Since $L_0^n = H_0 = 1$,

$$\sum_{\rho=0}^{\infty} \frac{1}{\rho!} t^\rho H_\rho(\xi) = e^{2\xi t - t^2}. \qquad (13.46)$$

It follows immediately on differentiating (46) with respect to ξ or t that the Hermite polynomials satisfy the pair of identities

$$H'_\lambda(\xi) = 2\lambda H_{\lambda-1}(\xi) \qquad (13.47)$$

$$2\xi H_\lambda(\xi) = 2\lambda H_{\lambda-1}(\xi) + H_{\lambda+1}(\xi). \qquad (13.48)$$

These identities can be combined to show that the Hermite polynomials satisfy the second-order differential equation

$$H''_\lambda(\xi) - 2\xi H'_\lambda(\xi) + 2\lambda H_\lambda(\xi) = 0, \qquad (13.49)$$

and the recurrence relation

$$H_{\lambda+1}(\xi) = -e^{\xi^2}\frac{d}{d\xi}\, e^{-\xi^2} H_\lambda(\xi). \tag{13.50}$$

Equations (47) and (50) provide the factorization for the differential equation (49).

It is possible to give a function space representation equivalent to the matrix representation that has been obtained. To do this, we multiply equation (44) by e^{iz} and write it as

$$\sum_{\rho=0}^{\infty} e^{iz}\, i^{\rho-\mu} e^{i(\mu-\rho)\phi} F_{\rho\mu}(t) i^\rho G_\rho(\xi) = e^{i(R+z)} i^\mu G_\mu(\xi - t\cos\phi)$$

or, from (10),

$$\sum_{\rho=0}^{\infty} \bar{\Delta}_{\rho\mu}(z, \phi, t) i^\rho G_\rho(\xi) = e^{i(R+z)} i^\mu G_\mu(\xi - t\cos\phi). \tag{13.51}$$

We consider now the space M of all complex functions of a real variable of the form $\Sigma\, a_\mu i^\mu G_\mu(\xi)$ where the a_μ are complex numbers and satisfy $\Sigma\, |a_\mu|^2 < \infty$. The space M is actually L^2, the Hilbert space of all square-integrable functions on $(-\infty, \infty)$, but this fact will not be shown here. Comparison of equation (51) with equation (6.5) suggests that we define an operator D in M by

$$[Df](\xi) = e^{i(R+z)} f(\xi - t\cos\phi).$$

If we put $x = t\cos\phi$, $y = t\sin\phi$, this becomes, in view of (43),

$$[D(x, y, z)f](\xi) = e^{i[z-\xi y + xy/2]} f(\xi - x). \tag{13.52}$$

It can be verified by direct calculation that the operators D defined by (52) satisfy $D(x, y, z)D(x', y', z') = D(X, Y, Z)$ where X, Y, Z are given by equations (3). Therefore, the operators $D(x, y, z)$ provide a group representation.

In this representation the operators $\tilde{Q}$ and $\tilde{P}$ that represent q and p are given by

$$[\tilde{Q}f](\xi) = \frac{\partial}{\partial x}[D(x, y, z)f](\xi), \qquad [\tilde{P}f](\xi) = \frac{\partial}{\partial y}[D(x, y, z)f](\xi)$$

evaluated at $x = y = z = 0$. It is seen from (52) that these are given by

$$[\tilde{Q}f](\xi) = -f'(\xi) \qquad [\tilde{P}f](\xi) = -i\xi f(\xi). \tag{13.53}$$

The Hermitian operators $-i\tilde{Q}$ and $i\tilde{P}$, which again satisfy (1), are the Born-Jordan representation of the quantum-mechanical operators (in momentum representation).

REFERENCES

CHAPTER 1

1. R. Courant and D. Hilbert, Methods of Mathematical Physics Vol. 1 (Interscience, New York, 1953), English edition.
2. P. M. Morse and H. Feshbach, Methods of Theoretical Physics (McGraw–Hill, New York, 1953).
3. E. D. Rainville, Special Functions (MacMillan, New York, 1960).
4. N. N. Lebedev, Special Functions and Their Applications (Prentice–Hall, Englewood Cliffs, New Jersey, 1965), English translation by R. A. Silverman.
5. L. Infeld and T. E. Hull, Rev. Mod. Phys. **23**, 21 (1951).
6. W. Miller, American Mathematical Society Memoir No. 50 (American Mathematical Society, Providence, Rhode Island, 1964).
7. B. Kaufman, J. Math. Phys. **7**, 447 (1966).
8. W. Miller, Commun. Pure Appl. Math. **17**, 527 (1964); **18**, 493, 679 (1965); **19**, 125, 251 (1966).
9. N. I. Vilenkin, Special Functions and the Theory of Group Representations (Publisher "Nauka," Moscow, 1965).
10. E. P. Wigner, Application of Group Theory to the Special Functions of Mathematical Physics (unpublished lecture notes, Princeton University, Princeton, New Jersey, 1955).

CHAPTER 3

1. E. A. Coddington and N. Levinson, The Theory of Ordinary Differential Equations (McGraw–Hill, New York, 1955), p. 12. Note that the differentiability conditions assumed here imply that the Lipschitz condition is satisfied.
2. For a proof of this, see L. Pontrjagin, Topological Groups (Princeton University Press, Princeton, New Jersey, 1946), p. 13.

CHAPTER 4

1. L. Pontrjagin, Topological Groups (Princeton University Press, Princeton, New Jersey, 1946), English translation by Emma Lehmer.

CHAPTER 6

1. G. Frobenius, Sitzungsber. Preuss. Akad. (1896-99).
2. I. Schur, Sitzungsber. Preuss. Akad. p. 406 (1905).
3. W. Burnside, Theory of Groups of Finite Order (Cambridge University Press, 1911).

CHAPTER 7

1. F. Peter and H. Weyl, Math. Ann. **97**, 737 (1934).
2. E. P. Wigner, Applications of Group Theory to the Special Functions of Mathematical Physics (unpublished lecture notes, Princeton University, Princeton, New Jersey, 1955).
3. M. H. Stone, Studies in Modern Analysis (Mathematical Association of America, 1963), edited by R. C. Buck.
4. A. Zygmund, Trigonometrical Series (Dover, New York, 1955).
5. E. Wigner, Ann. of Math. **40**, 149, 193-197 (1939).
6. E. C. Titchmarsh, The Theory of Functions (Oxford University Press, London, 1939), second edition, p. 13.

CHAPTER 8

1. E. P. Wigner, Group Theory and Its Application to the Quantum Mechanics of Atomic Spectra (Academic Press, New York, 1959), English translation by J. J. Griffin.
2. G. Racah, Phys. Rev. **62**, 438 (1942).

CHAPTER 10

1. H. E. Moses, Ann. Phys. **37**, 224 (1966).
2. M. Bander and C. Itzykson, Rev. Mod. Phys. **38**, 330 (1966), Appendix.
3. L. C. Biedenharn, J. Math. Phys. **2**, 433 (1961).
4. V. Fock, Z. Physik **98**, 145 (1935).
5. M. Bander and C. Itzykson, Rev. Mod. Phys. **38**, 346 (1966), Appendix.

CHAPTER 11

1. A. S. Wightman, Rev. Mod. Phys. **34**, 845 (1962).
2. I. E. Segal, Duke Math. J. **18**, 221 (1951).
3. E. Inönü and E. P. Wigner, Proc. Nat. Acad. Sci. U.S. **39**, 510 (1953).
4. E. Saletan, J. Math. **2**, 1 (1961).

CHAPTER 12

1. W. Miller, Commun. Pure Appl. Math. **17**, 527 (1964).
2. B. Friedman and J. Russek, Quart. Appl. Math. **12**, 13 (1954).
3. M. Danos and L. C. Maximon, J. Math. Phys., **6**, 766 (1965).
4. M. E. Rose, J. Math. and Phys. **37**, 215 (1958).

CHAPTER 13

1. W. Miller, Commun. Pure Appl. Math. **18**, 679 (1965), **19**, 125 (1966).
2. J. von Neumann, Math. Ann. **104**, 570 (1931).

INDEX